Memoirs of a
Mystic Misfit

BARBARA KORTE

Barbara's life has been uniquely multi-faceted. It was filled with difficulty and hardship until her mid-life awakening took her on a journey of healing, blessings and connections that would help her transform her life. While learning to follow her guidance, (often difficult, sometimes even a bit unbelievable) she opens up to a world of information and Beings that she never knew existed. Throughout the past 20 years of friendship, Barb has shared her amazing stories with me. It's been amazing to watch them come alive in her book. These stories are authentically and truthfully shared, often, with a sense of humor that will put a smile on your face. It is definitely a page turner! Enjoy.

- Jane K.

Raw. Real. Wondrous. Barbara's authenticity shines through as she shares the trials of her childhood, her tumultuous relationships with men, and how her world that may have seemed upside down suddenly turned right side up once she found the spiritual path she was destined for. Her stories take us around the world and open our hearts and minds to believe what many would deem unbelievable. Reading this book will not only change your view of the Universe, but it quite possibly may activate wondrous, seemingly unbelievable, experiences of your own.

- Carolyn Mager

Mystic

A person who seeks by contemplation
And self- surrender to obtain unity with
or absorption into the Deity or the absolute,
or who believes in the spiritual apprehension
of truths that are beyond the intellect;

A seeker of truth.

Thank you, Rick, Macie, Tanner, Brandon, and Logan, for always supporting me to find my truth. You will always be my greatest gifts! Thank you, Rhonda, Douglas, Dana and Jane for being my space holders and being able to reel me in and ground me when I most need it. Thank you, Danielle, for designing my cover. And thank you Carolyn, Jane, Lyle and Lori for helping me to edit and shape my book. It's been a long time in the making.

Prologue

LIFE IS A journey. We all pretty much come into this human life the same way. Each of us are born into specific families that help us to create foundations for adulthood. We attend school to learn what society deems important. Then we try to figure out what we want to be when we grow up. Many of us work various jobs while building our independence. More often than not we fall in love, several times, as we explore compatibility. Most get married, have children and build careers. Many get a divorce, and rebuild their life. Around the age of 35 to 50, we often go through a midlife crisis of some sort to help us review the places that need change. Most are gifted with grandchildren, retire, grow old and die. Of course, there are a great many variables. But for most, this is an adequate and bare-bones storyline of a human life.

It's all quite amazing when you think about it. You can be born red, black, yellow, white, or a blend. You can choose being male or female, even carrying traits of both. You can be a mixture of different cultures, as well as different sexual preferences. There are also many different religions and belief systems to be hardwired into or experience.

Through our thoughts, beliefs, programming, and actions, we create a push and pull of energy that shapes our life into a kaleidoscope of colorful experiences. Those experiences can range from mundane to extraordinary, harsh to extravagant, and hateful to incredibly loving. There's also every twist and turn of emotion and reaction one could possibly imagine.

People's lives have always fascinated me. Perhaps that is why I became a healer, life coach and spiritual counselor. I get to see into the lives of so many people. I've enjoyed helping others to see and work through the pieces that have caused so much pain, suffering, and misalignment in their life. Facilitating positive change for others has brought me a great amount of satisfaction and healing within my own self. It seems the more I experience and heal within myself, the more I can help others do it for themselves. I can also see that the more I heal myself, the more I create a morphic field of healing to open for those around me, including my children and lineage.

Through the years, I have worked with literally thousands of people. I have seen the beauty, dysfunction, patterning, programming, victory, loss, rejection, self-sabotage, denial, jealousy, hatred, anger, sickness, and love that has run through people's lives. I have also seen every shade and color of crazy and inspiration you could possibly imagine. These have been an amazing reflection of the very things that I have had to take a look at, or reveal within my own life. Each has had a piece in shaping who I am.

Throughout this journey of 66 years, there is one lesson that I have been very grateful to have learned. It is that one stays a little saner when they are able to come to a place of detachment, non-judgement, and humor, in all that they see. It helps to create a state of mind that makes things easier to deal with.

My prayer is that one day we cease to judge people for the way they are, or how they live their lives. We don't know what another person is here to do or to experience. Nor do we know the challenges or depth of pain that one has faced. Each of us has contracted a very mysterious and individualized journey. Sometimes it is full of hurt and anger, other times full of wonder, joy and love. Life vacillates to create a yin and yang of emotion that propels us into our experiences and growth. And, just like the snowflake that begins its descent being formed by all the elements of nature pressuring it into an intricate work of art, there are no two lives alike.

I believe that all of us are highly evolved "Spirits" that have incarnated into a human body. Each of us coming back over and over again to experience different facets of life. I feel we reincarnate with our individual Soul groups, each playing different roles for our collective and individual experiences and growth. Those experiences complete contracts, missions, and desires we made before birth. I also believe we are here to continually grow our eternal Soul. We do that through expansion, as well as the clearing of karma for our self, as a collective, and for our lineage. This can include missions of light work that many of us are involved with.

When we are first born, we remember who we are and have a strong connection to a higher power. Many choose to call that higher power God, Goddess, the Divine, Source, Creator, or the Universal energy that runs through all things. Unfortunately, that remembrance more often than not fades in childhood. It gets buried under the harsh needs of survival and programming from those who have already been hardwired into a certain way of thinking. Within every person is that spark that knows it is special. That feels how life should be, even though their outside reality reflects something quite different. How confusing and lonely it can be at times as we each try to figure out why we came here, and what our purpose is.

Perhaps as you read this book, a crack will begin to open into the remembrance of the magnificent Being that you are. Or maybe it will help you bring parts of yourself and your gifts forward so you can be a powerful ally for humanity and the planet. It may even spark a remembrance of what it is you came here to experience and do. Hopefully, it will help you to pay more attention to the universal thread of energy that magically steers your life for your best and highest good. And, if you begin to ask, maybe it could even help you to open up to new experiences. At the very least, my hope is that it helps create a more heart-centered life while you are here. Ah, how different life could be if we just loved ourselves and followed the promptings of the heart, instead of the mind.

I think I have chosen to have a very experiential life riding from one spectrum of the chart to the other so that I could help others to overcome, and embrace their own experiences. After all, it's pretty hard to have compassion and understanding when you've never experienced anything difficult or trying yourself.

I believe we are all born with many gifts and abilities. One of my greatest gifts is the ability to see the innate love that threads through each person, as well as the intricate beauty that they hold. It seems to activate their gifts and abilities to come forward as they work towards becoming their highest potential. I also have the ability to hold a field of love for people to heal and shift out of all the programming and beliefs, that have kept them from a heart-centered life. The other gift that I am so grateful for is humor. It's helped me to not take life too seriously.

This is my story. I'm sharing the dysfunction, trauma, and self-sabotage that I have experienced throughout life. Experiences that have created a dumbing down and misconception of the person I was capable of being. Those choices often reflected my lack of self-worth caused by what has played out around me. Sometimes that life was horrific, other times, incredibly magical. Your journey won't look the same. We all have very different make ups and reasons for being here. I share my journey into finding my truth through the expansion of my understanding of who I am and what I'm capable of. It is only through understanding your own story, that you can heal, transform, and recreate your life. By doing so you open up to a world you never knew existed. That is when you meet the mystic that you were always meant to find and to be.

Table of Contents

CHAPTER ONE

My Beginnings

I WAS THE second child born into a southeastern Minnesota family of seven. It consisted of my parents, two brothers, two sisters and myself. My mother wanted to be a doctor. My father had dreams of being a professional baseball player. Life threw them a curve ball, as it often does. At 16 they conceived a child, got married, and had to become more responsible than I'm sure either could have imagined.

There is a lot of my childhood that I don't remember, and interestingly, the ones I do remember are more of the harsh memories than those that were good. A lot of those memories were burned into my conscious mind and could never be forgotten. Others, started surfacing back up from my subconscious mind after I started my mid-life journey. **As is often the case when we have traumatic experiences, we tend to bury them deep within. It's like putting a bandage over a cut. A bandage stops the cut from bleeding and protects the injury from germs that could cause an infection. Physical, mental, emotional and sexual trauma creates a rip or cut within our psyche. A rip in one's psyche causes precious energy to leak which creates a depletion in our life force. To take care of it, our mind often compartmentalizes it, then stores the experience deep within the brain's unconscious, and subconscious holding tanks. Trauma is also stored within the body's cells. There it is locked away, and a wall is secured around it. The wall often shows itself through extra weight, addictions, control issues, OCD, constant anger, split personalities, memory blocks, etc. Burying the trauma gives much needed time for the person to mature before it comes back up again for review. That is usually when there is a good chance of it being healed.**

The good thing about burying trauma is that it allows a part of you that is unable to cope with it to shelter itself. That way you

can move forward and still live a halfway normal life. The bad thing about burying it, is that the subconscious and unconscious mind is where we manifest a lot of our reality from. That place of deep hurt, anger, and fear that we have tucked away on the inside, is often causing drama and resignation as a natural state of being on the outside. Dysfunction breeds dysfunction until you heal it and see your way through. More often than not, deep trauma stays buried for decades. Eventually the right time comes along and something triggers it to come back up to the surface. Then it can be seen, dealt with, and hopefully healed.

The earliest memory of my childhood is from when I was around the age of four. That was when I first remember being aware of my dad's drinking and the anger that often accompanied it. One night, my mom had made a boxed pizza for supper. It was a new product in the grocery store and she wanted to try it out. We were all sitting at the table, anxiously waiting for Dad to wash up and join us after he got home for the night.

After sitting down, he glanced at the food, raised his plate, and in a rage threw it up at the ceiling. It clipped the light bulb showering fine shards of glass everywhere. It was all over the food, the table, and all over us. Screaming ensued while we sat there crying, too petrified to move. After all the words had been slung, we were sent to our bedrooms, crying, hungry, and scared. This was the beginning of the fighting that we were to witness throughout the rest of our childhood.

Thank God when I was five, my parents purchased a beautiful lake property. Even though it was hard at times, living there was like salve for a wound. It had a three-bedroom house and four cabins that we rented out for extra income. It also came with a picnic area, 5 acres of farm ground, a food stand, and a supper club with an attached dance hall. That would be how we made our main income. There was also a beach that we leased out to the public during the summer. That meant a lot of opportunity to be with other people.

I was obsessed with the lake, and it became the center of my Universe. It was something my Soul deeply connected to. I loved floating on top of a mirror still body of water hearing no sounds except an occasional jump of a fish, or a call of a bird as it flew overhead. It was incredible experiencing the weightless embrace of my body as I floated gazing into the sky. It was like I was one with the lake, as if the lake ran through my veins. I couldn't imagine living anywhere else.

Of course, living on the lake with so much beautiful nature, my imagination soared. I went on excursions looking for ancient Indian ruins, Fairies, Unicorns, Big Foot and Space Beings. Nature was a place where I felt most alive and cradled. I was at peace and could be myself without worrying what was going to happen next. I could just be.

As a child, I had a fascination with storms. Often, I could be found outside watching a storm as it rode in with lightning and thunder crashing. I remember looking up and talking to a group called the Thunder Beings. It seems odd to me now as I write it, but I remember feeling very connected to them. Most people I knew were afraid of storms, but for me they had quite the opposite effect. Storms were electrifying, exciting, and totally mesmerizing.

Around the age of nine, I began to feel, and sense invisible Beings around me. There was usually two to four of them. It was always men dressed in dark suits and ties. I could feel them around me a lot. I could see them with my inner-vision. I never saw them as a physical presence. In the winter, I could sometimes hear the crunch of their footsteps in the snow behind me as I walked. I was afraid of them and didn't understand why they were constantly in my shadow. I never remember them talking to me. It was more of a feeling that they were observing me. That went on for a lot of my childhood and into my teen years. They weren't there continually. They popped in and out at random.

As much as my siblings and I loved living out on the lake, there was a downside. More often than not, we were left alone. We were also forced into having to be a little too responsible for kids our age. My parents put so much energy into the nightclub that we literally never got to see them. Tuesday through Sunday they would sleep until late in the morning. Then they'd start early afternoon to clean and get ready for the night business. The night business would keep them there until one or two in the morning. By Sunday they were too exhausted to do much, except recoup from the long week of work. That was the only time we seemed to be able to spend together. Typically, they would take us out for dinner, or we'd have a picnic. Usually, there was a water activity like skiing, fishing, or swimming to finish out the day. They were the times I looked forward to the most.

When we went to school, we would get up and make our own breakfast. If we missed the bus, there was hell to pay. I was so afraid to wake them up when lunch money was due. There were times I went to school knowing there would be no lunch. Sometimes, one of the cooks would sneak me a peanut butter sandwich if she saw I didn't go through the lunch line.

By the time we got home from school, Mom and Dad were already at work. If we had any problems, the telephone was usually our connection. It was too disruptive to go over and talk to them very often because it was always so busy. Sometimes we got to go over to the dining area and eat. Other times, we picked up a bundle of food to bring home. Most of the time it was a free-for-all. Children without supervision can get into a lot of trouble, and we were no exception. Whether she wanted it or not, my oldest sister Rhonda, got the brunt of responsibility thrown on her shoulders.

CHAPTER 2

Riding the Waves of Dysfunction

WITHIN ITS USUAL cycle, Mom and Dad's drinking spiked and waned. As time went on, there were more times where it spiked than waned. I don't know what was worse, the drunkenness, or the hurtful words and violence that spewed up like a volcano because of it. Eventually, Mom began drinking as well. I'm sure it helped her numb the pain when she was getting yelled at or being beaten. My siblings and I got our fair share of spankings and nasty words thrown at us, but those weren't as bad as hearing and seeing all the violence towards our mom. Seeing that created a constant fear wondering what was going to happen next.

I was startled from my sleep one night and jumped out of bed to look out the window. Dad was screaming at the top of his lungs calling Mom a whore as she lay crying on the top on the stairway off the back of the dance hall. Then he grabbed her by the hair and pulled her down a flight of wooden steps while screaming about how he was going to teach her a lesson. All she could do was cry and beg for him to please stop. No one must have been around in the dance hall, or they were too scared to come out, because no one tried to stop it. I'm sure a lot more happened, but I have blocked the rest out.

On one particular night it was especially brutal. It started out with the regular fighting and then escalated out of control. We were all up in our beds crying and scared. This time Rhonda went down to plead for them to stop. Dad had ahold of Mom and was beating her over the head with a toilet plunger. Rhonda screamed at them and was told to go back to bed. Instead, she walked to the phone and started to call the police. When Dad figured out what she was doing, he tore the phone off the wall and threw it on the ground. He then walked to the closet, brought out a rifle and started digging through the closet for ammunition. Mom yelled for all of us to run outside while she followed.

Rhonda climbed up a tree. The rest of us hid in the wet cold soybean field to the side of the house too scared to move. Dad stumbled out of the door with his rifle in tow, but didn't go any farther than the front steps. I guess he didn't see us, or must have forgotten what he was doing. After a while he turned around and went back in. We stayed there until we knew Dad was passed out and we were no longer in danger. Mom gathered us all back together with packed bags and clothesbaskets full of things we needed. Then we left for a safe place. We ran away several times during our childhood. Sometimes we went to our grandmothers, sometimes to other relatives.

Each time Dad promised that he would quit drinking and never hurt her again. I could never understand why she would take him back after the horrible violence, and the hurtful things he'd said and done. I guess her self-worth wasn't much after all that she had gone through. I could imagine the fear of raising five children on her own was scarier than the cycles of violence she continually endured. Of course, as the pattern dictated, before long the drinking and circle of violence would start all over again.

It does horrible things to a child's psyche to see and hear that kind of abuse from the people who they love and look up to the most. Especially from those who are supposed to nurture and protect them. It plants itself deeply in one's memory, as it shapes the foundation of every choice that creates their future. There is no discrimination in the fact that it affects everyone involved. It just affects each one in a different way. Everyone in our family experienced the same things, yet each of us seemed to have processed the experiences differently. I can clearly see how it has manifested into our own individualized dysfunctions.

CHAPTER 3

School Days & Puberty

SCHOOL WAS A blur, and with fitful sleep, it was incredibly hard to concentrate. I was always embarrassed by the dark rings that encircled my eyes. Looking back at our school pictures, it wasn't hard to see that there was something terribly wrong. I'm sure that in a small town there had to be others that knew what was going on. Yet, only once in all the years of school, did anyone intervene. Unfortunately, that one time was a disaster.

It started one morning when I woke up with a bad case of hives. I remember telling my parents that I had red spots that itched really bad and I couldn't get my shoes on. They were so tired and hungover they couldn't even open their eyes to look. They told me to go to school anyway. What else could I do? I packed my shoes in my backpack and off I went. Of course, it didn't take long for someone to see that there was a problem. I had welts everywhere, and my feet were so swollen I could only wear socks. My parents were called to come and pick me up so they could take me to the doctor.

Not long after, my youngest brother went to school and told the nurse that he had fallen down a flight of stairs and hurt his back. He said that he had tried to tell my parents, but they thought he was faking and made him go to school anyway. I assume it put up another red flag. My parents were called in once again. This time social services were called and we were forced to go to counseling through a county agency.

To say that it was a joke is an understatement. Several days before the appointment, we had "the talk" with our parents. They sternly suggested that if the child protection services thought that what was going on in the house was bad, they would take us away. We were told that we would have to go live with strangers and that each of us would be placed in separate homes. They alluded that we would probably never see them, or one another again.

The day we went in for the appointment they sat us all at a long table. I still to this day can't fathom the reasoning behind putting our parents straight across from us. Over and over, they asked if there was anything that was harmful or negligent going on at our house. With your parents sitting there staring at you while they are waiting for the answer, how could we dare say anything? Why would we say anything about what was really going on? What would happen when we got home? Now I felt forced to internalize all that we experienced. I would need to be extra careful not to let anyone know anything. It felt like I had to keep it all inside so I wouldn't draw any more attention.

Around the age of twelve, I began to have a unique phenomenon happen. I would be at school reading and the words would rise off my page and begin moving around. Of course, when that would happen it was impossible for me to read, let alone concentrate. I never told anyone. Who would believe me anyway? I think I was afraid that they would think I was drinking, or on drugs. Of course, I wasn't, but I was afraid that is what they would think. It became another deep secret.

It was a rare occasion that I could read without this happening, so in order to make it through class, I began to study the teacher. After a while, I would know what kinds of questions they were going to ask in tests. I earmarked that information to memorize it. I also used my intuition when tests were multiple choice to pick the right answers on tests by circling 1, 2 or 3 or A, B, C, D or E. It was amazing how good I got at it. I wasn't an A student, but I certainly did okay. It served me and I am sure because of it, I was a step ahead in tuning into my intuition.

I started to become aware of the way I could tune into people and began to use that as a tool to diffuse the time bombs at home. Whenever I would feel the energy shifting, I would become or do whatever I thought was needed to diffuse the anger that was building in the house, or towards myself. It was like playing a game of chess and I became an expert at making the right moves. I learned to manipulate energy. Sometimes honestly, other times I did and said what it would take to diffuse the anger and change the outcome. Whether right or wrong, it made things easier to deal with.

I was definitely a little ahead of the rest as far as maturing. My chubby adolescent body was quickly becoming a curvaceous and beautiful 36-24-36 work of art, and I hated it! As the other girls in my class were praying for their breasts to mature so they could wear a bra, I was praying to God to please make mine shrink. Boys would make jokes about me at school and call me all these weird names like Boobless, Barbie Doll and Brahma. They were always trying to look up my dress as I climbed the stairs and some would even go as far as to ask me if I stuffed my bra. I couldn't believe the lengths that they went to try to get a feel or see if they could get the best of me. The attention was relentless and it made me feel extremely self-conscious.

I was twelve years old when I began to menstruate. My first period started in school and I didn't know what to do. No one had talked to me about my period, and I didn't know what was going on. I remember crying in the school bathroom and not wanting to come out of the stall. One of my friends came in and asked me what was wrong. She was the one who explained what a period was. Then she bought me a pad out of the machine and after school I went home and asked my sister to talk to me about it.

I'm not sure why my mom never talked to me about that particular subject, but she did give all three of us girls a talk about bras. It was one of the most embarrassing talks I had ever sat through. She took us to a local restaurant and had "the talk" out loud with other people seated around us eating their meals. I couldn't have been more mortified that people were listening! I guess to live in this family, "embarrassment" was always going to be the norm.

CHAPTER 4

Surfing with the Boys

ONE AFTERNOON I was asked if I wanted to go out boating with some boys from the summer cabins and go surfing behind their boat. I loved to ski and thought it would be great to learn how to surf. I got ready and climbed on the surf board behind Dan who was one of the older neighborhood kids. We got up after a few tries and I proceeded to get up on his shoulders as planned.

It was a lot easier than I thought it would be. I was really enjoying it until Dan reached up and to my horror unhooked the top to my bathing suit. How the heck he was able to do it so quickly and easily was a stretch of the imagination! Knowing them, I wouldn't have doubted if they took turns putting on a bra and practiced with one another just for this very thing. Nonetheless, the girls were free and believe me, all eyes were glued right there. I promptly fell over backwards into the lake and began to swim back to the dock. What I was going to do once I got there was beyond me. At least I was getting farther away from them and closer to getting some help.

They picked up Dan and came back to get me. Of course, there was no way I was going to go anywhere near them after they had violated my trust. They kept telling me that they were sorry. Finally, one of them took off his shirt and threw it in for me to cover up with. I thankfully put it on and finished swimming to the dock.

By the time I got there they were already loading the boat up on the ramp and putting things away. I jumped up on the dock, walked over to Dan who was trying to cough out an apology and kicked him as hard as I could between the legs. I heard the kick echo as he doubled over and fell into the lake. The others scattered like rats as they ran off to their cabins. I guess they didn't want to stick around to see what was going to happen next.

I turned and marched down the dock fuming, but eventually noticed that Dan wasn't getting out of the water. Putting my anger aside, I finally waded back into the lake to help him get back up on the dock. At least then I wouldn't have any guilt about him drowning. He lay on the dock for hours and finally made it back up to the house. Part of me felt bad because he didn't come out of the house for several days. But then after what he did, I felt he had it coming. I don't know what gets into boys. Perhaps it's the proverbial thinking with the other brain. It seems like it takes over and they just can't control themselves.

CHAPTER 5

My Spiral Down with Men

ONE NIGHT AFTER the gate to the beach was locked up, there was knocking at the door. My sister, Sandy, went to see who it was and came back saying there were some boys. They'd asked for me to meet them in the parking lot to the night club. I couldn't even imagine the kind of trouble I'd get in if Mom and Dad knew that they were there to see me, so I went out to tell them that they needed to leave.

My mom came out of nowhere. I had no idea how she even knew they were there. She stood between the boys and me, drew her hand back, and slapped me across my face while she labeled me a whore. The boys' hurriedly left without me saying a word. The slap I could have overlooked, but the words seared my Soul. I didn't drink, smoke, do drugs, or swear. I decided right then and there that if she was going to call me a whore, I might as well deserve the name. I went out at the age of fourteen and had sex with a boy I barely knew. And as he took my virginity, I felt no pleasure. There was only a deep apathy for the words I had been branded with echoing through my mind.

My eighth-grade year, there was a teacher that I felt some strange vibes from. He was a skinny, middle-aged guy, with slicked back black hair and taught math. It didn't take long to notice he was a pervert. He would stand behind us girls when we were writing, and in the guise of helping figure out a problem, he would stand extremely close and grind his crotch into our elbow. It was so creepy! A bunch of us girls would often have collaborative talks about how to put a stop to it. At one talk, the idea was brought up that the next person who had it happen to them would promptly elbow him in the groin. After that, they were supposed to stand up. That would be the signal that it was time to go to the principal's office and report him together. That way no one would be singled out.

That day we all made a pact and waited for it to happen again. I should have known it would be me. Per the agreement, I elbowed him in the groin and stood up saying "Ok girls, let's go." Not one girl stood up. Not one! They all had their heads bowed and wouldn't even look me in the eye. Well, what could I do but go it alone? I couldn't believe what a bunch of chicken shits they were! The teacher had a report filed, but not much happened to him. At least not the way I thought it should. Part of me wondered if it was worth it, but at least I stood up for what I felt was right.

The summer I was fifteen I really wanted a guitar. I decided that if I were going to be able to raise the money, I'd need a more substantial job. My grandma agreed to take me in for the summer so I could work in town. I slept in her basement where she had two beds set up and that was just fine by me. It would be more private and I wouldn't wake her and my step-grandpa up when I came home from work after the night shift. My job would be deveining turkeys and taking the meat off the bones. The thought of it brought up vomit, but I swallowed my disgust and did it. At my age, who else was going to hire me for the kind of money that I would need to buy a guitar with?

One of the days after my grandparents left for work, the doorbell rang. It was a service man who said he was there to fix the washing machine. Later that day, I let Grandma know that he had come to complete the job. She informed me that she had never called anyone to fix her washing machine. The police came over to file a report but were surprised because nothing had been stolen. They told her that they would be patrolling the neighborhood to keep an eye on things.

That night I was startled awake by the sound of stone crunching under footsteps. As I lay there trying to figure out what was going on, I saw a shadow methodically cross each basement window. Whoever was sneaking around the house worked his way to the back door and gently jimmied it open.

The next thing I knew, a figure wearing a face mask and holding a pistol made his way down the stairway into the basement. I was para-lyzed with fear as he walked halfway across the floor leading to my bed. Thankfully the dog finally began barking. It was like a key that unlocked my voice. I started screaming as the man turned and ran for the stairway exiting through the back door. Of course, the police were called again, but he was long gone by the time they got there. They did figure out that he had taped the lock to the back door so that it didn't fully lock. All he had to do is stick a card of some sort through the lock-ing device to undo it. I had to wonder what he was after. Was he there to steal things, and if so, what was of value in the basement? The only thing down there was two beds, a wash room, a bathroom, a storage room and me. And if it had to do with me, why hadn't he acted on it while there earlier that day? While I may never know the answer to that question, I do know it definitely planted a seed of fear in me.

A month later, I was walking to my grandma's house after a school dance. Just as I was starting to cross a street, a white car with a red light in the rear window stopped in a way that forced me to go around it. The man driving it looked to be in his 30's with brown combed back hair. He rolled his window down and asked if I could tell him directions to a certain place in town. I got closer because I couldn't hear him clearly over the car noise. As I came closer, he grabbed my wrist and tried pulling me in through the window. I remember being shocked, but knew that I needed to fight. I started screaming and scratching at his face until I was finally able to break free. As I fell to the pavement, he tore off. I ran to a neighbor and they called the police. My grandma thankfully came to get me. I was too scared to walk home the rest of the way. I shied away from doing things with my friends for quite a while after that. I was beginning to feel traumatized by all that had been happening. Understandably, I was beginning to have a huge mistrust towards men.

By the end of my summer stay, I finally had enough money saved to buy my guitar and I was ecstatic. Playing the guitar was the one thing that I could put my heart and Soul into. I was able to release some of my anger and sadness through my songs.

CHAPTER 6

Bankruptcy, Loss of a Sister & Relocation

HALFWAY THROUGH NINTH grade, the bank came and repossessed our boat, cars and the property. I don't remember any mention of moving, or that there was financial trouble. It was a huge shock to all of us kids. We loaded up whatever we could fit into a large moving truck. Tons of our things were left behind, including a cat that we had become very attached to. This move ripped the very fabric of my being. I was so attached to this lake and our property that I was beside myself. My oldest sister, Rhonda, begged to stay with our grandma until she graduated. She left, our family became split, and my siblings and I lost our sister and protector.

The move to Sleepy Eye ended up being okay. It was a place where I made friends quickly. School also seemed to be easier for me here. When I read books, the words no longer floated above the pages. I became more of a freethinker, who got along with all the different classes of people. My personality also came out a little more. I was noticeably becoming a bit more rebellious. One of those times was when there was an unjust firing of a teacher that I felt to be exceptional. I brought together a group of people who felt the same and organized a sit-in. I also started a new fad by wearing army clothes paired off with combat boots that came from the local army surplus store. That went okay, but then I fashioned white sheets with hand painted Disney characters into clothing. I was told to go home and put on appropriate clothing. I don't think the school knew what to do with me. I walked home thinking I was going to get either whipped, or grounded. Surprisingly, Dad would show up at the door with a face I knew had been previously laughing. I wasn't sure I was ever going to be able to figure this guy out.

As a nature lover, I naturally gravitated toward going hiking in the woods bordering nearby rivers. I loved following animal tracks and exploring what scenery was around each bend in a river. One weekend several of my friends, my boyfriend, and I went on a canoe trip. We paired off into four canoes and headed down the river. At some point, Darin and I realized we were way ahead of the others. It wouldn't have mattered much except that the sun was starting to get low. We sat at the pullout point for a while and then he decided to paddle back upstream to see if he could find them. I needed to find a spot to go to the bathroom.

After a while, I started getting scared that something could have happened. I remember talking to God praying for everyone to be protected. As I was in my prayer, a huge beam of light came down from the clouds and enveloped me. It was warm and comforting like God himself was holding me in his arms and I heard the words "It's okay Barbara. They're all safe and will be here soon." I just sat there in the warmth and took it all in as my fear receded. There was no doubt in my mind that everyone was alive and well. Minutes later, shouts from the others sounded out. I gave thanks as I ran down to the river to help them all pull in their canoes. That was my first remembered encounter with what I felt to be God.

It was during this time of my life that I started having intense prophetic dreams. Here is an example of what it was like. I was walking to school one morning telling my friend that I had experienced a bad dream that night. In the dream, she and I were walking down the same exact street that we were currently walking down. In the dream, a smaller motorcycle came past, blew its front tire, lost control, veered to the right, and hit a tree. The driver flew off hitting his head on the sidewalk. As I told the end of the story, a motorcycle drove by and blew its front tire. He lost control, veered to the right, hit a tree, and flew off landing on the sidewalk. I don't know who was more freaked out, her or me.

Several dreams happened after that, like a grandparent getting cancer, some catastrophic Earth dreams that came true, some not. I asked for them to not happen anymore and they began to slow down and finally quit. I think it made people uncomfortable, so I was glad to not have to deal with it anymore. I wanted to feel more normal, as I transitioned into this new life.

Town living was so different from country living. Living here was the first time that people were allowed to come into our house. Mom and Dad took jobs at nightclubs, so they were still gone a lot, but the violent spells seemed to lessen a bit here. Maybe there was less stress since they were working for someone else and not responsible for everything themselves.

We could walk to school because it was only ten blocks away and I always enjoyed the clearing of the mind that it brought. During my five day a week sojourn, I was in my own little world. Not surprising that it took me a while to figure out that there was a car that was consistently following me. The first few times I saw him, I thought it was coincidence. After about the third time, I started putting two and two together. I figured if he made a move, I would start screaming and run to the nearest house to get help.

The next day as I was walking home, I could see him driving closer like he was going to come up to me. I was freaked out and was ready to run when out of nowhere a blue car pulled over and screeched to a halt on my side of the road. A lady opened the car door and screamed for me to hurry up and get in. I was so in shock I got in and closed the door. She proceeded to tell me that she had been taken and molested by the man that was following me. She wasn't going to allow him to ruin someone else's life. I got scared for a minute thinking that it could be possible that she was working in cahoots with this man, but she proved to be sincere. She dropped me off at my house and went to the school and the police to report him. The next day there were warnings about the car and man whom they had identified as a pedophile. He was considered a threat and had been spotted in the area following young women as they walked home. We were warned to walk in pairs or get rides from our parents until he was apprehended.

Sleepy Eye was where I first experienced the first death of a close friend. Tim was the captain of the football team and the class president. Everyone looked up to him. The only thing that I could see that was messed up was his relationship with his girlfriend. From outside appearances, he seemed to be totally obsessed with her.

At one point, she broke up with him (probably because of that very thing) and he really took it hard. The breakup caused him to shut himself off into a world of his own, that few were allowed to enter. One morning, he drove his car into her driveway and yelled until she came outside. It was said that when he could see her at the door, he took a gun, pointed it to his temple, and pulled the trigger.

We were all in shock. He seemed to have everything, and yet I guess he felt he had nothing. I cried for him and the families that were torn apart because of his actions. I prayed that they would be able to heal. That one day they could be at peace. **Suicide is incredibly cruel. I'm not saying that so much for the one who does it. I only have compassion for them and the demons they continually fight with. I'm saying it's cruel, because it keeps hurting those that they love the most. It rarely allows the grieving to come to a place of true peace or closure. They always wonder if they could have stopped it. Or blame themselves because they weren't able to catch it before it happened. It's a heavy burden for family and friends to carry.**

CHAPTER 7

My Late Teens, Ghosts & Loss

MY DAD LOST his job about a year after moving, and started to commute to a new job about an hour away. That job lasted for around six months and then we moved to Wells, Minnesota. That just lasted a few months, and then we transitioned to Easton, Minnesota, where my mom and dad became the managers of an American Legion. Moving to a new school halfway through my junior year was incredibly hard. Now I understood why Rhonda left to stay with my grandma.

I made friends, but they weren't the kind of deep relationships you make when you are at a school for a long period of time. The girls there seemed fickle and mean. I have never gravitated to snobby people, so I became more of a loner. I had friends; they just weren't good friends.

At first, we lived in an apartment in the top half of a creamery. The bottom floor was unheated, so it was really cold in the winter. The water pipes burst and created a waterfall of ice down our two-story stairway. That forced us to move to a house several blocks down the road.

The house was small, and we had to share bedrooms once again, but at least it was warm. I'm not sure why, but I ended up sleeping on an old box spring. Back then, box springs were only a bottom part to a bed that was made solely of metal. Its main purpose was to stabilize the mattress. There was no material or wood involved. It was just a metal frame and springs so I piled as many blankets as I could find on top. It definitely wasn't comfortable, but it was better than lying on the floor.

This was when my first ghost experience happened. Where he came from I hadn't a clue. Perhaps the house was haunted and we didn't know it. I had been in bed and was just beginning to fall asleep when I started to hear tapping on the metal frame. It was slow and rhythmic like someone who was getting impatient at a counter trying to get a clerk's attention. I thought it was Sandy playing a joke on me so I asked her to stop. From her side of the room she replied, "Barb, it isn't me. I can hear it too. I swear, it isn't me!" Pretty soon my bed started bouncing gently up and down. Desperately I begged for Sandy to please stop rocking my bed and again from the opposite side of the room she said "Barb, I swear it isn't me!" I was so scared I couldn't fully form words in my mouth. At some point, I got brave and opened my eyes. I could see a semitranslucent man around the age of 65 standing at the foot of my bed with one foot on the springs. He just stood there staring at me while he pushed up and down on the box spring with his foot. I started to try to scream, but only broken sounds would come out of my mouth. Sandy, on the other hand, had no problem running out of the room screaming.

It only happened that once, but it was so traumatizing that I had a hard time falling asleep after that. I was so afraid that it was going to happen again. At some point, I thought it might be a good idea to go over to the Catholic church across the street to talk to the priest. After all, a church is a church, and who knew when I would get to a Lutheran church like our family had attended. The priest told me he thought that the ghost was the Devil trying to take me over and control me. Not for a minute did I believe him. I actually thought he was probably ignorant about ghosts, so just improvised with demonic talk instead. I just let it go. The ghost never came to my bed again, so I guessed it was just a one-time experience.

Mom and Dad's drinking started going through another spike. One night they got home around 1:00 a.m. I could hear Dad looking for the bathroom. It shouldn't have been too hard to find, as it had always been downstairs in the same place. I guess with as much as he drank, he'd forgotten where it was. After stumbling around for a while, he started up the stairs. Coming around the corner of the stairway, I could see that he wasn't wearing a stitch of clothing. All I could think was "God forbid, now what the hell?" He proceeded to open a closet door in the hallway and peed all over the clothes, mine included.

After that, he decided to come in our bedroom and check in on us. I don't know if Sandy was awake, but he looked at her and kissed her head. Then came over to my bed, lifted up the blankets and climbed in. I was in a panic and asked him what the hell he thought he was doing! All he kept saying is "You know I love you, don't you? I do. Do you know that I love you?" I told him that he was drunk and needed to go downstairs and go to his own bed. I just kept saying it over and over while inching away. Finally, he slid out, and went back downstairs. That night I told myself that I was almost 18. As soon as I got a chance, I was getting as far away from this crazy ass house as I possibly could!

The next morning, I woke up to cars honking. I looked out the window to see what was going on, and there in the front yard of the house sat our car. Apparently, they were so drunk when they drove home that they ran into the tree in our front yard and left it there for everyone to see. Of course, it had to be Sunday. The Catholic church was directly across the road, and everybody was filing into town pointing. I was so embarrassed!

I was accustomed to our dad drinking a lot, but I have to say it got harder when Mom's drinking got out of control. She must have decided to drown her unhappiness in the same fashion. It's not that I blamed her. If I had to put up with what she put up with, I probably would have done the same. I knew that the Legion was a lot of pressure. They had to work around the clock. Night clubs were like that. The work didn't stop when the night was over. There was always cleaning up and prep that had to be done to set up for the next day. Working at places like this probably wasn't the best place for an alcoholic to work. Booze is way too readily available and free.

A year and a half into taking over the American Legion, Mom got really drunk. She fell backwards off a bar stool and was knocked out cold. An ambulance was called to take her to the hospital. There they told her that if she didn't quit drinking, she was going to die. I'd say that was probably what she was trying to do.

The boys were getting older now so things were getting a little easier for us all. I got to waitress at the Legion and all of us kept busy helping there in one form or another. I had just broken up with my boyfriend of several years and felt a little low. That is when I started drinking beer. Not a lot, just enough to fit in a bit.

I still think about the time when a carload of us went drinking while driving down the gravel roads. That was a usual activity for a small town with nothing for the teenagers to do. When I say drinking for me, it meant a partial can of Colt 45 malt liquor. During the ride, several of us girls had to go to the bathroom, so we pulled onto a gravel road and stopped. All three of us were squatting in different areas of the ditch when I noticed a light out of the corner of my eyes.

As I looked over, I saw a huge blue ball of light about the size of a small bedroom resting on top of an electric pole. It was absolutely stunning! The ball was a very soft opaque blue with a jagged whitish electric current running around the outside edge. There was an audible electrical hum emanating from it. As I watched, the ball lifted from the pole and started to slowly float down to the ground towards us. I wasn't as scared as I was intrigued. However, the others started screaming and pulled me to the car. We all hopped in and took off. It didn't chase us or do anything. What it was I hadn't a clue, but I was glad that we had all seen it. What I didn't question at the time was, why they were so scared, and why I was so curious and mesmerized.

Easton was a very small farming community of around two hundred people. All that it had for businesses was a post office, a grocery store, a cafe, a lumber yard and the Legion. The Catholic church was central to the livelihood of the town and the majority of those that lived there were of that particular faith. It was one of the most beautiful churches in the inside that I had ever seen. I loved going there when no one was around. I'd just sit and soak it all in. I think that I must have had past lives as being a nun or had a lifetime with knowing Christ because I felt so at home when I went to any Catholic church. It wasn't because of the teachings; of that, I am sure. I was more attracted to the statues and to the beautiful stained-glass windows depicting the Stations of the Cross. I loved the intricate carved pillars and vaulted ceilings. Every time I went into a Catholic church, I could literally feel Christ. It was his energy and the energy of his mother that I always seemed to gravitate to. It felt like I knew them and had a strong connection with each.

The other part of church was a mystery to me. I couldn't get into it, let alone understand it. Even as a child it just felt all wrong. It preached love and compassion, yet all I felt while sitting through a service was judgement and separation. Many times, I would study the people when I was in church. It always felt icky to me to see someone who I knew the very night before was drunk out of their minds and physically or emotionally abusing their families. Yet, the next morning, there they were, sitting in the front pew with their arm around their wife. Their children were well-dressed and sitting quietly, as the parents sat nodding their head in agreement with every word the priest uttered. Simultaneously, I'd notice them craning their heads around looking to make sure everyone knew they were there. I sensed that they needed to be seen as a faithful family of the community. I always felt myself to be an observer of actions and words spoken by others. And, as far as I could see, the whole church experience didn't feel right.

I didn't understand how the priest could talk about how a woman was to obey her husband because he was the head of the house. Not when I knew the amounts of violence that plagued a number of the families in town. He would also say it was a sin to get a divorce and start another relationship. How could it be a sin to divorce a man who was beating his wife and family black and blue with fists and words that scarred them for life? I guess maybe in a perfect world that might be a different story. From what I was witnessing, there were an awful lot of families that were silently suffering the effects of alcoholism and abuse. It was a huge problem in these small towns.

I also felt there was way too much emphasis on money during the sermon. I understand that it must take a lot of money to keep a priest, nuns, and an extravagant building for everyone to gather in. That's a no-brainer. But to make sure that ten percent tithing came up at least five to ten times during any given sermon seemed a bit over-the-top. It also bothered me the way they would post for everyone to see who gave what. To me that was a way to shame people into giving more. I'm sure that some could give more. But I also think that it caused families to feel even more shame for not being able to give as much as was expected.

Maybe that is why I chose to sit in church alone instead of during a service. There I could feel the truth of what our relationship with God was really supposed to feel like. No man's interpretation of the written word, but the truth of what my heart felt and knew. And that was far different than what I had heard or witnessed in any of the churches I had experienced thus far. To me it should be all about love, compassion and treating others with respect.

CHAPTER 8

Marriage & My First Born

EASTON WAS WHERE I met my first husband. We dated most of my senior year and he proposed to me right before I graduated from high school. Ron had a huge Catholic family that I loved like my own. They were a little quirky, but who was I to talk? I don't know that I really knew Ron all that well. I think I said I would marry him because he threatened to enlist in the army if I didn't. It was also a good way to get the hell out of the house. Those are good reasons to get married, right? As I got to know him more and more, I fell in love with him in the way someone who didn't know what love really was could. **Honestly, I think a lot of people fall in lust, and think that's love. It's pretty hard to fall in love when you've never experienced it, or had it modeled for you. When you've never experienced feeling that deep love, you can only guess what it would feel like. It's easy to think hormonal surges could be love.**

What concerned me was that Ron had a very jealous streak and liked to brawl. You know how they say you marry your father? Well, it seemed like that was pretty much what I was doing. We were about a month out from the wedding and I knew I needed to call it off. I went to my parents and told them what I was thinking. They responded by telling me that I had made my bed, now I could lie in it. They had already put money down for the wedding reception food, and over their dead body was I going to embarrass them by doing this. They assured me that I probably was just getting cold feet and it would all get better. Just ride it out. I caved in and got married.

I had to become Catholic to marry Ron. It was a sin for a Catholic to marry another faith. Another sin I didn't know about! I had to sign papers stating that I would bring my children up as Catholic, which I had no intention of doing, or we wouldn't be allowed to get married. I also had to take First Communion which meant I had to be confirmed again. That was to be my third round of catechism. I had already taken five years of it in two different churches. You'd think I would have known the Bible frontwards and backwards. I also had to absolve all my sins through confession.

I'm sure the priest in charge of converting me rolled his eyes more than once. I seemed to buck at every new piece of Catholicism he presented. To me, confession was an absolute joke. I told the priest that I didn't believe that I had to have someone else forgive my sins. I could talk to God myself if I thought I had done something wrong. I also told him that I didn't believe in purgatory or that God was a jealous and angry God that proclaimed us sinners. I felt him to be a kind and loving God, and couldn't understand why he was made to be so elusive and scary through the Catholic teachings. He really had more of an open mind than I had figured and we got into all sorts of philosophies together. I actually enjoyed our time getting to know one another very much. At the wedding, he announced to everyone that I was a "new" kind of Catholic, and I knew that he meant it with absolute fondness.

The wedding went off without a hitch, but I was extremely nervous through the whole thing. Not really having my heart into it didn't help matters. The only thing that broke it up was when the flower girl started sobbing in the front of the church as she stood next to me. I finally bent over and asked her what was wrong and with tears in her eyes she looked up at me and blurted out "I'm too young to get married!" The whole place went into a fit of laughter! It was priceless! I did explain to her that it wasn't her getting married but me, and finally the light went off and a smile beamed from her the rest of the time. Poor little thing, no wonder she didn't seem very interested in being the flower girl. **Children are very perceptive. Who's to say she wasn't feeling what I was feeling and just acting it out.**

The honeymoon seemed to be jinxed. I got my moon cycle on the very first night. We got in a few pretty big disagreements. And, I left my purse with all our wedding money at a restaurant when I went in to use the bathroom. I didn't figure that out until about 30 minutes down the road. Thank God an honest couple found it and held it for us until we got back. We didn't have a lot of money so we kept fairly close to home. After a few days, we went to set up our first apartment in Waterville, Minnesota.

Things were pretty normal, at least as normal as I could gauge what normal was. It didn't take long to figure out that I had to once again be a chameleon to keep the peace in the marriage just like I had to growing up in my home. My husband could be very moody and didn't like when I bested him at anything. If I wanted to keep the peace, I needed to lose in cards and playing pool, as well as never contesting him in any way. Whenever I didn't behave how he thought I should, he would wait until we were out driving, then drive as close to the ditch as possible at really high speeds. All the while telling me it wouldn't take much to lose control and roll the car with both of us in it.

Even though I was on the pill from the start of our marriage, I found out I was pregnant seven months later. The first pregnancy was an early miscarriage. I went back on the pill and six months later I was pregnant for the second time. This time there were no problems and I was ecstatic even though the pregnancy wasn't planned. While various people tried talking me into college, I had no interest in it. I knew from the time that I was little that I was meant to be a mother, and I was beyond excited!

My first born took 18 hours of horrific back labor, but the minute he was put into my arms everything faded but the immense love. I had no idea you could love someone so much! He was incredibly beautiful in every way. I couldn't wait to get out of the hospital and take him home.

Randy was an easy baby. He was really good natured and slept a lot. Sometimes I would try to wake him up just so I could hold him. Things went really well until around six weeks old. I had been warned to watch out for signs of a hereditary condition called pyloric stenosis that ran through the genes on my husband's side. It is a condition where the valve from the small intestine that connects to the stomach won't open to let the food pass through. Because it won't open properly, any food that is swallowed gets projectile vomited back out. For some reason, it is usually inherited by the first-born male in a family.

The projectile vomiting is literally like the vomiting that happens in "The Exorcist". You could be with him propped up on your shoulder in the middle of the room and his vomit would hit the wall. Poor little guy. We took him in to the doctor but they kept holding us off on the surgery. At seven and a half weeks he weighed less than he did at birth, and still the doctors kept putting us off. Finally, I told them that if they didn't do the surgery that I was going to take him somewhere else and get help. I think they were trying to stall us until our regular pediatrician got back from vacation. Hell, hath no fury like a mother protecting her child. His surgery was done the next day.

Because the surgery cost a lot, I knew I would need to find a job or we would never get it paid off. I took a manager's position in an ice cream store in the mall. All was flowing well until a day when I was in the back room making ice cream favors for a wedding. I had just served several people who were sitting on the other side of the wall contently eating their ice cream. The front door chimed alerting me to a customer, but I knew it was one of the owners. He always jingled his pocket coins as he walked. He also wore very distinctive cologne that I could smell well before he reached me. As he walked through the back entry, I told him hello without turning my head. I was fully into my task and didn't care to stop. He asked me how things were going and then playfully said "Hey, give me your hand!" I didn't think much of it, so reached my hand back behind me. I was thinking he was going to give me a piece of candy.

Instead, he placed his penis on it. I screamed and asked him what the hell he thought he was doing! He kept trying to hush me and would nod his head towards the front where the customers sat. He told me that I had asked for it with my teasing manner, and he knew I wanted it as much as he did. I told him he was out of his mind and that I had half a mind to tell his wife what he had done. I took off my apron, washed my hands, grabbed my coat, and left. This marked the start to unwanted older male advances that plagued me for a very long time.

Our marriage only lasted a few years. I found out that my husband would rather hang out at bars than come home and spend time with his family. It was something we just couldn't seem to work through. His family all advised me to divorce him. Yet, when I did, they all turned their backs and refused to have anything to do with me.

It was a long and painful separation. I tried to get him to go to counseling but he refused to go. Often there were drunken calls with him stating he had a gun and was going to kill himself unless

I came back. It didn't take long to figure out that it was his way of once again trying to manipulate me. After several of these threats, I finally told him that if that was what he needed to do, then he should go ahead and do it. Who was I to say that he should stay if he really didn't want to be here? He never called again.

In the three years of separation while waiting for the divorce, I didn't date. It didn't even cross my mind. I worked and came home to be with my son. One of my friends told me she thought I needed to go to a dance and just forget about stuff for a night. I had to admit, it had been a long time since I did anything fun just for me. I decided to join her and go. It felt good to do something proactive and fun again, perhaps it was time to start a new chapter in my life. I wasn't there for more than an hour and while walking to the bathroom, I was grabbed in a choke hold from behind. I was stunned and confused as to who would do something like this to me. Especially in front of all these people. As I turned to try and get a look, I caught a glimpse of my soon to be ex-husband. He was staring at me with so much rage and jealousy that it chilled me to the bone! All the Tae Kwon Do lessons I took and I couldn't even make a move to help myself. I was frozen with fear. I begged him to stop, but it was like he couldn't hear me. As I looked around, I saw people staring, but not one came forward to help. There were even four police officers standing up against a wall. It was like a nightmare where I had no control. I began to fade in and out and wondered if this was the way my life would end. Finally, anger kicked in and I got a surge of energy. I finally broke loose. I remember feeling so confused and enraged that not one person had come to intervene.

Writing this now I see the parallels with my mom the night that she was dragged by the hair down the stairway so long ago. The feelings of immobilizing fear and helplessness that most likely ran through her was what I had experienced in this situation. It really does make me wonder how tied into the karma of our lineage we are, and how it affects one's life. I do believe each generation comes in to help heal our family lines.

CHAPTER 9

On My Own Again

THE BILLS PILED up, the house payments were being missed and I cringed at the thought of it, but I finally had to take a job at a meat packing plant to keep everything going. My job was as a trimmer. Trimmers are the ones who stand on a grated steel bench about a foot off the floor, while moving lines of hams go by. They pull off a ham with their stainless-steel hook which they hold in one hand. With the other hand, they take an extremely sharp knife and trim off the fat and bad spots. Then they throw the meat back on the belt where it falls off into a big tub. After that, they press it together and make canned hams. Oh God, how I hated my job! But it paid the bills and afforded me to keep my house.

I worked 40 to 45 hours per week. There were a lot of nice people, but it really was an awful place to work. The workforce was mainly male with a lot of minority workers in the mix. The company treated us like slaves. Everything was about profit. We were continually being expected to put out more finished product, which became an unattainable goal. Literally, there were times where the meat would be piled up so high, that it would start falling onto the floor. You would think that they were smart enough to figure out that it wasn't a good way to keep the flow of productivity going. But then, there were many things not up to par with this company.

I had worked there about a year when I began to notice that fumes were starting to invade our workspace. It would make people get dizzy and nauseous. Several times I told them that something was wrong and each time they ignored it and said to just pay attention to my work. They'd take care of the rest. All the while they kept sending more hams down the line. It happened any time someone complained. I guess they thought it would scare us from voicing our concerns.

At one point, the fumes were so bad that I started to get incredibly nervous and shaky. A couple of the women fainted and fell onto the floor. One of them was six months pregnant. She fell with a knife still in her hand. I don't know what came over me other than an intense fury that I felt over the stupidity of what was happening. I walked over to the stop switch, and pulled it down to stop the line. Then I started shouting for everyone to leave the building. Several of the men helped the two women who had fallen and carried them out. Others were in a state of shock. It was like they were frozen in place and needed to be told what to do in order to break their stupor.

Once everyone was out, I called 911 for ambulances to come. Then I called OSHA and reported what had gone on. Several people were taken to the hospital, some just needed some oxygen and fresh air for their symptoms to fade. The company probably could have padded the incident without further harm and gone back to their production, but my call to OSHA had a repercussion that the company would not be able to sweet talk their way out of. For the next year and a half, there was a walkout of all workers. I became the secretary of the union, and a strike ensued.

Day after day we picketed the entrance into the plant, trying to thwart the new workers from going in. It was a very hard time financially. The pay while on strike was a fraction of what we were making previously, but we stuck it out. Finally, after a year and a half the company conceded and reinstated its workers with a pact from the union. Now, I'm not saying that I believe all places should be unionized. In this case I felt it was absolutely necessary in order to create a safe working environment.

Going back to work there was bittersweet for me. I was the one who had forced an evacuation of the building and reported them, which caused the strike to unfold. I'm sure they also felt that I was the reason the union was instated. The lead people were watching me nonstop looking for anything they could write me up with. Three write-ups in a short time and you are able to be fired. I knew what their game was. I was extra careful to make sure that my work was impeccable. After a time, I just couldn't take the pressure anymore. It felt like my time there was at an end.

I called the lead man over to me and looked him in the eyes. Then I shoved a ham in his belly as I said "Here, stick this up your ass. I'm sure it will fit because you're one of the biggest assholes I've ever met." I gave him a pearly white smile, put my tools on the bench, and left. There is no amount of money worth the compromising that I did in that workplace. All I could feel was peace flooding deeply into my body. Was I scared? Hell yes! I had no idea how I was going to keep everything afloat and make a good life for my son. But I knew that things would work out somehow. They always did.

After things had settled, I met a few of my previous coworkers for a beer at one of the local bars. It was one of the few times I went out. It was there that I met the man that would become my second husband. Sam and I dated for six months and then he moved in. During our time together, I began to have a continuous menstrual cycle. I went in several times to check into it and was referred to an oncologist. He told me I had a suspicious pap smear that looked to be cancerous and suggested that we do a freeze of that area and see if it would improve. I did the procedure but the bleeding continued. The doctor gave me iron shots to boost my blood count. He also took me off the pill, but it still continued. After 11 months I was given a D&C. He told me if that didn't work to stop the bleeding within a month, that I would need a total hysterectomy. My dream of having a big family looked to be fragile. I did a lot of praying for healing to fix it. Almost a year to the day, my bleeding stopped. I was warned that I would never be able to be on any form of birth control again, and that I may never be able to conceive another child. But something in me knew that I would.

During Sam's time living with us, I don't remember a time that he helped pay for groceries, or house payments, let alone the bills. Sometimes his mom and dad would come and bring some groceries. I think they knew what he was like so they wanted to contribute. I felt we were going nowhere and it was feeling more and more draining having him there and not contributing. I drew up my courage and decided that I was going to ask him to leave.

That night he came home from work and was acting really nervous. As I started down the steps to go outside, I started to open my mouth to tell him that I needed to talk to him. Before I could get it all out, he grabbed me by the wrist and blurted out "Will you marry me!" It was almost like he knew.

He explained that he had waited so long to ask because he had to feel secure that he had enough money to support me. I'm not sure that he ever thought about how it was off my back that he was able to save that much money up, but then that was just as much my fault for allowing it. I could have talked to him about it many times, but I just couldn't seem to get the nerve up to say what I felt. I've looked back at this point in my life many times. How could I be such an advocate for others, and yet not be able to do it for myself?

I thought about whether it was right or not for quite a while. We were just so different from one another. Part of me wasn't sure if it was going to work. Sam was handsome, a very hard worker, incredibly intelligent and could fix anything. It was also nice that we were used to one another. But then there was also that other side where he could be controlling, self-centered and stingy with his money. There was also a fear that he would never be able to be a really good father to Randy. He had been there for several years and I saw improvement, but he still tried to control a lot around him, and it made me uncomfortable. **My biggest advice to people out there contemplating a marriage with an instant family is to forgo it if you feel there isn't a willingness to try and have a relationship with your child, Watch carefully. Actions speak louder than words**. That was not to say that I was perfect. Just look at all the craziness I had been programmed with growing up. I'm sure he could have made a list just as long for me and perhaps even longer. The other part of me felt my biological clock ticking. I knew I wasn't getting any younger. Did I really want to put another four years into finding a partner?

I was really confused, so when I was at work one day, I decided to hash it over with a wonderful older man that I trusted and adored. After explaining it all he looked at me and said "You know Barb, I really love you, and think an awful lot of you, but I don't know how easy it would be to live with you." I took that to mean that all of us had faults and that I should be looking at the good and not the bad. Perhaps that was what I was doing. After all, none of us are perfect. My biological clock won. I married Sam on the first day of spring. I thought spring was an appropriate time for new beginnings.

CHAPTER 10

My Second Marriage

THEY SAY THE Universe puts obstacles in your way when you are going the wrong way. If the wedding was any indication of that, I was making a huge mistake. Sam's mom had a broken thumb. My sister, Sandy, who was the maid of honor, had been attacked the night before and scored a black eye. My dad had brain surgery two days before the wedding. And, the night before our wedding, a major ice storm hit keeping a lot of people from attending. Other than that, the wedding went off without a hitch. We had a home spun reception out at the family farm.

Our honeymoon night was spent going to the Mayo hospital in full wedding attire to see my dad. I hadn't been able to see him since he had his brain surgery. I knew he felt really bad about not being able to be at the wedding. We were only gone a few days, then settled back in at the house in Klemme, Iowa. Things went far better when we were married, than when we were living together. Maybe being married just made everything feel more relaxed because we both felt more secure. Sam was a good provider and the differences seemed to fade as we created more of a unified dream for the future.

During this time, my grandma called and asked me if I would be interested in becoming a manager for my great uncle who owned several pizza places. He wanted to hire new blood into several of his eateries and thought with my cooking skills I could possibly work out. He was in a town nearby, and said he'd like for me to come there so he could talk to me about it. We set it up to meet the next day at the Holiday Inn. A friend could drop me off and was going to wait at a sports bar until I finished. It was only a few blocks away, so that worked out perfectly. I could walk there as soon as I was done.

My great uncle told me to go to the front desk and ask to ring his room when I got there. When he got the call, he would come down to have supper with me. The receptionist told me he had left a message that he was running a bit late. I was supposed to go on up to the room and make myself comfortable. I thought it was a little weird but maybe older people were just like that. Our family had stayed with him and his wife several times when things went wrong at home. It wasn't like we were strangers. I certainly didn't feel like I shouldn't trust him.

I walked up to the room and knocked on the slightly opened door. As I walked in, I could hear the shower running so I yelled out that I was there. He yelled back to help myself to a drink while I waited. I didn't want liquor, so began to pour a glass of water. As I began pouring, I heard the door to the bathroom open and hurried footsteps coming towards me. Before I could turn around, he had jumped on my back buck naked! He had his arms around my neck and was using his legs to pull me backwards towards the bed. When I stumbled backwards, he threw me down and jumped on top. Holy Shit! This guy was at least seventy years old and I was just twenty-five. I couldn't believe what was happening! I fought with all I had and pushed him off and onto the floor. Screaming I asked him what the hell he thought he was doing. Then I ran out the door not willing to let anything else happen.

In hindsight, I should have gone to the front desk and asked for the police to be called. Instead, I thought how much it would hurt my aunt and grandma to hear what happened. I walked as fast as I could back to the bar where my friend was waiting for me. Once there, I decided to sit in my car for a while so I could think things through and calm down. Tears of anger and repulsion washed over me as I sat there and released the shock of what had just unfolded. Hoping that it would help to recenter me, I rolled down the window to breathe in the fresh air.

In the rearview mirror, I saw a car pull up behind me and stop. Out jumped my great uncle, begging for me to talk to him. I figured he wanted to apologize, but was sadly mistaken. He walked over, put his hands through the open window grabbing my face on both sides. Then he stuck his head in and tried to force me to kiss him. It was unbelievable! I reared my head back and kicked the door open as hard as I could. The force of it caused him to lose his balance and fall to the ground. When he fell, I got out and ran into the bar. I told my friend everything and when she followed me back out, he was gone. No wonder he needed to reorganize his business. He probably was doing similar things to other women.

My grandma called to see how it went and I told her that I was uncomfortable with it and it wasn't a good fit. I couldn't tell her the truth. I knew it would have hurt her deeply. Why make her feel bad? She had no idea what her brother was like. She was only trying to do me a favor. I did tell my parents, but it just seemed to make them uncomfortable, so I chose to let it go.

For the life of me I couldn't understand what makes a guy behave like that. I am a friendly person but I certainly had no thought of a sexual encounter with my great uncle. Nor any of the men who had tried to molest me. In fact, it was the furthest thing from my mind. The examples that I share here in these writings are just a sample of the times it has shown up in my life. How many women have the same kind of stories?

The statistics say that one in every three women have been sexually molested in their life. Some are leaning towards one in every two. Within those statistics, it was shown that more than half of the molestations were done by family members. It's no wonder that there is so much dysfunction around sexuality and so much healing that needs

to take place around sexual abuse. When I feel into it now, I can outwardly see the dismantling and destruction of the human consciousness around sex. There has been a desensitization in the sacredness of sexual intimacy. That has been done through, the sensualizing of women and children, all types of pornography, bringing too much awareness around sexuality at too early of an age into our school systems, and the inability to communicate comfortably with others. I feel that this has been done by design. It disconnects the heart from the act of intimacy, which is the most powerfully creative and healing emotion in the human consciousness. It is said that two people who are in love and know how to consciously create through their higher understandings, can bring new worlds into existence during their climax. They can also send healing out for one to three miles around them affecting all in their path. How sad that sex has become distorted for so many within humanity.

CHAPTER 11

My Second Pregnancy

THINGS WERE GOING well in Klemme. We had a few good friends and I really liked our neighbors. I could also see that Randy and Sam seemed to be bonding a little better. Randy was such an awesome kid. I loved his imagination, and how much he loved to share and please. He could be completely content playing with a shoe box, magnets, little animals and string. The only thing that he really ever asked for, and it was repeated over and over, was a baby sister. He'd been asking for one since he was three and at this time, he was seven.

In December, I found out I was pregnant. I knew it was a girl. I don't know how to explain that, I just knew. Besides, how could it have been anything else with all the wishes Randy was putting in? I worked through the sixth month of pregnancy and then my doctor told me that I wasn't gaining enough weight and I had to quit my job. It was either that, or I would end up on bedrest. It was so hot that summer, and I was so big and uncomfortable. Sam and Randy were constantly doing things to help me feel better.

One day they brought a giant squirrel cage fan from the farm to cool me off. Sam plugged it into the wall and turned it on with me in a chair three feet away. It was crazy powerful and it was heaven for a mama with raging hormones. I spent a lot of time in front of it. Another time, I was feeling really low and moody and they came out dressed up in fifties clothes. Their hair was slicked back with leather coats, and tight pants. I couldn't quit giggling as they led me outside to a chair with a BB gun leaning against it. The chair sat back a good twenty feet from the clothes line. When I asked what they were doing, Sam told me he and Randy had made up a game. It was guaranteed to help take my mind off how uncomfortable I was.

Sam explained he was going to pretend he was the duck at a shooting gallery. The clothesline was the perimeter for him to go back and forth. I was supposed to use the BB gun to shoot him. The rules were no shooting above the chest, and I had to make sure I didn't hit him below the belt in the front. Oh My God! I couldn't do that! I told him I couldn't shoot him, but he insisted that the gun was really low power. It wouldn't be able to hurt him or go through his clothes. He was too well padded.

They both begged me to, so I picked it up and aimed. Sam started walking like a funky duck away from me and I took a shot hitting him in the backside. He threw his arms up and jumped as he quacked, spun around and waddled in the opposite direction. At first, I was mortified! But then I broke out into fits of laughter! Ok, maybe they were on to something. I took another shot. This time it hit him in the chest. I broke out in laughter again as he quacked and spun. It was working! The laughing was clearing all the hormonal monsters I was dealing with. The ideas these guys were coming up with were pure genius!

Out of the corner of my eye, I spotted the couple next door standing in their upstairs bedroom window. They were staring at us with an expression of horror on their face. We were going to have to sort things out with the neighbors. I waved them to come down. When they got there, they asked us if everything was okay. Then there was the expected "What the hell are you doing?" After we explained the whole thing, they were in on the action. We were all laughing hysterically! It was exactly what was needed.

A lot of the time that I was pregnant, Sam had been working at a nuclear power plant in Michigan. The economy was weak here and there weren't many jobs to be found. He tried to come home on weekends but at times it was impossible. We made it work, but of course I would have rather had him home with us. His job in Nebraska turned out to be a short-term thing because he got overexposed too many times to radiation. The rules and regulations forced them to let him go. I was glad that he was going to be working somewhere closer so we could spend more time together. It was hard always being separated when I was pregnant.

This pregnancy actually hurt and I wanted it to be over with. I could literally feel the baby scraping her fingernails back and forth inside me. It was like she was sharpening them. I also had a lot of false labor. A couple of times I thought that it was time and went in. I certainly didn't want that to happen again, so I waited until I was having contractions three minutes apart. When we finally took off for the hospital, I didn't think we would make it in time. I had her 23 minutes after being admitted into the hospital.

There were several names picked out, but the minute they handed her to me I knew the name I had written down as a teenager was it. Her name was Paige, and she was one of the prettiest babies I had ever seen. The first thing my husband and I checked out when they laid her on my chest were her finger nails. Yup, they were sharpened to a point.

It took eight years, but Randy finally got his wish. He got his sister and was the best big brother anyone could have asked for. He adored Paige, and spent every minute he could with her. Several times during the early morning hours I would wake up to the sound of the rocking chair next to her crib squeaking. When I went up the stairs to check it out, I'd find Randy rocking with her cradled in his arms just staring at her. It melted my heart to see how much love he had for her, but it also became an every-night thing. I finally had to put a stop to it when the teacher let me know he was falling asleep in school. Paige also needed to be able to put herself back to sleep after a short period of fussing. It finally came to tying a metal crib spring on top of the crib so he couldn't get her out anymore.

She had him wrapped around her little finger and knew at an early age how to wield it. Randy would always rock her and push her around in homemade diaper box cars that he had expertly detailed. He helped her learn how to walk, and read to her constantly. Nothing could compare to the contentment that I felt being able to have these two beautiful children and stay home with them as they grew up. I loved being a mom and felt perfectly content in my life.

CHAPTER 12

Creating a Family

AS TIME WENT on, I began to see a start of a rift between Randy and Sam. I talked to Sam about it and noticed things would lighten up a little, but before long it would slide back to the same old behavior. There was a noticeable difference in the way he treated him compared to his sister, and my heart broke for Randy who was still such a little boy. I watched as his confidence started declining. Their relationship was definitely taking a turn for the worse. I was seriously considering leaving, and then I found out I was pregnant again. I prayed I was going to be able to help fix what was going on.

This pregnancy was a lot easier. The baby was a boy, and he hiccupped all the time. It was so funny to see my belly shaking up and down with each round. Thomas was born 15 months after Paige. When

I was giving birth, there were four women in labor, and only one doctor on duty. I had a monitor in the form of a tight belt wrapped around my belly. It was to make sure things were going okay with the baby. Unfortunately, the belt made the contractions hurt so much worse. In the middle of one of the labor pains I couldn't take it anymore and ripped it off. At some point, one of the nurses came in to check on our progress, and found out Thomas was in distress. They figured out the cord was wrapped around his neck twice. He was shoved back up the birth canal, and I was warned not to push until they could get it unwrapped. After pushing him out, he was quickly taken away. I could feel that things were off and I knew something was wrong. The other babies were pinkish after coming out. Thomas had a funny greyish hue.

When I nursed him, he would often quit breathing and turn blue. That would set off an alarm, and the nurses would come running and take him away. More often than not, I would have to go and see if he was alright. For some reason, they would never bring him back. Usually, I couldn't wait to go home and would leave a day after giving birth. This time I asked how long I could stay. I was afraid of what was going to happen at home if things didn't change.

When the doctor came to check in on me on day three, I could tell something was wrong. He told me that they believed Thomas was mentally retarded and suggested that we consider placing him in a home. I didn't understand and asked him what he meant. He then went on to tell me that there were places that take care of babies like this. Perhaps we should think about bringing him there. I don't know if I was more mortified or outraged. To think that parents would do that to their own flesh and blood was beyond my comprehension. I told him that I doubted we would ever consider doing something like that, and I didn't want him to mention it to me again. We were going to bring him home, and he was going to be part of our family.

The next day we were released from the hospital. I'm not going to say it was an easy path, but it was the path we chose. He had crossed eyes, so had glasses at six months, surgery for an eye duct by eight months, didn't sit up until thirteen months, didn't walk much until he was three, didn't talk until he was eight, and the list goes on and on. He started special education services when he was three. The hardest part was that he couldn't give a kiss or hug without pinching or biting. He also had no understanding of right and wrong. That meant you needed to watch him like a hawk, and put everything up. We couldn't have any plastic left anywhere that he could get at, and strings were the worst. Sometimes I would pull a two-to-three-foot string out of him while changing his diaper. He ate anything and everything. He was also extremely sensitive to sounds and quick movement. You literally couldn't go to anything that was too overstimulating. Because of the way he retreated from sounds and movement, we were also questioned by the school in case there was violence going on. Rearing him was not for the faint of heart. Life definitely got a lot more difficult.

CHAPTER 13

Another Move, Lush Gardens & The Rats

THE ECONOMY WAS still at a lull, things were slow, and Sam got laid off. He was offered a job outside of Austin, Minnesota, on a dairy farm. We packed everything up and moved into a three-bedroom trailer house on a river. It was actually pretty nice as far as trailer houses go, but one thing kept bothering me. When they showed us the house, I noticed a heavy square piece of metal laying on the kitchen floor. It was off to the side by the wall, and under the table. When I asked what it was there for, they told me that some pesky red squirrel had chewed through. They just hadn't had time to patch it up yet. I was assured that it would be fixed soon. We were told not to worry because they hadn't seen any activity since putting the piece of metal down. They also told us that they had put fresh bait out so not to be alarmed if we got a whiff of anything. It just meant the bait was working.

It was a beautiful place right on the river and there was an abandoned cattle yard that they told me I could have for a garden. I was thrilled! I had never been able to have one before. I was beyond excited to get it tilled up and planted. Sam bought me a big Troy-Built tiller and we worked up the soil for a huge garden. I can't tell you the amount of joy and satisfaction I got from planting and growing our own food. Here is where I found out I was pregnant with our fourth child. I felt this would be the last one and prayed he would be healthy and normal. One handicapped child was more than enough.

The garden grew like crazy and before long it was obvious that I was going to have to sell the overflow at a farmer's market. I loved watching everything grow. Because of the fallowed ground that had been covered with cow poop, everything grew to a monstrous size. The kids were very content playing outside when I was in the garden and Randy was awesome at helping out. For the most part, we all liked being out there on the river.

It could be really hard selling at the local farmers market with three kids. Thankfully, once in a while my dad would come and watch them while I took the produce in to sell. Dad did pretty well until the third time watching the kids. That's when I came home to him sitting on the front steps. He was white as a ghost and crying like a baby. I couldn't imagine what could have happened!

Evidently, Thomas had gotten ahold of a ripped off corner of a doggie treat bag, and had eaten it. Randy ran to his grandpa to tell him that Thomas was in trouble. When Dad got to him, he was passed out, blue, and couldn't breathe. He checked his mouth and saw a piece of plastic lodged way down in his throat. Unfortunately, he couldn't reach it with his fingers, so he started shaking him upside down to try and dislodge it. He thought for sure he was going to lose him. Finally, after what seemed forever, he vomited it out. That is when he went to sit out on the steps. All he could say was "Don't you ever ask me to babysit your kids again!" Poor guy, he was really traumatized.

Sam's job kept adding more and more hours. It was way over what had been agreed on and with no extra pay. The guy had him at his beck and call. We rarely got to see him. He would be gone early morning and usually come home after the kids were asleep. He'd be so tired he could barely keep his eyes open. I would try to stay up until he got home so I could at least make sure he had some good food in him before he went to bed. One night, I got up after a short nap and went out to fry some bacon for a BLT. There were paw prints in the left-over bacon grease. The darn squirrels had found another way in. There were tracks all over the counter!

At night when we were lying in bed, we began to hear running back and forth under the trailer. It would go on for hours into the night. More than once, the smell of a decaying animal seeped in. I was losing a lot of sleep because of the constant smells and noises.

My nephew, Dirk, came to stay for a few nights so he could hang out and help with the kids where he could. Since we didn't have an extra bed, I made up the couch for him. I had set a live trap with an ear of sweetcorn on top of the counter to trap the squirrel. He was to let me know if he saw or heard any action.

Around 1 a.m. I heard him quietly walk back to my bedroom. "Aunt Barb, what is all that noise under the trailer?" I told him it was squirrels and he said "Oh, ok." I guess he was satisfied with that because he went back to bed. An hour later he came back and said "Aunt Barb, I hate to tell you this, but those aren't squirrels, they're rats!" I asked him how he knew and he said he saw one peek out of the cupboard and climb up onto the counter. I went out into the living room and sat with him on the couch. Sure enough, the cupboard door squeaked open. A rat stuck his head out to look around, and it started to climb up onto the counter. Dammit! I hated rats!

I told Dirk that I'd leave the lights on. Hopefully it would keep them away. What else could we do at that time? In the morning we would get out and go to Grandma and Grandpas. I gave him a BB gun and told him he was free to shoot anything that moved. Unless, of course, it was a human. We needed to try to sleep until we could get going in the morning. At 3 a.m., I heard him on the phone talking to his grandma and grandpa.

He asked if they were up yet, and could they please come and get him. There were rats and he was too scared to stay out here. Well, I don't think they were up, but I don't blame him for wanting to leave.

The next morning, we packed everything up and went to my parents for a few days. Then we moved back to Iowa. Sam had talked to his parents. It was decided that we were going to take over the family farm. They were getting ready to retire soon anyway. Wow, we were going to be farmers!

CHAPTER 14

Moving to the Family Farm

IT WAS INTERESTING to me that I was in Iowa again. I really didn't like Iowa much. As far as I was concerned, the land was too flat and not pretty. There was hardly any natural water. The farmers took out all the trees to get every last inch of farmable land that they could. There were also way too many hog confinements there. It made me nervous about the aquifers that supplied the drinking water. Before I met Sam, I had thought about moving back to Minnesota. It's funny how life works out. I guess for some reason, Iowa was where I was meant to be.

The farm was the typical 160 acres with a farmyard that consisted of a machine shed, barn, work shed, some grain bins, and a four-bed-room house. The house was really old. It was pieced together from a general store, a corn crib, an old house that first sat there, plus an addition that was added on many years previously. Sam's great aunt and her husband bought and started the farm. His parents took over after his great uncle had passed away. Now, it was our turn.

I had never farmed before so this was another new experience. I was so excited to till up a space for our family garden and get a bunch of ani-mals. You know, I'm not sure why I never seem to be able to start out slow with things. I seem to always go just a hair over the top. We started out with buying 400 chickens, and then worked into thirty ducks, eight turkeys, two geese, four sheep, thirty pigs and ten cows. We also bought an incubator to start hatching out our own eggs. I did that more for the kids, because it was educational and a lot of fun. They really enjoyed the animals, except when it came time to clean up the poop. And believe me when I say that there was always an overabundance of that!

My favorite animal I raised was a Canadian goose that we hatched from an egg. The neighbors had brought it over from the nests built by wild flocks near their cow pasture. There had been a typical late snowstorm and the neighbor knew the eggs had been abandoned. We took in four eggs to incubate but only one hatched. We named the gosling Feiffer. He was the cutest little fuzzball on two legs I'd ever seen! I loved the way he peeped and followed me around everywhere. Sometimes we'd bring him in the house because he would throw a fit when I went in. Geese poop all the time, so in the house, he had to wear a diaper. I know, pretty ridiculous but it sure was fun, and we absolutely adored him!

Feiffer grew fast and I got the surprise of my life when I left one day to get groceries. I was driving down our gravel road, and next thing I knew he was flying right next to me! It was really awesome, but I was afraid he would get killed by an oncoming car, or cause an accident. After all, it's not every day you see a car and a Canadian goose going down the road side-by-side. I turned around and took him home. It broke my heart to think of locking him up in the barn. Instead, I decided to make a seat for him and let him get a taste of riding in the car with me. Then he could still travel with me and he'd be safe. I know, a little crazy, but I never did color completely in the lines.

I made a seat out of an old dish tub lined with tinfoil. On top of that I added a board that could hold his body up to the right height. There was a gap in the back with a splashboard so he could just poop into the tub under him and not get anything on the seat. I put Feiffer on his new throne and couldn't believe that he sat there so well be-haved. Our dogs didn't sit that nice. Ok, he made it through the first hoop, but that didn't mean he would sit there going down the road. When I took off driving, all was well. He absolutely loved it! I had the window rolled down on the passenger's side just far enough for his head to stick out the window and see. He'd stick his bill out and make these really cute noises as he slid his beak back and forth over the top of the window. It was hilarious! I don't know who was enjoying it more, him or me. Unfortunately, we had to turn around again. It seemed people seeing a goose riding in a car caused too many heads to turn. Turning heads, meant swerving cars. It was just too dangerous. Poor Feiffer was forever banned from the car!

After that, I knew I had to wean him off from human contact. I worked with him every day to stay outside and he finally seemed okay with being in the pasture with the cows. Sadly, one night he got attacked by an animal. Whatever it was had done damage to his right leg, and the vet didn't know how to help other than to put an antibiotic cream on it. We put Feiffer in a round partitioned fence with water and freshly gathered food around the clock. He really meant a lot to me, and I didn't want to see him die. Every day I would rewash and sterilize the wound and put new ointment on it. Unfortunately, it didn't seem like it was healing.

I was on extra alert for the animal that was starting to come in and take birds. I figured it was probably a weasel, a fox, or a coyote. I wanted to make sure that Feiffer wasn't going to be attacked again. One night I heard a bunch of ducks sounding off. I ran out of the house without even as much as putting my glasses or shoes on so that I could protect the birds. I was hoping the culprit would finally be caught.

All I could see was a black blob like one of our farm cats coming towards me. I started putting my hand down to give it a quick pet before going on. When it got about five feet away, I saw a white stripe running down the middle of its back, and took off running across the yard. No matter where I ran, the skunk was chasing after me. It must have been quite a sight. A skunk chasing an eight-month pregnant woman in her nightgown with bare feet. I started yelling until my husband finally heard me. He came out with a gun and shot it. I'm pretty sure it had rabies. It was certainly abnormal behavior. There was no more going out to check on things. I promised to wake Sam up if things went bump in the night after that.

On the fourth day after Feiffer was attacked, my mother-in-law came over and asked if she could see him. I thought it odd, but brought her over to the pen. She picked him up, looked at his wound, and walked back to the grove of trees with me in tow asking her what she was doing. When she got to the trees, she took a knife she had hidden from my sight and stabbed Feiffer in the chest. Then she threw him in the grove. Holy Shit!!! I couldn't believe what I had just seen! I was shocked that such a sweet lady would do something like that! She said she was sorry, but somebody had to put the poor animal out of its misery. I grieved and was angry, but in my heart, I knew that she was right. He more than likely wasn't going to make it, and he was probably suffering. It was just a very hard thing to see and experience. It would be one of my many heart pulls of getting too close to farm animals. They become such pets, and yet the day comes when they are going to be sold, or butchered.

We bought a bunch of little piglets from my friend, Bree, to raise. I liked when we bought them from her, because I knew she gave them a lot of love. When I got our new batch in, I was baffled. Every time I did chores, they kept rolling over on their back and kicked their legs in the air. I could tell they were trying to make sure I was looking. Afterwards they would look puzzled, get up, and check out my pockets. I couldn't imagine what they were looking for! Finally, I called her. She explained in a shy voice that she would bring M&Ms with her while doing her chores. Often, she would roll them over onto their backs, rub their bellies and give them an M&M from her pocket. Of course, I now had to follow suit!

The piglets grew so fast! Before you knew it, they were grown up and ready to be sold. I always had a very hard time with the animals being loaded up into a trailer. I knew what was coming for them and it was hard to think about. I waited around until the help came, then I was going to go to the house. Sam had asked a few men to help load the pigs up and they were all standing there ready to do the job. One had a hammer, one a board and one a steel rod. It didn't take too long to figure out that they meant to make sure the pigs knew who was boss. I was mortified, and wasn't going to have any of it. I told them that you could just walk them into the trailer nicely. They needed to put their implements down. One spouted out "Oh ya? Well maybe you should just show us how to do that!" I told them I'd be right back and load them myself. I'm sure they were having plenty of laughs talking about me while I went to get my supplies.

I went to the house, grabbed a bag of M&Ms and poured them out onto a tray. When I walked into the pig pen, I rattled the pan and put it low so the pigs could see. Then I walked up into the trailer pigs in tow. They followed me like the Pied Piper. Once all the pigs were in, I made a line of M&Ms down the middle of the floor. As I backed out of the trailer, I told them how much I loved them, then swung the door shut and latched it. Before I left, I looked at the guys and said "See, you can do it a nice way." They all stood their speechless. Of course, I cried for hours after the trailer pulled out.

CHAPTER 15

My Fourth Pregnancy

THIS PREGNANCY WAS a pretty easy one. I still had false labor, but it didn't seem to start as early as the others had. Again, I knew this one was a boy. And if all the flipping he did in my womb meant anything, he was going to be an athlete. I was glad that the drive to the hospital would only be twenty minutes this time. We even got there about two hours before the actual birth. Everything felt good and I didn't even worry that this would be another handicapped child. I just knew everything would be fine.

I'm one of those women who become very internal when in labor. I don't like to talk or be touched. Especially when in a contraction. Poor Sam could never do anything right. I wanted him there, but half the time I think I was yelling at him to not touch or talk to me. In the next breath, I'd be asking him to rub my back.

The hardest thing about this delivery is that I got a nurse that would come in constantly. She asked me all sorts of unnecessary questions when I was in a contraction. And, she couldn't get a needle in to start the IV to save her Soul. I kept it together for a little while, but on her fourth try she botched it again. Blood started spurting everywhere. I finally lost it. I put my foot against her stomach, and shoved her back while yelling "If you don't know what the hell you're doing, get someone in here who does! You are not going to stick me again!" She flew back, hit the wall and slid down landing in a sitting position on the floor. Oh my God! I still can't believe I did that, but one can't be held responsible when they are in labor, can they?

Brent was born on December 22nd in the middle of a snowstorm, and after he had been delivered and the nurse had taken him off to clean him up, I grabbed the doctor by his tie and said "Ok, this is it, I'm done! Can you please talk to my husband about getting fixed?" He just looked at me and smiled. Guess it wasn't up to the doctor. We were going to have to have "The Talk."

I fell into a deep sleep after getting cleaned up. In the morning, a nurse brought Brent in and laid him in my arms. I was anxious to get to see him again. The night before was a blur. I looked down and saw the cutest little boy, but I was puzzled. I looked at the nurse and said "He's really cute, but where's my baby?" She looked at me confused and assured me that it was. I said "This is not the baby I carried." She told me that I was the only mother in the hospital that had given birth. She assured me that there was no other baby but this one. It had to be my baby. They watched me for a while. Perhaps they thought I had postpartum depression. I guess in their place I would have wondered the same. Why else would someone say something like that? I didn't understand what was happening, and I was certainly at a loss as to why I felt the way I did.

That day haunted me for a very long time. The whole thing was so bizarre! I thought about it off and on after I brought him home and wondered what was going on. Part of me felt so horrible to think that I said that to the nurse. She must have thought I was crazy. I never told Sam about it. It was one of those things that were unnecessary to ever repeat again.

Brent was a precious little boy, and I wouldn't have traded him for the world. He was the perfect addition to our growing family. I think he had it a little harder from the start because Thomas was still in a very fragile place. Normally babies at least get a little spotlight time. Brent had some serious competition. I had to watch him constantly to make sure that Thomas was behaving around him. He would think nothing of grabbing Brent's leg and pulling him off wherever he was lying. I think that was when I grew the proverbial eyes in the back of my head.

CHAPTER 16

Wishing on a Well

DURING THE NEXT few years, we grew our farming operation to incorporate 600 instead of 160 acres. Sam also decided to go to work at a local factory. I had to give him credit, he wasn't afraid to work. I helped him as much as I could, but one can only do so much when they have four children, a garden to keep up, and animals to take care of. That on top of all the cooking and household chores that needed to be done. It definitely seemed that there wasn't enough time in a day.

Sam's friend, Tim, lived just a few miles down the road and lived with a woman named Sharon. Tim used to put me on edge because he could be a very crude person. It took me a while to feel somewhat comfortable around him. His partner Sharon, had a really strong personality, but was very sweet. She would come to visit every couple of weeks so the kids could play together and we could visit.

When her kids were very young, Sharon found out she had a terminal brain tumor. It grew really quickly and she ended up in the hospital. On one of my trips up to see her, she was having a particularly rough time. I decided it was best to take her daughter out of the room to a little park area. I figured that it was a much better place to be until things stabilized a bit more. In the park, there was a little fish pond with tons of quarters in it. She wanted to know if I had a quarter that she could use to make a wish. I thought that was an excellent idea. Danielle took the quarter, held it tight in her little hand, and squeezed her eyes shut while she focused her prayer into the quarter, and threw it in.

I looked at her and said "That was really sweet, Danielle, what did you wish for?" She smiled at me and said "I wished that you would have another baby boy." Confused, I asked her why in the world she had wished for that? She looked at me with such innocence as she replied "Because you're supposed to!"

Two months later, I found out I was pregnant again. To say that I was in a state of shock was an understatement. I think the whole family was shocked. Damn that wishing well! This would be my last pregnancy come hell or high water! I talked and argued with Sam until he finally gave in. The vasectomy was scheduled four months before the baby was to be born. Honestly, the procedure really only took around a half an hour from the start of us coming in, to the finish of his one or two stitches to cinch the small incision up. What the heck! How could there be any question as to which sex should be sterilized? Thankfully, there were no problems after it was done. Otherwise, I would never have heard the end of it

CHAPTER 17

Riding the Line Between Sane and Crazy

THERE WAS ALWAYS so much work to do with farming and having a large family. I was tired and overwhelmed a lot. Sam worked his job at the plant and farmed, so he could rarely take care of the kids. I pretty much had to do everything on my own. It was a major deal to get ten minutes, let alone a few hours, to myself. With Thomas in the mix, there weren't many people who offered to babysit. I was always so thrilled when I thought I finally had a babysitter that was going to work. Sadly, after one time, two tops, they would never come back. So, whatever was needed to be done was done with the kids in tow. Grocery shopping was the worst!

I'll just fill you in on this one incidence and I think you'll understand why I rode the line between sane and crazy on a regular basis. On this particular trip, Randy was visiting his dad, Paige was six, Thomas five, Brent two and I was eight months pregnant with Linden. We were really low on groceries at home so I knew this was going to be a two-cart full mission. I put Thomas in one cart, and Paige pushed Brent in the second cart. It didn't take long before I knew this had the possibility of turning into a disaster.

We were just getting started and I noticed that Brent needed to go to the bathroom. He was being potty trained and had the thick underwear instead of a diaper so I had to take him quickly. Paige watched the two carts and Thomas, while I took him in. When we got back, he wanted to walk for a bit and that was fine. If he started to act up, I'd just put him back in the cart. I started smelling something almost right after the bathroom break and checked Thomas to see if it was him.

That is when I noticed Brent kicking his foot as if trying to get something off it. As I looked closer, I saw what I thought was a little round turd sitting on the top of his shoe. So much for potty training underwear on an outing! He started squealing while trying to kick the proverbial turd off his shoe. As I started walking over to bring him back into the bathroom, he gave his little foot one last sharp kick. The little turd went flying through the air, and landed near the feet of a lady standing nearby. I quickly picked it up with a tissue and a humble apology as I hauled Brent off one more time to the bathroom. This time he went back into the cart. I couldn't afford any more delays.

Everything that I put in the cart with Thomas, he started grabbing and throwing back out onto the floor. I'd bend over to pick them up, and he'd nail me in the side of my head with another thing! Well, one jar of applesauce and three new lumps on the head later, I finally figured out that I would need to put everything in the front of the cart where he could no longer reach them. I could now help poor Paige push her almost full cart and pull the other cart with Thomas in it behind me. Unfortunately, now that he didn't have things to throw, he began to grab and pull things off the shelf. After a jar of mayo came crashing to the ground, I knew I needed to stay in the middle of the aisle as much as possible.

This worked way better, but soon Thomas was signing to me that he was hungry. I told him that if he was patient, I would buy everyone a treat for the trip home. Lucky for me, as we got to the end of the aisle there was a lady giving out free pizza samples. We were each handed a small slice and then she informed us that she was also making root beer floats. I politely told her thank you for the pizza and no thank you to the root beer floats. She insisted it was no problem, and took it upon herself to hand each kid a small one anyway. Oh, well what could it hurt? I'd hoped it would keep them busy for the last few aisles. By the time the sugar kicked in, we would be done and able to leave.

I rounded the next aisle and noticed a lady from the store kneeling down on one knee stocking the shelf. She had beautiful curly blond hair that was piled up high on top of her head. I thought I had cleared her with plenty of room but because of the scream I heard, I guessed not. When I looked back, Thomas had a sinister look on his face with pizza firmly gripped in one hand and his other one buried in her hair. Evidently, he had pulled her over onto the floor. I was mortified! I quickly went over to her and unwound Thomas's fist out of her hair while profusely apologizing! Then I helped her to get up as I started smoothing her hair back into place. (Like I'm sure that really made everything alright!)

Thomas's fist was full of his prize and he wasn't going to give it up. He hurried and stuffed it in his mouth. Dang him, he was going to try and eat it! I dug as much out as I could, but I knew he had swallowed a bunch of it. I was so exasperated!

I told the kids that I needed to grab some orange juice, and then we were going to leave before anything else happened. We would just come again another time and get the rest. I left the cart with Thomas in it at the end of the refrigerator/freezer section while I quickly went to grab the juice. I heard Paige sternly say "Thomas how could you! That was a very naughty thing you did back there to that lady!" Thomas let out a war cry and threw his root beer float way up into the air! When it hit the ground, it exploded, hitting everyone and everything in its path. We were all in a state of shock!

I'd have given anything for the ground to swallow me whole! There was root beer and ice cream all over the doors to the freezer cases, in people's carts, which meant all over their groceries, and worst of all, over two or three shoppers. I had never seen such a mess! One elderly lady actually had one of the globs of ice cream on top of her head and it was dripping down the sides and front of her coat. I profusely apologized again, and said I would go and get some help. By this time, tears were running down my face. I told the kids we were just going to go pay for the groceries and go. I couldn't just leave them after all the trouble we'd caused. Over the loudspeaker I heard, "We need several people to help in the freezer aisle, again, we need people to help in aisle four."

The cashiers were kind and pulled us into a closed checkout line and started ringing up our groceries. The lady was wiping off each package that had been splattered with pop and ice cream and I told her that it was ok. I just wanted to get out of there as soon as possible. I told her that I'd wash them off when I got home. Unfortunately, the groceries wouldn't scan until they were cleaned and dried. You can imagine how long this whole process was going to take. Eventually, we made it through one cart, so I pulled the second cart with Thomas into place. The other lanes were three or four carts deep. A lady who wasn't in the know pulled her cart behind ours. She kept trying to talk to Thomas and had her cart way too close for comfort. I told her that things hadn't gone well. It would probably be to her benefit to back up a bit. He was known to take things out and bite them. She, of course, laughed and said it was perfectly fine. She had several children of her own, so no worries. Well, ok!

As the second cart was being scanned, the checker said "Oh my, I'm going to have to get you a new package of hotdogs, there's a bite taken out of this package!" I assured her that it was probably Thomas and it was ok. I just wanted to get out of here before anything else happened. There were several of those strange bites in packages. I told her again it was fine, our fault entirely. I gave a sigh of relief as she scanned the last of the groceries. Soon we would be out of this nightmare!

That's when we heard the lady behind us yell out "Oh, no!" As we all turned around, Thomas had a hold of the front of her cart, head bent, and was throwing up over all her groceries. Well, what do you know? Hot dog chunks, pizza, pop and the missing hair, all over her groceries! Nothing could have made me feel any worse than I already did. All I could do was apologize once again, as workers went to replace everything in her cart.

I think I cried the whole way home. I had so much frustration raging through me. I finally had to pull the car over and get out. I screamed and screamed at the top of my lungs as I spun around in circles. My poor kids didn't know what to do. At one point I heard little Brent ask Paige if I was alright. All she could say was "I think so Bubs, I think so." The next grocery adventure was my husband's!

CHAPTER 18

My Fifth and Last Child

AGAIN, I KNEW this pregnancy was a boy and that he was healthy. This one was a very quiet baby, and I rarely felt him kick or turn. Sometimes I was afraid he had died in utero. I could literally go weeks without feeling movement. Once in a while, I would shake my belly just to see if I could feel a little protest. Every time I went in for a checkup, they assured me everything was fine. What could I do but give it up and just allow things to play out? Like I had any control over it anyway.

Linden was born right at the start of corn planting on May 3, 1990, much to the dismay of his dad. I think this one was really undecided as to whether he wanted to come out or not. The labor would stop and start and stop and start. The doctor's patience was finally at an end. He said we needed to induce labor. I really didn't want to put drugs into my body knowing it would go into the baby's bloodstream. I had never had any drugs with any of my other children. The doctor assured me that women did it all the time. There was no ill effect on the child. I finally conceded.

The contractions while in induced labor are even more intense than normal. Things still weren't progressing the way they thought it would. So, he broke my water. Finally, Linden decided to make his debut. I was shocked because he looked almost exactly like his brother, Brent. It was amazing how two different babies could look so much alike.

Let me tell you, having a baby in your 20's is far different than having one in your 30's. I couldn't believe how much harder it was. I could tell that my muscles weren't as strong or supple. It also took longer to recuperate and gain my strength back. To say the least, I was glad this was my last birth.

CHAPTER 19

The Move Changed Him

I REMEMBER WHEN we moved out onto the farm my mother-in-law pulled me aside and told me that being a farmer's wife could be a lot of non-stop work. If I helped out in the field, he would always ask me to work with him. She said, "Take my advice and act dumb. Then they'll do it themselves or hire someone to help." I thought that was a horrible thing to do, as well as manipulative. Looking back at it now,

I think they were wise words from someone who had been there. The more I tried to help, the more he asked me to do.

Saying no has always been one of the hardest things for me to do. I had a hard time standing up for myself. As I write this now, those words seem silly. Here is a woman who structured a whole school sit-in and started a strike at a meat packing plant. Yet, in my relationships with men, I could never seem to stand up for myself. It was like there was something inside me that didn't feel like I had the right to. I also think I was afraid our relationship and family would be torn apart. Instead, I was passive aggressive. I was pissed off a lot but kept it all in, later to come out sideways. Unfortunately, this was usually in inappropriate times and ways.

Knowing what I know now, I understand that we attract that which we are most familiar with. In my case it was men who didn't value me and always tried to shut me down. We also attract what we most need to work through. For me, that was taking my power back from those I willingly gave it away to. I needed to learn to voice my opinions and stand up for what I believed and knew to be right. I also needed to quit dimming my light or shrinking who I was to keep the peace. Relationships are a hard, but beautiful, mirror to show you things about yourself. Sometimes you see it and work it through. Other times you can't see it to save your Soul, and end up attracting another person to you to help you grow.

I had an alcoholic father and my first marriage was to an alcoholic man. My second marriage was to a man who was a dry drunk. That means that he held qualities of an alcoholic, but no longer drank. So goes my proverbial quote to the many: "We spend our whole childhood getting fucked up, and spend the rest of our adult life trying to get un-fucked from our childhood."

Since moving to the farm, I saw a difference in Sam. Not so much right away, but there was a noticeable difference as the years went by. Before we moved, he was a bit more even keeled and we got to spend at least a little more time together. After moving to the farm, he seemed to take on a different persona. We were together a lot more, but I couldn't have felt more alone. I could see the kids pulling away from him as well.

The farm seemed to be more important than our family, our marriage, having a social life and everything else that most families deemed normal. It was like he had some deep need to prove how competent and successful he was to somebody. Maybe it was to everybody. But ultimately, it seemed he had something to prove to himself. He became obsessed with how the yard looked, how much land he could farm, and how people perceived us.

His mind was always racing ahead to what needed to be done next. There was little down time. The poor kids could seldom just be kids. They were always expected to be working. He would always rant "God Dammit! If I have to work, then you guys can too!" What he couldn't understand was that he was the only one putting pressure on himself to make everything perfect. The kids and I would have rather had his time. None of us cared about the money. Family and time spent together were more important. It wasn't that any of us minded working, it was just we didn't want to work all the time. There was this silent code that if they heard him coming up the steps from outside everyone would throw stuff on the floor and start picking it up. Or throw some dishes in the sink and pretend they were washing them. This became our farm life reality.

I asked him to go to counseling several times, but he would never consider it. I think he was more afraid of someone knowing he was going than the actual going in itself. **Doing the counseling work that I do now I feel that one who keeps too much in the work cycle and stays too busy, usually doesn't want to look at what they hold inside. They're afraid to feel their way through the things that have happened to them in their individual lives. They keep all their hurt and anger buried and don't want to deal with it.**

In reality, it is imperative for each of us to take time for ourselves. It is only through being still and looking inward that we can see the unhealed places, and begin to unravel them. It is also the only place that we can get guidance for our lives. It is there that we wake up to the understanding of who we truly are. The understanding of what we came here to do and experience.

I understand men think differently than a woman. The book "Men are from Mars; Women are from Venus" didn't get famous because it was only another good read. There are actual differences

in the way men and women think. Men tend to think in terms of making sure that their family is taken care of and being proud of what they've built to be their legacy. They're providers. Women tend to think more about the emotional and physical stability of the family. They want their children nourished in love and imagination. Women are nurturers. I see these roles blurring some today and love it, but back then I still saw the proverbial mom takes care of the kids and the house; dad makes the money and builds the empire. Both are intricate parts in having a family as long as they are in balance. When things get out of balance, it creates a home out of balance. Our home was definitely a home out of balance.

CHAPTER 20

The Breakdown & Healing Through Love

SOMETIMES THERE ARE experiences in life that crash us. Those crashes often create a catalyst to our awakening. Although they are very hard to go through, crashes often create an opening within you that can forever change the trajectory of your life. Crisis can, and often leads, to an awakening.

Sam and I had talked about my upbringing before. He knew the one thing that was the most traumatic for me was when someone yelled at the supper table. One night, it finally happened. He yelled at the supper table and it instantly catapulted me back in time to the night when my dad shattered the lightbulb all over our food.

I calmly got up from the table and went into the bathroom so the kids wouldn't see me crying. I decided that maybe it would be a good idea to run the tub full of hot water and just soak. While lying there soaking, I begged God to take me. I told him that life was too hard and I wanted to leave. I didn't much care how, as long as I could go.

I told him that the kids were old enough now and I thought they'd be okay. I just didn't want to be here anymore. I cried and cried, until I didn't think I could cry anymore.

While releasing the tears and sadness, I began to notice that the burgundies and creams in the tiles were starting to separate. The burgundies gathered to the burgundies and the creams to the creams. I was mesmerized as I watched everything shifting and merging together in solid, yet separate colors. When the process finally stopped, there was a perfect silhouette of Christ's head. It was about ten inches high by six inches wide, and rested where the tile met the side of the tub. I couldn't believe my eyes! I kept tracing the outline in awe wondering how on earth it could have happened.

Out of the corner of my eye, I could see the same movement start at the foot of the tub. Colors from the tiles started separating and merging until the perfect silhouette of Mother Mary formed on the wall. As it was all miraculously unfolding, unconditional love was being flooded into every cell of my body. I allowed the energy to flow through me as it fed all those places that had felt and experienced so much lack. It was incredibly intimate and beautiful! I can't even come close to describing what I felt. It was a love that was so pure and encompassing that it literally transcended the hurt that I carried in my heart. There was also a knowing that was emitted as it washed over and sank deep into my cells. I knew that it wasn't my time to leave yet. I still had a lot that I was here to do and experience. This next part of my life was going to look very different. As I was able to feel deeper into the energy, I knew that it was true. I told them that I would stay.

I'm not sure how long the experience lasted. Time felt suspended while I was in it. After stating that I would stay, the energy began to dwindle. I knew the experience would soon be done. I so wanted to share the silhouettes with my children. As I put on my robe, I opened the door and called for the kids to come to the bathroom. Of course, by the time they got there, the silhouettes had already vanished. It was a personal experience and wasn't meant to be seen or experienced by anyone else.

Later that night, I told my husband what had happened. I thought maybe it would open up something in him, but instead of being able to talk about it, he begged me not to tell anyone. He said he was afraid it would cause a bunch of nut cases to camp on our yard waiting for the apparitions to show up again. Honestly, I think there was more fear around what people would think of us. I had no intention of telling a bunch of people about it. I just wanted to share it with the person who was supposed to be my partner. I wanted to share what I was going through. Maybe I thought that if he listened and understood, it could help him work through some things in his own life as well.

Why is it that women always think they can change people for the better? Especially the men they are supposedly in love with. I would hear stuff like this all the time. "Well, he may be a little rough around the edges, but I feel once we're married, he'll change." It's like they could see the potential there on the proverbial horizon. If they could see their potential, they could overlook the way that they were now. Somewhere inside they believed they would magically change once their feminine influence came into play.

My daughter came to me one day in her early teens and said "Mom, I think I know why there are so many divorces." "Oh ya?" I countered back. "Tell me, why do you think that is?" She said "Women always look at a man and can see his potential. They say "He'll change, I know I can change him," and he never does. Men on the other hand look at a woman and think I am attracted to her just the way she is. They hope she never changes. And yet, they always do." The girl was incredibly perceptive.

The experience in the bathtub had created a lot of questioning in me. I knew that I had been expanded in ways I couldn't explain. Things in me had shifted and I didn't exactly understand what that meant, or how I felt about it. All I knew was that things were different. I felt different. The experience was an opening of some sort. I had more compassion and strength in me. For that, I was incredibly grateful. My oldest sister, Rhonda, was the only other person I shared my experience with. Through the years, we had become closer to one another. We both felt there was a spiritual nature to this existence and we both wanted to understand it at a deeper level.

Several months later, she told me about a reading she had experienced. She had gone to see a psychic and thought maybe it would be good for me to do so as well. After hearing the tape of her session, I thought she was getting taken advantage of by an absolute crazy woman. I honestly have to say that I was worried that she was being taken for a ride. I decided to make an appointment and check her out.

The day of the appointment, I was more than a little apprehensive. To pass time while waiting, I paged through a book that was lying on the table. It was hard not to notice there was a lot of talking going on in the room that the reading was taking place in. I could hear a lot of soft mumbling and laughter. The longer I sat there, the more nervous I became. I started to wonder if I should just leave, but the door opened, and I was called in as the other person left.

Joyce seemed to be a nice enough person. She broke the ice by telling me how much she enjoyed my beautiful sister. Then she wanted to know if there was anything specific that I wanted to know. If not, she would just begin and see what came through. I told her that I was open and would just see what came through. Besides, why would I want to give her any kind of information that she could glean anything from? I wasn't going to say a word.

My sister didn't warn me that Joyce went into a trance and could look a little strange while doing so. That may have been helpful information to have had beforehand. I sat there almost frozen as she slumped in her chair with her head bowed down to her chest. It was odd, but I could sense an energy hovering in the room, and an energetic connection being made. Finally, after a few minutes, her head started to rise and face me with her eyes closed. She had black lines running down her face from her mascara. Then her face contorted as she began to speak in a different voice. The first thing that popped out of her mouth was that they knew that I was there checking her out to protect my sister. They told me that was fine, because it got me there. Okay, I started to get a little freaked out.

The energy that was talking always referred to itself as plural. They called me Mary over and over. I know she knew my name was Barbara, as she had said it several times before she went under. After that, they told me that I had been placed in a sweet spot. It was important for me to be in the Midwest, because I was safe there. They told me nobody would know who I was. (I was really confused. What the hell were they talking about?) The voice went on to say that it knew that my heart was troubled by what was going on in my life. It said I would always be surrounded in protection and love. I was told not to worry for things were going to change.

They went on to tell me that I had been a monk several lifetimes and that I loved baking bread. Baking had always been a very holy practice for me. When I baked, I put Christ's energy in it. I was also told that they had taken a rib out of me to make more. They said that in this life it was important that there was more than one of me because I had a lot to accomplish, much more than one physical lifetime could achieve. The reading went on with some truths, and a lot of things I didn't fully understand. The pinnacle was at the very end when she leaned over to me like she was telling a big secret. Three times she repeated "They switched your baby at birth you know." Holy shit! I was not expecting that! It went on to explain that there was another son that was to be born and had often gone in and out of the fetus while I carried him. At the last minute there was a switching of the birth order. The other son, for whatever reason, needed to be here sooner. There had been a switch. If I had had false teeth, they would have been laying on the floor! That one piece of information was invaluable to me. Now, I could finally make sense of that birth that had happened so many years ago. It finally put all the dots together. I could now let go of the guilt. It also helped me to understand the reason why the little girl at the wishing well had said what she said. There indeed needed to be another baby, or the one who had given up his birthing order would not have been born. My mind was blown!

I reeled the whole way home. I didn't know what to think! I decided not to share anything that was said with Sam. He was already becoming uncomfortable enough with me the way it was. Why give him any more to worry about?

CHAPTER 21

My Life in Constant Motion & The Fall

BY THE TIME the kids were all in school, we were farming 1,000 acres. We also had cows, pigs, chickens, turkeys, ducks, sheep, cats and dogs that needed tending. I was headmaster in the local farmers markets and starting the schematics of erecting a bakery. Sam had a full-time job. The kids were in five different school districts. That meant five different parent teacher conferences, musical programs, sporting and after school events. I felt like the van never quit rolling down the road. We were all in constant motion.

Randy and Sam really started banging heads together about this time. Sam was incredibly hard on him. Several times I caught him kicking him in the backside while yelling at him to do things faster. I tried to talk to him, but it would only change for a very short time before starting in again. Randy was really struggling. Finally, he and I agreed that it may be easier for him to go and live with his dad for a while.

This decision was by far the hardest thing I had ever gone through. It felt like my heart was literally being torn in two. I believe I held a lot of resentment towards Sam because of it. In the back of my mind, I decided that when the timing was right, I would be asking for a divorce.

After that, every time Randy would come home to visit, Sam would purposely make everyone so busy they could barely spend any time with him. Why I seemed to have lost my voice, I simply cannot explain. I can't tell you how many times I cried myself to sleep at night. I just kept swallowing the hurt, and stuffing it in so no one could see it. Looks like my staying here and putting up with my marriage, was no better than what my mom had done. At least she tried to leave, I was too scared to.

With Randy gone, Brent was now the oldest able-bodied boy to help his dad. It was time for him to become Sam's new butt shadow. The poor kid's attitude started changing from a free spirit, to an angry young man. Several times he came to me and asked if I should get a divorce. I told him that there was no way that I could get a divorce right now and take care of everyone, especially Thomas. It took two parents to raise him.

Things became more and more hectic with all the responsibility we had in keeping the farming and extra jobs, plus the kid's schedules flowing smoothly. It was affecting us all. There were many times when I was afraid of something happening to one of the kids. Sam didn't seem to understand how dangerous doing things on the farm was for those that didn't fully understand how to be safe.

At one of my farmers market days, we were halfway through market and I started to have a horrible feeling in the pit of my gut. I knew I needed to hurry and get home, so started packing up. There was an incredible amount of angst running through me! Before I was finished, a police car pulled in. I knew without a doubt in my mind that something bad had happened to Thomas. I felt my stomach lurch as they told me he had fallen off one of the grain bins and was in pretty bad shape. He had been transported by ambulance to the nearest hospital and I needed to get there as soon as possible.

Driving to the hospital was one of the longest rides of my life! I could only speculate as to what had happened. My heart sank when I saw him lying there with his grandma standing next to him. It was evident that he was in a lot of trouble. Half of his body seemed to be swollen twice the size of the other from the waist up. He lay there with so much pain in his eyes I didn't think I was going to be able to keep it together. I made eye contact and told him I was so sorry and I would stay with him and not leave. All that he could do is repeat "I hurt," over and over again.

The doctors explained that they were unable to give him any pain medication until they fully understood what was wrong. Because he was mentally handicapped and couldn't explain exactly where the pain was, they felt they couldn't help him. They weren't equipped to treat him at this particular hospital. He was to be transferred to the Mayo Clinic in Rochester, Minnesota.

I looked at his grandma and asked her if she knew what had happened. She told me that Sam was cultivating at a farm away from home. Evidently, he had left a note on the table for Brent and Paige to level off two of the grain bins as soon as they got home from school. You never let kids up in a grain bin without supervision. Sometimes a crust forms on the top of the grain. If they break through the crust they could sink, and there would be no way to pull them out. Evidently, they were up in the bin leveling, and Thomas decided to join them. The note had told Linden, who was then 8, that he was supposed to make sure that didn't happen. How he thought an 8-year-old child was supposed to take charge of his big 14-year-old brother who is mentally handicapped was beyond comprehension.

Paige and Brent tried to help Thomas down the ladder, but his foot slipped and he fell 18-feet landing on his butt and back. Linden said he tried to catch him, but he missed. Oh My God! My head and heart reeled with so much anger and fear! All I could say to Sam's mom was "I will never forgive your son for this, not ever!" Poor Grandma, it wasn't her fault, I just felt so helpless and angry. In reality, it was as much my fault for not leaving this situation before now. Had I left, my poor son wouldn't be laying here in so much pain right now.

Thomas was transferred to the hospital in Rochester, Minnesota. Those three days were without any medication. They had found some internal bleeding and said if meds were used, it could cause complications that he wouldn't be able to alert them to. His stay had to be medication-free until they knew exactly what was going on. I did everything I could possibly think of to help soothe him, but of course it couldn't stop all the pain that he was dealing with.

Finally, they came back and said the bleeding had stopped. They could now give him pain medication and work on setting all the broken bones that had been caused by the fall. One of his shoulders was in bad shape and he had a broken bone at the top of his arm. He also had broken several of his toes, his pelvis, and a leg. They said there were 13 breaks in all and they were going to have to put Thomas in a full body cast. He also needed to be in traction for a month in the hospital.

The doctors were going to start that day by putting him in the body cast. During the procedure, he would need to have screws put in his right knee for the traction to be hooked up to. When he came back to the room, it was obvious that they had put the screws in the wrong knee. I could see where they had taken them out and started over on the other knee. Not one word had been said to me about it until I point blank asked them if that was what happened. It was then that I knew I couldn't leave Thomas alone for a minute. He had no way of advocating for himself.

The next day they put him on an x-ray platform to reset and pin his arm back together and put it in a sling. I slept and ate in his room for all but one day of the month that he was there. Thankfully, my parents were able to come and stay for a day while I went home to grab some things and check in on the other kids.

Being in the hospital for a month, and away from Sam, seemed to help me gain a clarity that I could not have had otherwise. It gave me enough of a break that I was able to see my marriage for what it truly was. I also understood I desperately needed to heal some things within myself. I finally saw that I couldn't change him, but I could work on changing myself. I decided I was going to start taking time to do that, however I could.

My husband and the kids came up to see Thomas and me several times. Sam came up once by himself. It was several days after being admitted into the hospital. I knew that there was a lot that I needed to say to him but this was not the time, nor the place for those kinds of words to be spoken. Thomas was the only thing that mattered, and I needed every ounce of strength I had for helping him recuperate.

Even though it had only been five days since we were all at home, my husband now felt like a complete stranger to me. Perhaps it was the change that was happening in me. I had begun to earnestly take a look at the truth of what my life had become and my piece in all of it. I also felt I had closed my heart down so it didn't hurt so much. There was a palpable difference in the way that I felt, and I didn't know what to do with it.

Thomas was discharged a month later in a full body cast. We had to put him in the back of our van with the seats taken out to get him home. He was going to be in a wheelchair for several months and needed constant supervision. All in all, he did really well. I was amazed at how quickly he healed. When he finally got his cast off, we were all in shock. He was literally several inches taller! Perhaps being in traction had lengthened him out a little.

Sam was never able to see that he had put the kids' lives in danger that day, nor was he ever able to take responsibility for any of it. Why, I will never understand. I suppose we all have those ghosts in our closets that have caused us to act in ways that leave others scratching their heads in wonder.

I know that so far this seems to be a one-sided account, and of course it is my life story as I felt I'd experienced it. If you asked him his experience, I'm sure he'd tell you a whole different account of what he believed to have happened. In my marriage, I believed Sam to be an aggressive and overbearing man who always thought of himself first. Everything revolved around what he wanted. I guess you'd have to say he was a narcissist.

I, on the other hand, was a passive aggressive woman full of anger for not being able to speak her mind. I held everything in, letting it come out in inappropriate ways, so I didn't have to address it full on. I didn't take responsibility for what I needed to voice. Is one better than the other? Both ways are a manipulation of energy to gain something. They just look different. **Maybe we draw the perfect person that will help create a balance within ourself. A person who will draw out what we most lack and need to see.**

What if life is far different than what we perceive? What if one of the pieces we are meant to do in our life is to walk through the things that we most fear? There are two fears. One is there to keep you safe, like not touching fire. That kind of fear is obviously not the kind that I am speaking of here. I am talking about a perceived thought around something that makes one paralyzed or to remain in turmoil. Because of the paralysis, there is no forward motion. Every time we walk through a fear, it has no more power over us. It can't stop us from doing what we need or want to do. Nor can it stop us from being who we are meant to be.

Just think of what you could do with no fear. When we walk through a fear, we create freedom for ourself. We are no longer tied to that which paralyzes us. What if when we create freedom for ourself, we create a pathway to freedom for everyone around us?

CHAPTER 22

Starting a Bakery & My Higher Learning Begins

ONE CANNOT FULLY understand what happens to your life when you make the choice to connect to the Creator and the limitless energy of the Universe. To ask for help to understand yourself and what life is truly about. Your life opens up to a world of infinite possibilities. Your world changes. My life was about to change dramatically.

Several months after Thomas was back to his normal routine, we started ironing out the details for a bakery. I know it seems crazy erecting a bakery when you feel you're nearing the end of your marriage. I'm sure we were both feeling it would be helpful for me after the divorce as it would continue bringing in a steady income. It didn't seem like it took very long to take shape once we were both on the same page. We started the arduous journey of erecting a bakery from the ground up. When I was done with it, or had moved the business to another location, the building would be turned into the place where Sam could work on his farm equipment. It was built according to those specifications, and he was incredibly helpful getting the building erected and finished. He also did a lot of the work to get it up and running.

When it came to the financing, he wanted to make sure it was all in my name so that it would build up my credit. It was almost like he was making sure I had a good start once I left. I was ok with that, and actually very grateful for all of the support. I was just to the point that I needed to know where to put the equipment so that it was efficient. I also needed to purchase more equipment. To say I was frazzled was an understatement. I knew nothing about putting together a bakery. That night I prayed for help. I asked God to please send me someone who could help guide me.

The next morning, I got a phone call from a man who had just moved to the area. He told me he had heard buzz about a new bakery I was putting up, and wanted to know if I needed any help. I told him that at the moment I didn't know what I was going to need as far as help went. If he wanted to come over, I would see what he was thinking, and keep him in mind. He answered back that I didn't understand. He was actually a retired baker who for the last 20 years was hired by bakeries to come in and advise them. Before that, he had been a baker for 22 years. I told him that I didn't really have money to pay for his services right now. Again, he said "You don't understand. I am offering to come and help you get set up, and see what you need for free. I just feel I'm supposed to help you out." Thank you, Jesus!

He showed up the next day and we set up the whole bakery! He was an incredibly kind and patient man and I liked him very much. He gave me a name of a person nearby who sold equipment for a good price. Then he came in to teach me how to roll buns and make tight bread loaves. This guy was amazing! I was able to get everything up and running within a month.

Before long, I was delivering to six grocery stores, three delicatessens, gas stations and store outlets along with special orders up the wazoo. Each day that I baked consisted of 100 or more loaves of different breads, 30 dozen cookies, 40 packages of cinnamon and caramel rolls, 15 to 20 dozen buns, 20 strudels, 20 trays of bars, 10 to 20 dozen donuts, 10 dozen breadsticks, 40 loaves of sweet breads, and lots of other wonderful delicacies, in addition to all the special orders. All products were from scratch and had no preservatives. Because of that, they had a short shelf life and needed to be delivered every other day.

In the beginning, I was the mixer, baker, cleaner upper and deliverer because I felt I had to understand each position before I could hire and teach someone else. A typical day was a 2 a.m. start with getting the doughs rising and baking usually until noon. Then I would package and clean up as much as possible. After that, everything was sorted by stores, and loaded in the van. Then it was off to deliver on the road until at least 7 p.m. It was exhausting! Very fulfilling, but exhausting. Farmers markets I could pick and choose when I wanted to sell. It could work around a busy family schedule. There could be no missed days with the bakery.

It didn't take long to figure out that I was going to need to hire help, or wear myself into an early grave. I hired two beautiful woman who were neighbors that lived nearby. They would come in around 7 a.m. to clean up and package all the products. It helped me to concentrate on the baking and expansion of my line. I decided to continue the delivering until I understood grocery stores better.

About six months in, I started losing sensation in my fingers. There were times I would just drop things because I couldn't hold on to what I was carrying. I knew the signs pointed to carpal tunnel because I crossed paths with several people who had just had surgery for it. **It's amazing how synchronistic events or people show up when the Universe is trying to show us something.**

I didn't want to go through surgery. Not one person who I had talked to had said it made much difference. Besides, they had to wear a stiff brace for years after the surgery was done. I began to ask people if they knew of anything other than surgery that would help with it. One woman told me I should try energy work. She'd had good results with it and heard a lot of good things about it from other people. Energy work, I'd never heard of it before. What did I have to lose? I would look for someone who did it, and give it a whirl.

Two weeks later, I found myself lying on a massage table at a private home trying my first healing touch energy session. It was a very pleasant experience, and I don't think I had ever been so completely relaxed. As she ran energy through my body, I could see colors and

STARTING A BAKERY & MY HIGHER LEARNING BEGINS

shapes, even though my eyes were shut. I could also feel different pushes and pulls of energy run through me as she placed her hands on, and above, various parts of my body. Often, it would create uncontrollable jerks or warm and cold spots that affected different parts of my body. I could have stayed on that table the whole day. It was so incredibly relaxing and mind provoking.

Towards the middle of the session, something unexpected happen. I saw Jesus and Mother Mary walk into the room through the closet. They weren't in full physicality. It was more like looking at pixels on a TV set that aren't fully formed to make a clear picture. At first, they stood next to me and lay their hands on my body in several places, like they were helping the practitioner. I don't remember a word being uttered by either of them. I also don't believe the practitioner was able to see them, as she never said a word about them being there. When the two of them were finished, they backed away close to the wall. Behind them I could see another woman. She had long wavy auburn colored hair and her face was hidden by a shawl that she wore over her head. I watched them for some time through my third eye until they disappeared. The session lasted around an hour, but it felt like it had only been ten minutes. I felt like I was in an altered state of awareness.

The practitioner told me that healing touch worked with the principal that everything is energy. When we have an illness or hurt it is because our body is trying to get our attention by bringing disease of thought and emotion into physical form creating a disease or imbalance. When she works on people, she can see and sense where things are out of balance and uses energy to release or move the blockage of energy that was causing the problem.

On the drive home, my mind reeled once again. Just what was this healing touch all about? I promised myself that I would learn more about it during my five hours of alone time while I was getting the bakery up and running for the day.

For three days my shoulders, arms, and wrists hurt more than the previous day. It was a deep ache that never let up. I promised if I woke up with the pain one more morning, I was going to give the practitioner a call and ask her what to do. Things were actually hurting far worse than before I had gone there. It was another restless night of sleep, but the next morning I woke up pain-free. I had full range of motion in my hands and arms. To this day it has never come back. **I guess it just needed time to work through all the blocked areas and emotions that I had buried in the tissue that were causing it. I was also noticing that I felt a lot lighter within myself and had less tiredness and stress.** I decided right then that I was going to become a healing touch practitioner. I had to understand what it was all about.

I loved the early morning time in the bakery because those five uninterrupted hours gave me so much time to think and learn. I was being more and more pulled to study spirituality, so I got books and tapes that I could listen to while I worked. The tapes were by Lazarus, Esther & Jerry Hicks, Eckhart Tolle, Wayne Dyer, Neale Donald Walsh, and many others. Two of my favorite books were healing books by Barbara Ann Brennon which were the "Hands of Light" series, and another by Louis Hayes called "You Can Heal Your Life." I studied these books like they were bibles. I also was guided to listen to a year-long study on becoming an interfaith minister. I was surprised at how much everything in it resonated with me.

For those of you who don't know what the term interfaith means; it is the study and honoring of all faiths and religions. That means whether you're Christian, Muslim, Native American, Buddhist, Christian Science, A Druid, Wiccan, (and so many more), that your way is acknowledged. It is honored as one of the many pathways to the same Universal Omnipresent energy that directs life. It seeks unity in the threads of the common truths that each teaches its followers. Interfaith churches try to bring all people together so they can break down the walls of separation from one faith to the next.

All of the things I studied seemed to wake me up from a deep unconscious slumber. It made me question everything I thought I knew. I could see that my life was going to be uprooted and set on its head and I was excited to learn everything I could.

I also committed to going every three months to see the lady who had given me a reading as well. There was nothing like that around where I lived, and I needed to understand the things that were opening up in me. I got glimpses into some understandings through her readings, but what I really wanted was a teacher. I was so far away from anywhere where the information I was seeking existed.

My sister, Rhonda, gifted me a Soul Retrieval for my birthday that year. **A Soul Retrieval is where someone can look or travel into your past to see where you had trauma and if a fragment of your Soul left to protect itself. In this case, it was a Shamanic practice where the practitioner travels through their Astral Body to follow the fragmented Soul pieces back to their origin. Some say they travel to the realm of the Underworld. Of course, this is not the only way practitioners are able to do Soul Retrievals. It is just how it was done for me in this session.**

I have to say it was a really awkward experience. I went to a house where a husband and wife invited me in and showed me to a room. There I was supposed to lie on a blanket face up. The lady who was the practitioner laid with her head in the opposite direction touching hips. I was supposed to bring a piece of jewelry that I wore often, which was used as a tracking device of sorts. As we started the session, I handed her the piece of jewelry. I was asked to hold space while she traveled to track down pieces of my Soul that had fragmented off. Well, I had no idea what she was talking about, but I was open. She told me to call out to my Soul pieces that needed to be found. When they started coming back, I was supposed to welcome them home. It all sounded pretty bizarre to me. I was more than a little skeptical, but I decided to keep an open mind and see it through to the end.

We both lay there with our eyes closed while her husband held space and drummed a particular beat. It was almost like a heartbeat that lulled you into a trance-like state. The process went on for probably half an hour. I have to be honest, the whole time I was in my head judging how strange it was, and how uncomfortable I felt. After what seemed to be forever, she opened her eyes and had me sit up.

The lady told me that she found three Soul pieces that had fractured off. One was right after I was born. She said I was dropped on my head onto a cement floor, and part of my Soul exited. Another part she told me had fractured off when I looked to be around three and was lost somewhere where there were lots of trees. The lady said she saw a big cat like a lion, or tiger, and I was scared. She also saw that I had an umbrella. Okay, now she's got my attention. I actually did get lost when I was three at Como Zoo for quite a while. I had an umbrella because it was sprinkling and when I walked past the lion's cage, he lifted his leg and peed, some of it hitting me. That was burned into my memory bank. The third piece was when I was getting a divorce from my first husband and she said he was still holding on to part of my Soul. She had gotten it back, and now I needed to invite all the Soul pieces back in and thank them for coming home. She also gave me my spirit animal, which I was never to share with anyone, and that was the end of the session.

When I got home, I decided to call my mom and ask her if she had ever dropped me when I was a baby. The phone went silent for quite a while. Finally, she asked me how I knew. I told her that someone said they saw it and I was just checking to see if they were telling the truth. Mom told me that she and Dad had just brought me home from the hospital and was giving me my first bath. She had just taken me out of the water and was trying to get me over to the dresser where she had a towel laying. I slipped out of her hands and fell head first onto a cement floor. Well, that could explain the learning disabilities I had growing up! Maybe even the words floating off the pages when I read! She said that for three days after it happened, I had a huge angel that stood next to my crib day and night. I asked her how she knew that, and she said that both she and Dad had seen it. They thought that I was going to die. They figured that the angel was waiting to take me. She said that they were really scared, and could barely sleep after it had happened. I was shocked and asked her why she never told me. She replied "Well, you never asked!" What the hell???!!!

As far as the last piece, I am sure that it was the night that my ex had tried to strangle me in front of a room full of people, including the police officers. I wasn't sure what to think. All I knew was that I was beginning to experience things that I had no context for. I was beginning to think that there was a lot in this world that the majority of us weren't seeing, and I wanted to know a lot more. I dove deeper into my devouring of books.

Some of the favorite books I read were ones by people who had extraordinary things happen to them while walking their spiritual path. Things they couldn't explain, but seemed to be triggered by their continual search for the truth and service to a higher power of love. I was in awe reading about how things would just show up for them when they were in need, and the incredible things that would happen while out in nature. I couldn't imagine what it must have felt like, and could only hope that I would get a taste of it myself some-day. Studying spirituality was like breathing air to me. It felt way more in alignment than the life I had been living up till then.

One book I read was about a woman who lived in a remote place in Africa. She started the awakening process and had no one to teach her but her books. She said she would say things out loud and let the Universe teach her. It was how she learned pure informa-tion. Not through someone else's filter, but directly from source energy. I believe source energy meant God, or whatever one happens to call that all-encompassing energy that directs life.

So, one morning after reading one of the chapters in a book about chakras, energy fields, and the universal energy field, I needed clarity. I was starting my bread doughs in the bakery and decided to try my hand at it. I said out loud that I wanted the Universe to teach me about energy fields, as well as the Universal energy field. I didn't really understand how the book had ex-plained it and needed to be shown. Asking for understanding worked for the lady in the book. Why not give it a try for myself?

Around ten minutes later, I heard a voice. It said to turn off all the machines and go outside. It was going to explain what

I had asked for. I said "Right now? I can't leave all of this right now! My dough would raise into a huge mess by the time I'd get back!" (Nothing like arguing about something you had just asked for.) Again, it told me to shut down all the machines and come outside. It wouldn't take long, and nothing was going to happen with the bread dough. Well, who could argue with that? I shut everything down and excitedly went out the front door.

The sun was just coming up creating the most glorious sunrise I had ever seen! The colors were otherworldly. The voice came through again and said "Look around. Do you notice a thin line of energy that is emitted from and around everything?" I looked at the tree, and could definitely see the line of energy that followed the shape of the tree. It was several feet out from it and looked to be a translucent whitish field of energy that I had never noticed before. The voice told me to keep looking at everything around me individually, and I did. The bushes, a flower, the grass, even the weeds. They all had that same field of energy around them. The smaller they were the smaller the field of course, but everything had it. I was told that what I was seeing was an individual energy field.

Then the voice said "Now look into your whole yard. What do you see?" It took me a while, but as I stared at the yard and softened my gaze, I saw all the fields of each individual plant, tree, bush, flower and grass meld together into one unified field of energy. Again, it was a translucent white and it permeated everything. The voice continued **"Everything is made of energy, and everything has a field of energy that it emits. Each field separate in its own right, but it is also part of the one Universal energy field where all individual energy fields converge. That is how one person can affect the many. Whether they do an act of kindness, or harm, it creates a ripple like throwing a rock into the pool. The ripple goes on and on as it washes over others in its path. At first, an act affects only the one, but as its effects ripple out, it alters the lives of many."** I stood and stared for another five minutes reveling in the beauty of this most amazing sunrise. Even more still, that the Universe was here to teach me if I asked. I said thank you and my heart was overflowing as I finally turned to get everything going once again in the bakery. (Oh, and when I returned to the bakery, everything was as I left it.) I was blown away!

I began to share little things with my kids and my niece, Mattie. I'd have to say my daughter and my niece were the most open to at least hear a little bit at that time. With the boys and Sam, it was a constant struggle. They were afraid of the changes that they saw in me. Or maybe they were being influenced by their dads' projections. I guess I couldn't really blame them. Change can be a scary thing. Sometimes I was afraid that I would change so much that I would scare everyone away. Then what would happen? At times, I played in that fear a lot. I often toyed with quitting my search and just going back to the old ways. I could just let everything morph back into the way it was. But in my heart, I knew there was no way that could ever happen. I had to move forward and open to the mystery of where my path was taking me.

CHAPTER 23

Bleed Throughs & Here Come the Ghosts

MY NIECE, MATTIE, called one day and asked if she could ride along with me on one of my delivery days. I was thrilled to have some company on my long drive. I told her to come out to the bakery and we'd take off from there. It didn't take long before she started asking questions about what I was learning. Mattie was very curious and open. I enjoyed our time together very much. Unfortunately, while driving the route, it started to rain. Since it was winter and cold, the rain started turning into sleet. We still had one more town to go to and driving in a big rear-wheel drive van was incredibly nerve racking on slippery roads. I told her we were going to have to ride in silence for a while. I needed to place my full concentration on the road.

The cars were all going super slow. I asked for Arch Angels to be put at the four corners of my van to make sure we were protected. We'd only driven about two miles when we both heard a rustling. I asked her what was going on and she said she didn't know. A few minutes later, we heard it start in again, only this time it was even louder. It was coming from the floor on the passenger's side. As we both looked down, we saw a chip bag that looked like it was blown up and moving around. She started screaming and I told her to pick it up and see what was going on, but she was too scared. She thought a mouse had gotten into it and was now caught in the bag. The bag moved around for a minute longer, and then it just stopped. She finally picked the bag up. There was no hole in it, so it couldn't have been a mouse. We both looked at each other with a confused look. There was absolutely no logical explanation.

A few seconds later, we heard a Harley Davidson motorcycle pull in behind us. I knew it was a Harley because the noise their motor makes is unmistakable. What in the heck was a motorcycle doing out in the winter on a night with freezing rain? Again, we both looked at one another confused, then turned our heads to look back. The motorcycle kicked into another gear as it started to come around the side. It passed us, and pulled back in when it got to the front of the van. The weird thing was that there was a truck right in front of us, so where was the Harley? We could hear it, but there was no motorcycle there. A minute later, it pulled out from in front of us and took off down the road. We were both dumbstruck! The only thing I could chalk it up to, was what I had just read regarding different realities. In the book, it explained that there were many realities coexisting in the same space. Sometimes, when a person raises, or lowers their frequency, there can be a momentary co-mingling between two separate realities. They call it a bleed through. That became the mode of discussion for the rest of our drive together.

There was another teenage girl who was like a daughter to me. (The one who wished for my last pregnancy.) She called me one day and I could tell she was upset. When I asked what was wrong, she replied that there were some strange things going on in her bedroom. Was it possible to come over and help her with it?

The hair on the back of my neck stood on end. I hated stuff like this! She explained that she and a couple of her friends had been playing with a Ouija board. At some point, the marker started moving by itself. It started pointing to different letters over and over, and then things started flying off shelves. She was pretty shaken up. I told her that playing with Ouija boards was inviting in lower astral entities and ghosts to converse with. It was important for her to get rid of the board and never play with stuff like that again. She, of course, had no idea a Ouija board could conjure things like that. They were just trying to have a little fun. I saw the male ghost fade in and out while I was there, but think with the board being burned, he released and went away. Whether he went into the light, or somewhere else, I wasn't sure. I just know he didn't bother her there again.

That encounter must have opened up something in me because after that, I had one ghost experience after another. Usually, they would ask me to tell something to someone they loved. It would happen most often when I was having a one-on-one conversation with their loved one. One particular time, I was driving the last stretch home from delivering my bread. An older lady wearing a white terrycloth bathrobe with pink curlers in her badly dyed red hair materialized in the rider's side of my van. She scared the crap out of me! I had no idea they could materialize in a moving car! Of course, I asked her who she was and what she wanted. She replied that she was a Great Aunt of a friend and asked me to please not give up on her. I was the only real friend she had. I told her that I had tried for years to help her get out of her negative state. I couldn't do it any longer. I had to cut her loose. She didn't seem to be able to change. She kept saying "Please, don't give up on her. You're her only hope." To get rid of her, I told her I would give it one more try. After that, it was up to my friend whether or not she was ready to change. That was all I could promise. It wasn't up to me. With that, she left, and I asked to have that gift taken away. I didn't want to talk to dead people. Ask and you shall receive. The ghost experiences went away. At least for a while.

CHAPTER 24

Jesus & The Hawk

SO MANY THINGS began to happen as the months went by. One of the most beautiful things was that Jesus started showing himself to me. He would come to me several times a week and I would never know when it was going to happen. Sometimes we would talk through mind telepathy. Other times, he would just be there with no conversation. I wasn't scared by any of it, because it all felt very natural to me. It seemed he was there to help strengthen me for the next stages of what was to come. And for that, I would be forever grateful.

It was shortly after his visits started that I began to notice a big hawk hanging around a lot. I thought it curious for a hawk to stay around a farm where there was only open ground with a grove part way around the building site. There was no river, or natural forest where they would normally hang out. Instead, this one seemed to like sitting on wooden fence posts and the electric pole by the barn.

I decided to keep Thomas home a day when I was going to be hauling corn into town. I knew he would enjoy riding with me, and who knew how many more times we would be able to do this together. I could feel the time coming closer for when we would be placing him in a home. Especially since we had been having trouble with his school. For the past year, there had been many things that had occurred that made me wonder if he should even be there. The line of right and wrong had been crossed too many times. Sometimes I wondered if maybe it would be better for him to be in a home rather than leave him in this classroom. I had voiced my concerns many times, but didn't seem like anything was changing. Everyone seemed to be scared of taking charge.

Thomas was super excited as we climbed into the tractor and took off down the road. I started talking to him about school and how he'd be graduating before too long. While riding, I'd casually slip in about how when children graduate, they move away from home. I thought it was good to start getting him ready. Then, when the time came, I hoped it wouldn't be so hard on him. Just talking about it started the tears falling down my cheeks.

Just then, Thomas started jumping up and down with excitement pointing out the side window. I looked over and there was that beautiful hawk, flying right next to the tractor! Every so often, he would turn his head to look in at us, just like Feiffer used to do when I took off in my car. The hawk was incredibly regal. As he soared next to the tractor, you could see every detail of his beautiful body. The wings were a literal work of art with the intricate patterns of color that wove through them. Every piece of him was amazing to behold, but it was his eyes that made a spontaneous connection to my Soul. He accompanied us for several miles on our ride into town, flying near us for short bursts, then flying off, only to come back again. It was an incredible experience, and I was so glad Thomas got to share it with me. I'll never know what he thought, or received, but I'm sure the hawk was there as much for him, as it was for me.

CHAPTER 25

The Man in the Store

THE BAKERY BUSINESS was growing by leaps and bounds. People seemed to know me wherever I went. They were eager to talk to me about my product. I had several newspapers call and ask if they could interview me for a story. One store took a giant picture of me and put it up on their wall. It made me stretch past my comfort zone to be so visible and share my story so openly.

I still laugh when I think about one time when I was delivering to a grocery store and needed to pick up a few things after I had finished. I walked up and down the aisles grabbing what I needed. Midway through, I could hear someone sniffing. I'm not talking about sniffing like when you have a cold. I'm talking taking a deep sniff to really smell something sniffing. I walked on to the next aisle and again I heard someone taking a deep sniff. Three aisles and several sniffs later, I Finally turned around and there was a middle-aged man behind me looking embarrassed. I asked "Are you sniffing me?" He looked like a child caught with his hand in a cookie jar. He finally blurted out, "Oh my God, you smell just like a cinnamon roll! I'm sorry I just couldn't help myself!" I started laughing and told him I'd better figure out how to make it into a perfume. He retorted "I would surely buy it if you did!" We laughed as I showed him to where my bread was located in the store.

I would also get the crap scared out of me every once in a while, by an unsuspecting trucker who via the exhaust fan had smelled things baking. Sometimes they would follow the smell right to the bakery door. They would just randomly show up and walk in. It happened more times than you could imagine. I could totally understand it. To me, there is nothing better than the smell of fresh bread, pies, cookies, or cinnamon rolls coming out of an oven. Really, a lot of baked goods are like that. They remind you of your mom or grandma who made them for you when you were little. I guess it is natural that we equate those smells with the most beautiful momma love.

CHAPTER 26

Wake Up, the Universe is Talking

THE DEMAND FOR my baked goods grew, and more demand meant more and more time spent in the bakery. I was working way too many hours and not getting enough sleep.

During this time, I attended a funeral of a man who I had worked with as a teenager. He was getting old so I wasn't shocked. I just wanted to go there to support his wife and children. On the way there, my mom and dad warned me that his wife had severe Alzheimer's and probably wouldn't recognize me anymore. I could see by the blank stare on her face that it was true. As her children and friends came by to give their condolences, she held a blank stare. There was no emotion, no hug, no recognition, nothing. Just a blank stare. I could see that she was no longer there. When I finally got to her, she grabbed my hand hard and looked deeply into my eyes as she said "You are working too hard, Barbara! If you don't stop, it's going to kill you!" The eyes went blank again as she released my hand. I stood there in a state of shock as I tried to process what had just happened. **I had heard that spirit can talk through others to deliver messages, but this was the first time I had experienced it, at least that I was aware of. I knew in my heart it was a message that shouldn't be taken lightly.**

I loved creating at the bakery. I was right at the point that I could have expanded my business. I also knew how much my body was revolting from taking on so much work and so little sleep. There was always so much to do, even on the days I wasn't in the bakery. The house had to be cleaned, and I still needed to help on the farm. Brent had basketball games which I thoroughly enjoyed and didn't wish to miss. And, I wanted to spend more time with the kids. Randy had started at a vocational school and Paige was researching colleges to attend. I think it was in these couple of years where my devious sideways passive aggressive behaviors started showing up in quantum leaps. Oh, believe me, they've always showed up, but at this point they were a little out of control.

CHAPTER 27

My Sideways Passive Aggressive Humor

MY DAUGHTER HAD met a boyfriend when she went to a college program in Missouri. As is normal for a teenage girl, she pined for him when he was gone. We decided she could invite him to come and visit us for a week. During his time there, I figured him to be a real Mama's boy. He seemed so sheltered about the world. I know, a harsh judgement, but alas, it was true nonetheless. He was nice, just very ignorant about life. He was also very shy and didn't seem to know how to laugh. Perhaps he was just nervous, but I felt his world had never had much fun or gone outside the box much. That can happen when you're born way later than your siblings and your parents are old enough to be your grandparents.

One night, we decided to take a drive to a neighboring town. I told them I would drive and they could sit in the backseat. I would pretend to be their chauffer for the night and was at their command. As we drove along, he would make comments about different things that he saw to make small talk. At one point he asked "What's that?" I looked over and said "You mean the car wash?" He nodded yes, "I haven't seen one of those before." "Really, they don't have those in Missouri?" I asked. "Would you like to see how it works? This car is pretty dirty and could use one. We'll just go through it so you can see how it works." He thought it would be pretty neat to experience.

I lined the car up, chose the wash I wanted, and drove up to the red flashing light. The water started coming out of the sprayer in the front of the car ready to go around the sides. Now was the perfect time. I rolled the back windows down and switched to automatic lock. Paige started yelling as she franticly tried to shut her window. "Mom, what the hell are you doing? We're going to get all wet!" The water started gushing into the back seat of the car through the open windows soaking their upper bodies. They were definitely hopping up and down! Around and around the spray bars went. Next up, was the pink foam. They barely were recovered from the first round and got hit again. This time they were sprayed full of bright pink suds! Both were franticly brushing the soap off their faces and spitting the soap from their mouths when the flapping, spinning, cloth went by flipping more soap into their already fully colored space. They were huddled together in the middle of the seat screaming. I have to admit, they were definitely trying their best to not get hit! The rearview mirror was the perfect TV screen to watch it all play out, and I was laughing hysterically! Time for the last rinse! The final crisscrossing spray to take all the suds off. One more blast of cold water and we'd get to go through the dryer. (Awe, come on! You can't tell me there aren't a lot of you out there that haven't thought about doing the same thing.) It was pretty darn funny!

I rolled the car through the powerful dryer and pulled the car around the side of the building where I stopped. While releasing the locks on the windows and doors I turned around and asked "Well, what did you think of the car wash?" They both just looked at me like deer in headlights. There was dead silence. Then we all broke out in laughter. We laughed our butts off! We were laughing so hard we couldn't stop. One person would finally quiet down, and the laughter would start up all over again. People were driving by staring, so we finally got it together and started brushing out as much water as we could. The experience definitely broke his shyness. I'm not sure if he ever shared everything about his crazy visit with his parents, but I'll bet he's never forgotten his experience at the car wash.

Poor Sam was often the subject to my crazy sideways passive aggressive behavior as well. On one particular night, we were watching a little TV before bed. Like him, I had been working all day. On top of it, I had cooked, cleaned, helped the kids with what they needed and put them to bed. I was exhausted!

He decided he wanted to take a shower and on his way to the bathroom yelled out for me to go and get his pajama bottoms and a pair of underwear. Now, at this time I understand that all I would have needed to do was say, something like "Are your legs broke? I'm pretty sure they aren't, because I see you walking to the bathroom." But I was a martyr besides being passive aggressive. Oh, I'll get his underwear and pajamas all right, but he was going to wish he hadn't asked!

I got the stuff he wanted, stuck it in the bathroom, and sat back down to watch the show that was about to start. It took him about ten minutes before he started figuring it out. He kept shifting around on his chair like he was starting to get uncomfortable. Evidently it got worse as the time went on, because he started wiggling around like he had ants in his pants. I could see the confusion on his face and could barely keep it together as he took a big sniff and said "God dammit Barb, did you put Bengay in my underwear?" I just looked at him with a big smile before he returned to the bathroom. There are many stories, but I think you get the picture.

All of that being said, I do know that passive aggressive behavior is a very dysfunctional pattern. It is often a result from peers that mentally, emotionally, physically, or sexually abuse those weaker than themselves. As a child, it is easy to lose one's voice and feel powerless. When that happens, they turn to other methods to get their way or fight back. It has taken me most of my adult years to be able to at least somewhat say what I mean, and not be afraid to challenge, or argue my point with people. I believe that the Universe has brought forward certain situations in my life in order to help me see and break through those unhealed ways of coping. I'm not saying I don't still have a mischievous streak, but now it's about fun, instead of payback.

CHAPTER 28

Healing Touch

AT THIS JUNCTURE in my life, I decided to take the first level course in healing touch. It was incredible and felt very natural to me. I didn't share that I did energy work with many people because I didn't think everyone would be receptive to it. If my own family was having difficulty with it, I assumed everyone else would as well. **That being said, I now know that if one has a fear, the fear is often reflected back by those around them. Once they work through it, they often clear up the mirrors to reflect something quite different. It is not the case 100% of the time, but most generally it is how it works.** Every now and then people would ask me to do work on them, but at this time, it was seldom.

I got a call from a woman who was having a hard time with her five-year-old daughter not being able to keep food down. She had taken her many places and each had come to the same conclusion. It was all in her head. They could find no physical proof that anything was wrong. They suggested she go to a psychiatrist who could put her on medication for high anxiety and depression. She wanted to know if she could schedule an appointment with me. While making the appointment, she asked if I would make sure that no one knew or saw them at my house. She was afraid someone would find out.

With the way she felt about the secrecy, part of me wanted to say no, but of course I couldn't. I felt I was supposed to try and help this little girl. I had them come over when I knew no one would be there and put her on the table. I explained what I was going to do, then told her to just relax and maybe she would see some cool colors come across her eyes. She was such a sweet little girl.

While working on her, I could see that she had a twisted gut. As I worked on it, I could physically feel the untwisting of it under my hand. I started to see pictures run through my head about what was going on in her life that caused all the distress she was feeling. I talked to her for a while about how to cope with uncomfortable things she may be experiencing and then she excitedly told me about how she saw fairies, flowers and a beautiful river during the session. She also said that waves of colors came through. She was so incredibly open and innocent. I enjoyed working on her very much.

I explained to her mom that while doing the work I was shown that she and her partner were fighting all the time in front of the kids. It was literally making her child so nervous and scared that her gut was getting twisted in the process. Either they needed to get some relationship counseling, or take their fights somewhere where the kids couldn't hear them. I told her that if they continued their fighting, her gut would twist all over again.

If people could tune into the effects of turmoil, stress and emotion on the body, they could understand what it does. Perhaps then

they could unravel the energy that has affected and buried itself in the tissue of the body. A lot of times, the issue is in the tissue. I teach a lot about how one can talk to the parts of the body that are in distress. Once you understand what the main issue is, the body will share how to address it. Once that is done, it will often dissolve away to nothing. The pain is like a fog horn that is trying to warn you about a piece that is out of balance in your life. This is not true for everything that happens to us, but it is true a majority of the time. I feel it could be stated for 65 to 70 percent of what goes on in one's body. Sometimes it is just the luck of the draw, part of your individualized plan, being messed with, needing to learn something, or genetics.

CHAPTER 29

The Divorce Talk

IT SEEMED THE more I opened and learned about spirituality, the more I became aware of things. And the more I became aware of things, the more distanced Sam and I became from one another. I could see through so much now that I wasn't able to before. I knew Sam and I could both see the writing on the wall. I'm pretty sure the whole family could.

I relished the time before I went to bed each night, and used it to pray, connect and do a bit of reading. One particular night I had lit a candle and set it on the stand in the corner of the room. I was told that lighting a white candle brought spirit in. I also liked the soft light when I was in a meditative state. While sitting on the bed praying and connecting, I heard Sam's footsteps coming towards the door. As he opened the door and began to walk in, a voice came through and I clearly heard the words "This is your light." With that, the candle flame grew huge! It looked like it was touching the ceiling and at least a foot across. I stared in shock as the flame lit up the room. Then the voice said "This is what you allow him to do to your light!" And the room went pitch black as the candle went out. Sam spun around and quickly walked out of the room as he spat out "What are you, a witch?" I sat there in utter shock! I had no idea what in the world had just happened.

Weeks later, I was standing in a hallmark shop going through the cards trying to pick one out for our 20th anniversary. I must have gone through 30 cards, but I couldn't relate to one of them. I stood there with tears in my eyes at the realization of what needed to be done. Instead of a joyous honoring of one another, we needed to end it. No more pretending our marriage was okay. No more pretending our family was alright. It was killing me to stay in a marriage that neither of us wanted. I was scared, but I think I had finally gotten to the place where I knew everything would work out. Everything was going to be fine.

I was taught that when you have a family, you should stay together no matter what, for the sake of the kids. I think that staying together just for the kids' sake is disastrous. Staying together for the kids puts them right in the middle of a constant fight between the two people they love the most in the world. A bad marriage filters out through their fragile emotional systems causing damage that they will have to deal with the rest of their life. Children are incredibly perceptive. They know what is going on no matter how well you think you are hiding it.

Everything that I had experienced in my childhood that had created my foundation, was the very thing I through non-action around staying in a marriage long over, was creating in my children's lives. I was staying out of fear. It saddened me to see this piece clearly. I didn't know how I was ever going to make it up to them. All I could do was to move forward in what I knew in my heart I needed to do.

I think Sam was as relieved as I was to finally bring everything to an end. We both agreed that this was the right time for Thomas to be placed in a home, and that he would be the one staying on the farm. After all, it was the farm passed down on his side of the family. I promised I would not ask for a split in the farmland and he would have no right to my bakery or anything to do with that. I would try to sell or liquidate the bakery and its equipment. We also agreed to share a lawyer to get the divorce instead of both fighting over everything. I would find a house to rent in a nearby town and we would share custody of the kids. If I stayed close enough, they could go back and forth until they graduated. It was only the two youngest one's left to finish school. Everything seemed supportive and easy and we both took a deep sigh of relief. This was finally going to happen.

CHAPTER 30

Miracles & Thomas's New Home

MY DAUGHTER WAS coming home from her college in Indiana for a weekend visit. We didn't get to see her as often as I would have liked, because it was a ten-hour drive. I didn't know if this was a good time to break the news, but I couldn't wait a few more years for her to finish. When she got home, it was time to talk to the kids and tell them what we had decided. I knew she wasn't going to get home until late, so I decided to take a short nap. Then I could be awake when she got there.

At one point, I shot straight up in bed from a dead sleep as a horrible wave of panic washed over me. I didn't know what was going on, but felt that Paige was in imminent danger. I shouted out for the Angels to surround and protect her and started praying while my mind reeled to understand what was going on. After a few minutes, Paige called and was crying. She told me that she was driving down the highway and there was a semi coming straight down the road at her. She knew she couldn't avoid what was about to happen. The next thing she knew, she was sitting on the side of the road and didn't know how she had gotten there. I gave thanks to the Angels for saving her and for the power of connection and prayer.

The kids took the news of our divorce pretty well. You could tell they were scared, but they knew it wasn't working. They were very supportive. Brent wanted to stay to finish out high school in his home-town. Linden would come with me. The town we were going to live in was literally only 20 minutes from the farm. The boys could go back and forth as they felt they needed.

We found what we thought was the perfect place for Thomas. It was a fairly close place where there were people just like him. It was a beautiful community where they lived 16 people to each complex. Half of the complex was for the women, half for the men. They shared a dining area. The property had extensive paved paths for riding bikes and taking walks, and an incredible pool. There was also a large gar-den to grow food in.

The clients that were able, were allowed to mow the grounds. Some helped in the greenhouse where they potted and grew beautiful flowers and vegetables. Often, they would sell to the public through a retail store that was used to create revenue for the complex. There were also work opportunities assembling windows for a window company. Some tore down wood pallets and bundled clothing in a recycling center. Others did janitorial duties in the office building. The place felt really good.

We needed to put him on a waiting list for the village. As one per-son left, there would be room for another. Once he was placed on the list, it would go according to order and whether it was a good fit or not. I went in to meet with the staff, filled out the piles of paperwork, and talked with the head of admissions. She was a beautiful young woman who looked to be about six months pregnant. I felt I was be-ing directed to talk to her about it, but decided to hold back. I felt it was none of my business. All of a sudden, the words just blurted out of my mouth! "I'm supposed to tell you not to worry. Your baby is perfectly healthy." Crap! Honestly, it was like I had no control over it! She looked at me in shock and burst out crying.

I said that I was sorry, but felt God was pushing me to give her that message, and asked her what it was all about. She told me that they wanted to give the fetus a test to see if it was carrying a certain gene which would mean that perhaps she should have an abortion. She and her husband were in a lot of turmoil over making the decision. I asked her what she and her husband would do if they found out the gene was there? She told me that they would take the chance and deal with it after the birth. I told her that she needed to listen to her own intuition and make up her own mind. I was just guided to give the message. I did what I was being prompted to do and now I could let it go.

We were called several weeks later and told that there was an opening for Thomas. I went into a state of panic. I knew it was coming, but I wasn't ready for it. The village told us that it was important for Thomas to be dropped off only by the parents. It was too hard on them when the whole family came. It would be harder for them to work with Thomas when he was in an emotional state. Based on their experience, it was better for the parents to set up the room with the child. Then leave and let the process for becoming part of a new community set in. They told us to talk like we would to a college student, while dropping them off. Then, they didn't seem to have as hard of a time. They also said that it was important to wait at least two weeks before checking in with him by telephone or for a visit. That would give him time to settle in. Of course, we could always check in with one of the staff.

The kids said their goodbyes before school and when the car was packed and we were ready, Sam said he couldn't do it. I was left to take him there by myself. I was more than a little upset at him for not coming with, but what could I do? It seemed every time something hard had happened with Thomas, Sam would just disappear. Why would now be any different? I really don't think it was because he didn't love him. I think it was because he was afraid of losing it and crying.

Thomas and I got in the loaded car and took off for his new home. I could hardly contain myself on the ride there. No matter how I tried to hold back my tears, they still flowed freely. I opened the sunroof hoping that more fresh air would help to slow the tears. Nothing could stop the pain and sadness I felt welling in my heart as I drove this precious young man to his new home.

We were halfway there going down the main highway, when the hawk showed up. I could hear the wind moving through his wings as he hovered above the sunroof. He was so close I could have reached up and touched him. The hawk would look down at Thomas and me as he flew. Waves of love flowed through as we drove down the road, exactly like in the bathtub. I knew we were being looked after and was incredibly grateful. Everything was going to be okay.

He flew with us for several miles. Unfortunately, I could see the heads cranking and cars swerving as we went down the road. I'm sure they were trying to see if they had seen what they thought they had seen. I thanked the hawk and told him he could go. He stayed with us another mile and flew off.

As we pulled into the village, Thomas grabbed my hand, turned to me and said "Mom, it's okay, I feel normal here." They were probably the clearest words I had ever heard come out of his mouth. Thankfully, it put my heart to rest that we had made the right choice.

CHAPTER 31

Sound Advice from a Lawyer

SAM AND I agreed to meet at a lawyer's office at 3 p.m. for the initial appointment to start our divorce. It was another bittersweet trip to another ending, and I was pretty emotional. Things were changing so rapidly, I barely had time to brace myself for the next closing down of this old life.

As I left, the hawk was sitting on the mailbox at the end of the driveway. Ah, my friend was there once again to support me. During the half hour drive, I met at least five hawks sitting on signs off the side of the road. They felt like sentient Beings holding space for the old to be flushed away. Was it possible that they were all the same hawk? Their presence was so strange, and yet so comforting. Every time I passed one, I kept hearing "It's all going to be okay." It helped so much. There was a sense of calmness I highly doubt I would have had without their presence. I really did feel everything would be alright.

Sam and I met up, got all our paperwork together, and walked in for the appointment. The lawyer looked a little puzzled as he walked over to introduce himself. We both walked back to the office with him as he asked what it was that we needed. He was puzzled because he thought he was being asked to do a divorce. We assured him that that was exactly what we were there for. It was an amicable divorce, and we were agreeing on things, so we thought we could just share a lawyer. He looked at the two of us like we were crazy and said that it would be totally unethical. To do so would mean his license. He would represent one of us, and only one. It would be up to us which one that was.

I looked at Sam and said "Well, guess we're going to have to flip for it! Do you have a quarter?" I asked him which he wanted, heads, or tails. He picked tails. I knew before the coin landed it would be in my favor. Yup, it was heads. Poor lawyer, I don't think he knew what to think. Sam handed me the papers, and walked out the door. I'm sure he probably wasn't too worried. Things had fully been worked out between the two of us.

However, the lawyer took a look at the papers and threw a fit. He told me that I was committing financial suicide. How could I agree to a crazy lowball figure? How did I think I was going to live off from what I had agreed to? He assured me with the number of children we had together, how long we had been farming, and the years we had been married, that half of the farm was legally mine. I told him that I would not budge on the farm and wanted no part of it. It was a family farm, and needed to stay in the family.

We took a break and I got to know him a little better. I asked him what was going on because he had a very underlying sadness to him. He told me that he had cancer. It was his second time around and he didn't know if he was going to be able to fight it off this time. He told me not to feel bad. Cancer had been as much a gift as a curse. His experience through it had helped him to put things into perspective. He understood how precious life really was.

The lawyer told me that he could feel that I was a very good-hearted woman, but I wasn't seeing clearly around the settlement. He said "You helped farm for almost 20 years and gave him five beautiful children. Now you say you don't deserve part of the farm and want to keep it in the family and don't want child support. I am telling you that I feel very strongly that this is not right and I cannot sit back and watch you do this to you and your children."

He pleaded for me to at least ask for half of what the house was worth and half of the value of the machinery. It was only right. That was even too low, but at least it could buy me some time to start making some money. If I couldn't do that, he couldn't be part of what I had chosen. He couldn't represent me. I thanked him for being patient, and for explaining things so gently, and then I told him to put the agreement together. I would take it back to Sam, explain it all and see if he would sign it. Otherwise, I guess there would be two lawyers involved.

It was another strangely liberating day. On the way home, I felt through all the words that had been said. Thank God I had this beautiful man to help me see it all. Sam was, of course, pretty taken aback when I showed him the papers. It was quite a change from what we had agreed upon before we left. Within a few days, I brought back the signed papers.

CHAPTER 32

Letting the Bakery Go & The Divorce

IT WAS MY last day of work and my last delivery to the stores. Another very emotional day. I could see that it was almost as hard on Sam as it was on me. I think it was the last time that he gave me a hug. He surprised me when he said that he knew he didn't say it much, but he wanted me to know that he was really proud of me for the job I did and for the name I made for myself with the bakery. Looking in the rear-view mirror, I could see that he was crying as I pulled away. There was the hawk once again, sitting on a sign at the end of the driveway. I thanked him for being there once again. Just like the other times, I met him several places sitting on signs close to the side of road holding space for this transition.

Part of me felt like I was dying. I knew I would always be a mother, but who was I without the titles of wife, farmer, business owner and baker? I was headed into a place where I had never been, and I didn't know what to expect. The fear and sadness were overwhelming, but I knew I needed to walk through it.

With the bakery closed, I had time to get everything ready and packed up for the move. Sam and I actually got along pretty well during this whole process. It was like the suppressed monkey had finally had its day in the lime light and didn't need the attention anymore. Most of the tension and pressure was gone with the knowing it was almost over.

There were several things that I found interesting as we all went through this transition. First, was how upset the town was that we were getting this divorce. Sam and I often joked that they were taking it far worse than we were. Evidently, they thought us to be the perfect marriage and family. Our divorce was a dissolving of an idealism that they had created from within themselves. Honestly, I think we had become masters of illusion.

Most dysfunctional families have that going for them. Not just within themselves as an individual, but within their uniting as a family unit. Their family's illusion is built off the squashing of the truth through the dreaded code of silence. They put on that happy face no matter what and pretend everything is okay. Never daring to talk about how they feel for fear of saying something mean about someone they love. It's such a crazy thing. After all, how is anything going to get resolved if it's hushed and never talked about? So goes the crazy cycle of dysfunction, working its way through one generation to the next. How much of these dynamics is created in this one lifetime? How much is carried over from

generation to generation through our DNA? And is it possible that we take on some of it through the collective consciousness?

I once heard that the most difficult thing in people's lives, especially women, was to unlock their voice. I can understand that. There has been a huge energy of men being the authority and women being subservient. We were programmed to conform from a very young age. We were also taught to give despite ourselves. In my generation and those that came before me, women were reared to make sure that everyone's needs were put before their own, all with a smile on their face, and their true emotions deeply hidden. I am hopeful that things are becoming more balanced with each generation coming forward.

The other thing that happened through our divorce was a bushel full of rumors about me. Evidently, I was in a cult. Someone claimed to have followed me to a basement in a church in the cities. There I put on a robe and mask and stood with many others who were dressed the same. All of us were holding a white lit candle and started chanting as we walked in a circle. They ran back to the car not wanting to see what was going to happen next because they were afraid.

I guess someone needed some more excitement in their life. I could only assume that my soon-to-be ex was beginning to talk to others about what he felt was his excuse for not being able to stay married to me anymore. Unfortunately, the kids had to deal with that coming at them from different directions. **It is the saddest part of divorces as far as I am concerned, when children are put in the middle of things that they don't need to be aware of. Or, when they have to deal with things they shouldn't have to deal with. Unfortunately, talking bad about one's partner is often because of a need to feel justified in the decision to get a divorce. One has to feel right about that choice and often looks for validation from the outside world.**

The hardest thing, of course, was that the two boys left at home were going to be each living in a different place. I again felt like I was being torn away from another son. And although we weren't more than twenty minutes away, it weighed heavy on my heart.

I had found a two-bedroom house with more than fair rent within 11 miles of the farm. I would have liked another bedroom, but felt this would make due for now. Linden could share his bedroom when one of the other kids came, and there was always the couch and recliner if need be.

One of the neighbor boys brought over a stock trailer to help the kids and I get everything moved. When we pulled out the driveway to move to our new home, I intuitively knew it would be the last time I would see the hawk. Again, he met me at the end of the driveway and followed me for several miles. After he left, I knew his job was done. He had helped hold the energy for me while I went through all these transitions.

As we drove to our new start in life, so many emotions flowed through me. It was a strange dichotomy from extreme sadness and feelings of failure, to immense freedom and relief. I didn't know what was around the corner. I needed time to work through things, and figure out where my life was headed.

Once we had everything unloaded, we all sat at the table to get something to eat and drink. I remember sitting there feeling an immense relief come through as I took a deep breath and let out a loud exhale. It was the first time in 23 years that I felt I could fully breathe! I felt completely at ease, and there was no anxiety in me whatsoever. I was literally feeling a new sense of freedom washing over me and I began to get excited for what was ahead.

That night, before I fell asleep, the voice came in. This time it told me that I was not to work for one year. I needed time to heal my physical and emotional body. I also had a lot I needed to learn. Right away my mind went into defense mode. "Oh my God, how was I going to do that? I couldn't go without working for a full year! How would we live? What would people think of me? Everyone would wonder what was wrong with me. They'd think that I was lazy." And then I was gently reminded of the settlement, and told me that we would be fine. I didn't know what to think. Who was this voice that kept coming in to tell me things? Did I trust it? Why was it so interested in my life anyway? Yet, everything it has said and shown me had been true so far. I'd sit with what information I was given, but ultimately, I felt it was my choice. At least that's what I thought.

I think one becomes addicted to being busy and having a lot of drama in their life. And when it's not there anymore, things begin to feel dull and lifeless, like something is missing or wrong. I see it in a lot of people's lives. They're always talking about how busy they are, or about how many things are going wrong in their lives. They talk about how pressured they feel, or how much stress they have because of all they have to do. They wear it like a badge of honor. Then, when they don't have all those things to contend with, they become bored.

Why is it that we are all so incredibly busy? Is it that if we were to be still, we would have to look at our own stuff instead of everyone else's? If one was given the opportunity to slow down, would they gladly take it? Or, would they be so programmed by life that they would automatically choose to create more chaos to divert them from doing so?

I guess I was about to find out.

CHAPTER 33

Transition & Another Ghost

THINGS WERE ACTUALLY going really well at our new home. Linden was making some friends in his new school, and we got to see Brent on a pretty regular basis. I also started getting some much-needed alone time when their dad had them. That is something I had never experienced before. Little bits and pieces here and there, but not like this. At first, I didn't know what to do with myself. I'd find all sorts of things to fill my time. It took a while, but I began to realize how nice it was to just be. To not have to worry about anyone, and sit in your own thoughts.

The other nice change was, I didn't need to worry about having someone over. I could never do that at the farm because Sam would always put company to work. It was embarrassing, and not something you wanted to have others experience. Here, I could invite a friend over and just sit and talk over a nice cup of coffee. I could talk about spiritual things and do energy work on people without having to worry about what anyone else thought. I could actually get my healing practice off the ground. I was beginning to see that this divorce was not just a good thing, but essential for my growth. There is no way that I could have known or prepared for what was all going to show up for me. This was to be my time for incredible learning and expansion.

About a week after moving into the new place, I got a call from the young woman who had the Ouija board experience. Danielle was in her own place now and was engaged to be married. She asked if I could help her because the place that they had moved to had a ghost who was throwing things around. I often wondered why it was that some people attracted things like this, and others didn't? I'd hoped that this was going to be the last of it for her. Doing ghost work was far from my favorite thing to do.

I came to her house fully supplied with sage, Epsom salt and rubbing alcohol. We talked about how we were going to proceed to flush the ghost out. By the sounds of it, this one was angry. I hadn't come across one that shoved candles on the floor, or made books fly off the shelf. I have to admit I was a little wigged out that it was probably going to start happening. I could tell that he wasn't very happy about this new family in his house.

I got a look at him when I went to the bathroom before we started. He showed himself to me right inside the door and just stood there staring at me while I sat on the toilet. I'd have to say it was pretty uncomfortable. Part of me wanted to bow out, but then who would she find to help her? It wasn't like it was common to find people who did this kind of thing, not that I deemed myself an expert.

I made her do the clearing with me and we went from floor to floor clearing out any negative energy and hopefully, the ghost along with it. I had to admit the house was feeling awesome by the time we were done and I couldn't feel the ghost anymore. But something didn't feel quite right. It almost seemed too easy. But because I couldn't feel any ghost energy, I assumed it was gone.

Imagine my surprise when I got home and within minutes things started happening there? Evidently, the ghost had hitched a ride home in the car with me! And I thought I knew what I was doing! Now I had to de-ghost my own house. It was a good thing none of the kids were home. Well, if nothing else, I guess it was a good learning experience. I now knew to always help the ghost cross over before clearing the house. **Clearing doesn't get rid of a ghost. You need to locate them and help them understand that they are dead. It is also nice to ask them why they are still here. Is there something they need to talk about? Then, ask them if they want to cross over to be with their loved ones, or go back to the heart of God. If they say yes and are done here, then call in Angels, Arch Angels, and/or God to help open up a white tunnel of light. That's where the ghost can see their loved ones that have already crossed over, or have a connection to God. When you feel the ghost is ready, ask for the Angels/God to lead them through the tunnel to the other side. After they go through the tunnel, ask that it is fully closed and sealed**. I started over with my new learning and he was gone within minutes. I guess I should have thanked him for helping me to understand it all better. Who knows, maybe that is one of the reasons he was around.

Two weekends after that, my youngest son was supposed to go visit his dad. He was having fits and didn't want to go because one of his aquarium frogs had gotten out. Last time it was a crab, now it was the frog. I promised him I would look for it so he didn't need to worry. He just needed to go and have a good time.

After he left, I checked every place I thought it could have gone, but it was nowhere to be found. Finally, I took a break and decided to make some popcorn and watch a movie for a bit. The frog was probably gone. That's just the way things are sometimes. Linden would just have to deal with it.

Just as I heated up the oil and put the popcorn in the pan, I heard "Turn off the popcorn, the frog is in the basement shower under the mat." Here we go again! I went down to the basement, pulled up the mat, and there was no frog. Hmm, I guess this time the voice was wrong. I went upstairs and turned the popcorn back on. Again, the voice came through with the same message. I argued that I had looked and it wasn't there. It said "You didn't look close enough. It's under the mat, stuck between the suction cups. Look on the backside of the mat." Well ok, I'd give it another a shot. I went down and pulled the mat up once again. The frog was right there, wedged between the suction cups, just as the voice had said! Amazing!

CHAPTER 34

Meeting Buddy Piper

I STARTED GETTING a little more involved with a spiritual center. It was the one place that I could go to get inspired and find comradery with like-minded people. The lady that I went to for readings started it. At one of the meetings there was a special guest named Buddy Piper who was giving a talk on Share-International. Buddy was there to talk about Maitreya, who supposedly overshadowed Christ while he walked the Earth. He said Christ had come back to Earth as this body of energy called Maitreya. Buddy shared that he could manifest into physical form from time to time during which he would often perform miracles. Most of the time, he was in energetic form, and talked through a man called Benjamin Crème. They referred to this form of communication as overshadowing.

Buddy was a beautiful older gentleman and I was extremely attracted to him. Not in a romantic sense, but in a sense that I was supposed to meet and talk with him. That he was part of my Soul family sense. **I'm sure you have all experienced those beautiful people who you meet and feel a strong sense of familiarity and connection. It's like you know them, or, that you've met them before. Sometimes there's a strong magnetic pull or attraction to them. Those people are part of your Soul Family. I feel it's our destiny to meet them at certain times in our life.**

At the end of Buddy's talk, he asked several of us out to dinner. He and I ended up sitting next to one another. Through our conversation, I found out that he was Red Skelton's second-hand man. They had acted together on his comedy show for years. I was floored! I remembered that when Red Skelton died, I cried and cried. Deep down I always thought that at some point in my life, I was supposed to meet him. After his passing, I knew that would never happen. I felt such a huge loss, and yet, it felt ridiculous. Why would I think I was supposed to meet Red Skelton? But now here, in this restaurant, I was meeting him through his friend and sidekick, Buddy Piper.

What I noticed about Buddy was that when he talked to you, it was as if you were the only person in the room. I'd never experienced that before. It made me feel like I was really being heard and acknowledged. Sitting next to me, he looked deeply into my eyes with so much love and said "Barbara I can tell that you have had a hard start to life. You're struggling with your parents. I know it's hard, but it's important to love those who have hurt you the most. They've come here to play a hard role in your life. They're here to be some of your biggest teachers." It made me wonder how he knew? Did I wear it that closely to the surface, or was it that he could see that deeply? I really felt like his saying it with so much unconditional love, lifted and unlocked something in me. Perhaps I could now start healing those deep wounds. I was very grateful to have had that one experience with Red Skelton via Buddy Piper.

CHAPTER 35

Spirit Puts a Stop to It

IT HAD BEEN a month since we moved out and I swear every time I went somewhere, I was offered a job. Not just a mediocre job, a really good one. It was like there was a contest to see who could get me hired first.

One was really inviting. I was offered the managerial position at a store bakery. The salary was more than I had ever made. I thought about it a lot. I just couldn't seem to get into the "There will be no working for one year" plan. I was going to talk to them the next morning. Besides, what could it hurt to check it out?

Later that day, I decided to mow the lawn. While doing so, the lawnmower took off on its own as if it was possessed! At one point, it threw me off balance. I went rolling down the hill the house was built on and slammed my foot down on the sidewalk. Pain shot through me as I sat there dazed. Finally, a neighbor came over to help get me up and I was taken to the doctor. Two hours later, I came home with an air cast and a pair of crutches. I'd broken my foot in three places.

They weren't sure how long it would take to heal, because they were unable to line the bones up. The doctor told me that it was very important to not put any weight on my foot at all. I was to keep it up for a week only getting up to go to the bathroom. If I was lucky, the bones would come into alignment and I wouldn't have to get them pinned. At the one-week checkup it was getting better, but it still wasn't where they wanted it to be. The doctor wanted to schedule me for surgery. I refused. I wanted one more week to try to get things lined up. If it didn't work by then, we'd talk about it. I went home and called my friend, Jo, who was a Reiki Master. Thankfully, she came over and did a bunch of energy work on my foot. I definitely kept it up as much as I could. I didn't want pins put in my body, let alone having to go through surgery. I was going to get this foot lined up come hell or high water.

I thought about this accident a lot. It seemed a little suspicious that I had decided to look into a job after being told not to work for a year, and all of a sudden, bam! A fall causing my foot to have three breaks. Some unseen energy was making damn sure that I took this time off, whether I wanted it or not. Who was this voice? Was it God? Was it a more evolved part of myself? Could it be one of my guides? I swore I was going to figure out who was talking, and how was it possible for it to cause that accident.

CHAPTER 36

My Invisible Teacher

MY FAVORITE PLACE to spend time was out in my three-person swing. It was my nirvana. Anytime I was anxious or needed to ponder, this was the best place for me to sort things out. It seemed every time I went there, I was taught. The teaching voice was a different voice. It didn't sound or feel like the same voice that I had heard before. This voice was more like a telepathic mind link. The other voice was almost audible. It seemed very matter of fact, yet authoritative. When hearing the swing voice, it was more of a gentle teacher who was here to help me see what I needed to understand. To help me heal, and uncover truth about my life. I let it flow through in automatic writing to make sure I didn't forget what was said.

The first time the teaching voice came through while on the swing it asked me why I thought I got the broken foot. I said "Because I went against the advice I had been given and was going to take a job." It asked me if I knew why it was so important that I took a year off. It explained that there had been a reason that I was so tired all the time. I had literally exhausted myself through constant work and the stress I had experienced on a daily basis. It told me all I needed for proof was to look deeply into my eyes in a mirror. They would show me what kind of state I was in. Ouch! Of course, I didn't need to look. I had been exhausted for a long time, and I knew it without looking into a mirror. It went on to say that I had not been able to speak out my anger, hurt and frustration that I had experienced from childhood on. Because of it, all that emotion had gone inward. It had moved inside my body within my cells, and was causing a breakdown of my immune system and body. Unexpressed thoughts and emotions stuck inside one's cells can cause any number of ailments, including cancer. When people are under large amounts of

stress, it does a lot to the physical body, none of it good. The fact that I was harboring a chance to contract a chronic illness, or cancer was never said out loud, but it didn't need to be. This was my wakeup call. It was imperative for me to take this time to heal my body and emotions so I didn't leave early. It now had my full attention.

A week after my second visit to the doctor, I went back for another x-ray of my foot. This time, we saw a lot of improvement. She looked at me curiously and asked how I was able to get the bones to line up. I told her that I and another energy healer had spent many hours working on it. She said she knew there was something different about me. She asked if I could explain about energy work and the principles around it. I was a little surprised but was more than happy to share. We talked a good 20 minutes and she thanked me for taking the time to talk with her. She also said that she felt the foot would take almost a year to heal. Unfortunately, it would be in a cast for that whole time. We set the next appointment up for six months out.

A whole year in a cast! I guess that was better than having surgery and the three pins. I then told her that I had put money down on a trip to Catalina Island that was three weeks out, and asked if that would be a problem. She assured me it wouldn't, as long as I didn't overtax myself. She also urged me to use a wheelchair when needed.

CHAPTER 37

Off on an Adventure

WITH LINDEN AND Brent at their dad's house, my sister, Rhonda, and I took off for California. I was really looking forward to getting away and going on a trip. I had never really taken off like this before and was definitely up for the adventure.

The trip started out in Hollywood. We went to have a personal experience with Benjamin Crème, and Maitreya. He was presenting a channeling in an auditorium near where we stayed. Afterwards, we were to join a three-hour meditation for world peace. The talk was interesting and I could see another energy body hovering in and out of Benjamin while channeling a message. It reminded me of the lady I went to see where she channeled during her readings.

I was fine with the channeling, but the meditation piece was hard for me. I could barely do one hour, let alone three. An hour in, I had to get up and leave. Meditation and repetitious chanting are not my cup of tea. In fact, I have an adverse amount of repulsion around doing them. Instead of sitting there putting out bad vibes, I decided to leave. I did the same the next day at the Yogananda meditation center as they were meditating. I didn't seem to be fitting in very well.

One of the things that bothered me in Los Angeles was the dichotomy between wealthy and poor. I saw great big sky scrapers and endless traffic, so I knew there was money. I could also see the homeless were everywhere. I really hadn't been exposed to homeless people before. Part of me was appalled. I felt I needed to do something to help them while there. The next morning, I decided to go to the nearest grocery store before everyone got up. I was going to buy juices and fruit to hand out. I hadn't factored in the nearest grocery store being six blocks away. I had to admit, my foot was hurting quite a bit by the time I lugged everything back and started handing it out.

People were generally pretty nice, but to be honest some were a little scary. I even got yelled at by an old homeless lady. There were several who had sores all over their body. I couldn't imagine how much it must have hurt! I just kept praying I could keep my heart open and be nonjudgmental. I tried to make sure I gave eye contact. If they asked for a hug, I gave them one.

Things were going okay until I got to this one man who was definitely different than the others. He was pretty well groomed with longer dark wavy hair, and his mind seemed crystal clear. Even with that, there was something about him that I just couldn't put my finger on. He accepted what I gave him with gratitude. Then he looked deeply into my eyes and said "You know, what you are doing is nice, but you have put yourself in danger. You cannot trust all of these people. Do you understand what I am saying?" I was quiet, but nodded my head. Then he said "Do you think your doctor would approve of how long you've walked today? Especially with all the extra weight that you've carried?" I answered "No." He then said "Why would you do that to your body? You need to go back to your hotel and rest." With that he turned around. Who the hell was this guy? And how in the hell did he know?

I went back to the hotel to lie down and rest. As I lay there, I thought about the words that had been spoken. **Why is it that I would feel more need to help another than to help my own self? Why would I put them at a higher importance than taking care of my own basic needs? There are many people with this same theme playing out. Perhaps these basic acts are what we think we need to do to feel like we are good and worthy of love. Perhaps we don't want people to suffer the way we have. Maybe we are trying to create an outer action to heal an inner belief about our self that was hardwired into our psyche though our life experience. Maybe it's just that we can't stand to see injustice in the world.**

When you're on a plane and it's going down, they tell you to first put on your own oxygen mask. Then go help others. If you help yourself first, you have what you need to keep mentally and physically aware and strong. You are then more able to help others for as long as is needed. There's a better chance to save them. If you choose to help others first, there is only a limited amount of time you would be able to help. Without essential oxygen, you would become weak and disoriented. Eventually you'd die from not feeding your body with the vital life force of breath. With that course of action, you would only be able to help a few.

CHAPTER 38

Healing Miracles

A FLOW OF people started asking me to do energy work on them, which I was grateful for. I loved doing that more than anything. My favorite client was a little 14-month-old girl. She had an enlarged heart and was scheduled to have open heart surgery in a few days. I told her parents that I had never worked on something that serious before, but I would certainly give it a try. They came three days in a row and I worked with her. I can't say I knew I was doing anything more than just running energy into her, while sending her love. But I had enough faith that if something was supposed to happen, God would take care of it. I just needed to get out of the way.

They called late in the morning the following day and were ecstatic. They'd arrived at the hospital with 16 medical personnel waiting to take their daughter into the operating room. The parents had let go of her thinking that they wouldn't see her again for a very long time. A short time later, they brought her back to the waiting room. They said that there must have been a mistake made the first time it was diagnosed. When they had taken a picture of her heart to see its condition before surgery, it was only slightly enlarged. The medical staff must have made a misdiagnosis and were so sorry to have put the family through this. Thank you, God!

CHAPTER 39

Profound Occurrence & Past Life Visions

I BEGAN INTERACTING more with my older neighbor lady. She was very interested in spirituality and would often come for a morning cup of coffee just to discuss it. Sometimes, she would go home scratching her head, but it didn't seem to stop her from coming back. On one visit, I told her about a Soul portrait a friend of mine had just gifted me. I explained that Lisa would use colored chalk and have spirit show her what to draw. While sketching, a channeling would come through which she recorded. She was curious and asked me if she could see the drawing, so I took her upstairs to my bedroom where it was hanging on the wall. The picture was a very simple but beautiful chalk drawing on black paper that looked exactly like a Madonna with her eyes closed. She walked to it and bent over so she could get a better look. Next thing I knew, she was flying backwards through the air screaming as she landed on my bed! I stood there stupefied as she quickly scrambled off the bed and ran down the stairs. You could tell she was scared shitless!

I tried to call her, but she wouldn't answer the phone. Several days later, I began knocking on her door. She would just yell that she couldn't talk right now. A few weeks later, things must have finally settled. She told me that when she got close to the picture for a better look, the Madonna's eyes opened. When they opened, a blast of energy hit her. The next thing she knew, she was flying through the air. We really didn't talk much after that. I'm sure she couldn't wrap her mind around what happened. But then, neither could I.

Not long after that, I was sitting at the table writing out checks to pay bills while listening to some Native American flute music. All of a sudden, I was thrown into a past life where I was in the woods near a marsh. I was a Native woman around twenty years old. By the looks of it, I was about ready to give birth. My belly was big and I was uncomfortable. My husband and I were walking through the woods, looking for specific herbs that would be needed to help with the birthing process. We were both so excited for this child to be born.

In the distance, we began to hear the sound of footsteps coming towards us. We could tell by the sound they made that it was white men. My husband took me by the hand and started pulling me across a marsh to get away. He let go as he turned around and yelled for me to run. He pleaded that I not look back, no matter what happened. He just kept yelling to run! I heard several shots being fired, and as I turned around, I saw my husband lying face down in the marsh. My heart was ripped from my chest as I turned back around and ran with everything I had. The three men continued coming for me, and before long, I collapsed in a fit of exhaustion. After they caught me, each took a turn raping me and then they hung me by the neck in a nearby tree. I was hovering outside my body as I watched one of the men take a knife and cut my belly open. As he pulled the baby out, it took its first breath. He then smashed its skull against a rock bragging about how he'd stop another red skin from coming into this world.

Next thing I knew, I was sobbing at the foot of a cross. I was aware of Mother Mary and John being next to me as well as many other women. Jesus was nailed to the cross, hovering between consciousness and unconsciousness. There was a knowing in me that I had been prepared for this to happen. I knew that I was there to hold Jesus energetically while he played out his death. I also knew that there were two other women holding the energy with me. It was incredibly hard to see someone who I loved so much experience what he was going through, even if it was some divine plan. I could feel the pain and sadness that wore heavy on his heart, and I began to sob even harder. I was then thrown into a beautiful golden meadow. The grass was up past my waist where Jesus and I were alone together. I could feel the love we shared for one another as we danced in circles, hand in hand, and heart to heart. He kept tracing my face with his fingers and we fell to the ground laughing.

With that, I was back sitting in my chair sobbing, as I let go the last vestiges of what I had just experienced. While in these visions it felt like I had been gone lifetimes, but in reality, they had only taken minutes to play out. I knew that the visions were past lives. While in them, it was as if I was right there experiencing every part of it. I could feel every emotion and a 360-degree visual of people, color, and nature, as well as every aspect of what was unfolding. I can still see the visions as clearly today as the day it happened. Why was it shown to me, and what purpose did it serve? That I didn't know. I guess I'd be shown when the timing was right.

CHAPTER 40

Moving Back to Minnesota

I ENJOYED OUR first house we rented after the divorce. It was the perfect place to learn about myself and heal my foot up. I was beginning to worry that if I didn't buy a house pretty soon, I would use all the money on other things. I wanted a place to grow roots, and Iowa definitely wasn't where I wanted to spend the rest of my life. My heart was pulling me back to Minnesota. It had always been pulling me back to Minnesota. I felt Mankato was where I was supposed to land. I had a deep knowing that living there was an important step for me.

I talked it over with Linden and Brent. Brent assured me he was doing well and wanted to stay with his friends and graduate in Iowa. Linden resisted at first, but we struck a deal. If I promised he could get a cat, he was open to the move. An added plus was that my oldest son and my oldest sister both lived there.

I spent months looking for the right house. I'm sure my realtor was getting more than a little frustrated with me. Every time we went, I'd tell him the energy was off or it didn't feel right. After a while, I wondered if he even understood what it was that I was looking for. Nothing he set up for a showing was even close to what I had told him I wanted. Finally, I decided to go looking on my own. I'd just start driving and see if I could feel my way to it. I had barely hit the backside of Mankato and I was pulled to go down a road where there were several realty signs. The road was one of many in a subdivision that wove around the area. I loved the beautiful mature trees and that the houses edged a ravine. Even though you were in town, you felt like you were bordering the country.

As I followed the road to the back of the subdivision, I saw a house with a for sale sign in the front yard. I knew without a doubt in my mind that it was going to be my next home. It had the perfect amount of lawn and sat on a cliff next to a ravine with a creek running through it. The house had a fireplace, three bedrooms, a double garage with ample parking, and was on a dead-end road. What I loved the most was that it had large windows all the way across the back of the house with a magnificent view. It was everything I had put down on a sheet of paper that I wanted. I brought Linden with me to look at it the next day. When he saw it, he said, "Mom, this is the house I saw in my dream last night. The one where there was a hawk on the mailbox." I guess the hawk was still around guiding me! (smile)

Once we were finally able to have a showing, the realtor looked at me and said he finally understood what I meant with all that talk about energy. He told me he could feel this was a good house for me, and that it held a lot of peace. He finally got it! Six weeks later we moved in. Unfortunately, that was right after my sister moved to Rochester and my oldest son moved to Colorado. I was really disappointed, but I guess we were all being pulled to where we needed to go.

One of the first things I had to do was make good on my promise to Linden and get a cat. We decided to go to the humane society and save one of them from being euthanized. That day we started the hunt for the perfect cat. There were literally rooms full of them! I went off in my own direction so Linden could have his treasure hunt without my interference. While checking things out I prayed for a good cat that wouldn't tear up my leather furniture and didn't pee or make messes in the house. It seemed like I turned my head for one minute and next thing I knew, Linden had a large grey and white cat lying across his neck. I pretty much figured that it was the one, but it didn't seem to detour him from checking out every other cat he could. If there was anything Linden was, it was meticulous and thorough. Finally, he figured out that the cat on his shoulders had picked him, and he was the right cat. His name was Jasper and he was a young Maine Coon which is one of the bigger breeds. Jasper was a strikingly beautiful, long haired grey cat with four white paws and a white chest. And by the looks of it, he knew what he wanted and went after it.

I was soon to find out that cats were far more aware and amazing than I could have ever imagined. At least this one was. At first Linden had the monopoly of his time and Jasper slept in his room at night. But after things relaxed a bit, and the newness wore off, he would often come to sleep with me.

The first few nights, he jumped up on the bed and lay on my stomach and chest. Soon after, I could feel an immense amount of energy running from him into me. It was spreading out into specific places like my lungs and stomach. I knew on some level that he was doing healing work on me, and it felt wonderful. The fourth night in it was a different story. I was lying with my legs positioned in a number four ready to go to sleep, when Jasper plopped down and cradled in. Evidently this night he didn't feel like he had enough room. I could feel pulses of energy being bombarded at me as he energetically pushed me further up the bed. I mean I was physically being pushed up the bed until my head actually hit the headboard! I don't know why I didn't freak out. Maybe it was because I already knew he was a healer. I mean, how much weirder was it than anything else I had already experienced? So now we had a cat that could energetically shove you around on a bed? I figured that this cat may not be a typical cat.

Several weeks later, I was doing a session on a young lady who I felt had been sexually molested. She was having a hard time lying on the table. As I was doing energy work on her, I could feel her pulling inward because of her uncomfortableness. Minutes later, I heard the door making noise. It was gently being rocked back and forth. When I went to check it out, I found Jasper on the other side. He ran in through the crack, jumped up on the massage table, and curled up right between my client's legs. I gave a humble apology and told her I didn't know what had gotten into him. He had never behaved like that before. She asked to please let him stay. Her cat had died a week earlier, and it was really comforting to have Jasper there.

As I continued the energy work, she started opening up about how she was adopted by her grandparents. She had been brought over from Germany at the age of eight. It wasn't long before she found out that she was to be used by a group of men in a particular meeting space. There, she was continually passed around by her grandfather. Then she let the tears free. My heart hurt for this young lady that had been treated so poorly. All I could do is tell her how sorry I was and send her love.

After finishing with energy on the front, I asked her to turn over and worked the back side of her. The session finally felt finished, so I was going to rub her feet and let her know it was done. Jasper beat me to the punch. He stood up, stretched, and gently bit her on the butt. I stood there in shock! I didn't know what to say! We both looked at one another and burst into fits of laughter! I coughed out an apology, but she insisted that it was absolutely the perfect way to end the session.

Another time, a friend of Linden's came over to visit. He told me he was doctoring for heart issues. I felt it was caused by the energy drinks he was drinking, but told him I'd see if I could help him out. I was having a hard time with the energy in his body so asked Linden if he could hold and ground his ankles while I did what I needed to do. He felt too uncomfortable, so I proceeded on my own.

Again, the door started rocking back and forth, and Jasper started meowing. I knew he wanted to come in so I asked if it was alright. When I opened the door, he jumped up on the table and put his front paws on the client's ankles. I couldn't believe it! He was doing exactly what I had asked my son to help me with! I could see green energy running from Jaspers paws up the young man's legs. From then on, when Japer asked to come in, I knew there had either been sexual abuse, or I needed more energy and he was going to be my backup. He was one amazing cat!

Several weeks later, I found another thing he was capable of. I was sitting on the couch reading, and Jasper jumped up behind me on the back of the couch to take a nap. After getting settled in, he gently laid his paw on my shoulder to connect. When he'd finished his nap, he jumped down and went to the door and asked to go out. I got up, let him out, and sat back down to finish reading my book. A few minutes later, I felt something to my left. As I looked over, I saw weighted footprints walking across the back of the couch coming towards me. Then I felt a heavy pressure plop across the back of my neck and shoulders. I knew it was Jasper without a doubt in my mind. I had just let him out, and now, he was here, invisible on the couch with me. What else could this cat do?

CHAPTER 41

Tuning in to Nature

I DIDN'T REALIZE it, but the land in the ravine had once been a golf course. After it went belly up, the city had it gifted back to the landowners that bordered it. Because of that, I owned a pie shaped acre of land that bordered the creek. I often tuned into it as I sat on the top of the cliff and connected in to the wildlife that lived there.

On one of my nature tune-ins, I heard continual splashing coming from the bottom of the ravine. It was so constant that I decided to sneak down to see what was making all the noise. On the other side of the creek there was a handful of deer. It was mostly females and their fawns. The adults stood in a group interacting with one another, while the fawns played in the water. They ran from one side of the creek to the other jumping and splashing as they kicked their feet up in the air. You could tell they were having a ball cooling off on a hot summer day. It was not unlike what human children and their parents would be doing. I felt incredibly honored to have this peek into their family units and how they interact. The more

I observed the beautiful wildlife here, the more I realized how intelligent and like us they actually were.

I never really saw anybody walking down in the ravine. I guess people didn't like traversing the steep hill. We tied rope to several trees and used it like a hand rail to get to the bottom. At least that way if you started losing your footing, you had something to help regain your balance. Our family was down there exploring all the time.

It was around this time that the voice came in and I was told to stop eating meat. Perhaps with all the enjoyment I was getting from the animals it was the perfect timing to address it. I wasn't really given any reason for why I needed to do it, but I felt it was to raise my vibration. It wasn't that hard for me to give up eating meat, but every once in a while, a craving would sneak in. Whenever that happened, I was shown a pig hanging on a meat hook. It was hung by the back of its neck, swinging back and forth with blood squirting all over from the cut in its throat. It wasn't that hard to put a hamburger down after that. I had to give it to this guidance; it knew exactly what to show me to help curb my craving for meat.

I began to notice that I could hear drumming. Usually it happened late at night, but sometimes I could faintly hear it during the day as I sat tuning in. It sounded far away, almost otherworldly, and I felt it had to be the drumming from the Natives that used to live there. I could almost see them when I tuned in to the land below.

My son often took his friends down in the ravine at night with headlamps. He'd take random snapshots at night on a regular digital camera. One night, he called me into his room to show me one of the pictures he had taken. It had three Native men peeking from behind trees. One had a coyote or wolf headdress with only his face and chest showing. One had a headdress with small feathers sticking everywhere like a bird head. The third had a single feather on a leather headband. Their images were more translucent, but you could clearly see that they were there. I was amazed that he had captured their image with a snapshot. Soon we would come to understand that there were more than just other-dimensional Natives who lived down there.

CHAPTER 42

Our Thoughts Can Hurt Others

OUR NEW HOME was perfect for starting up my healing practice. The third bedroom made a beautiful healing space and I was ready to put what I had learned into use and make a living with it. I knew it would take some time to get a practice up and going. Especially to the point where it could make my house payments and pay all the bills. I decided to start a cleaning business with a former high school friend. For three days a week, I would put my time into the cleaning business. The other two, I'd start a healing practice. I could always change my schedule as the practice grew.

The cleaning company was going to focus on helping impoverished women get back on their feet. My first job out was an experience I'll never forget. I should have known when she asked me to bring my vacuum that something was off. I had to go in at 6 a.m. and only had two hours. That was all she could afford. It sounded like she had a pretty small apartment, so I didn't think it would take a ton of time. Funny how we can have such delusional expectations of how things will work out.

When the lady opened the door that morning, my jaw hit the floor. It was beyond filthy! There was black dog hair everywhere! I couldn't even tell what color the carpet was underneath it all. It only took a few minutes and the vacuum was plugged so tight that it couldn't suck anymore. Thankfully, I could blow it out the hose to get it unplugged. I reversed the hose and turned it on. Black globs of hair spew everywhere! She and I both looked at each other and then she said "Well, that's not going to work, how about we take care of the kitchen?"

I almost started crying. There were dirty dishes with mold and dried on food stacked to the bottom of the hanging cupboards. There were also maggots crawling up the cupboard from where the dog dish sat. I stood there in sheer horror as I fought back the dry heaves. I didn't want to hurt her feelings, but I just didn't know if I was going to be able to do this! I told her that I would start in the bathroom and then finish off with the kitchen. That would give me time to think things through. Maybe I could do that and leave. Crap! No wonder she wanted to pay in advance!

I'm not saying the bathroom was any better, but at least it didn't have maggots crawling around. Imagine my horror when I discovered I had left my rubber gloves at home. All of the cleaning was going to have to be done with my bare unprotected hands. What the hell was I thinking when I agreed to do this? As I started scrubbing the toilet, I was having an internal hissy fit. "Why was I taking on this shitty job! This place should be condemned! I can't believe I'm here in this life to scrub other people's filthy toilets, and clean up their shit!" It's probably a good thing that the voice came in, or the rant would have gone on the whole time I was there.

It said it knew that this was hard on me, but could I find it in my heart to look at it in a different way? I asked what kind of way could make what I was doing okay? It said "Barbara, this lady has been struggling for a very long time. I know that you couldn't possibly know this by looking at her, but she is actually a Nano scientist. She used to work for the government, and was one of the brightest." I asked what had happened and was told that she had experienced a nervous breakdown. She was trying really hard to get her life back on track, but it was all so overwhelming for her. "Do you think you could find it in your heart to clean and put love into what you are doing? It could be the very ray of light that helps her to get over the hump and out of her mental prison."

I got it. Clearing the clutter and dirt was helping her to clear the clutter in her head and life. Me spewing negative words was only adding to the continuous overwhelming negative cycle she was already in. I was causing her harm. I felt remorse as I changed direction and started to take everything on with a silent prayer for her to be able to heal. I repeatedly put energy and light into what I was doing.

As I cleaned, I wove the intention for a new start to life. When I left, I could feel a shift in her and the house. I just hoped it was enough to make a difference. On the way home, I said out loud that I was ok with this one house, but I was never to be sent to another house that dirty ever again.

It only went up hill from there. The people and houses that I began to take on after that became very important to me. They were all very special people that became good friends and family. At some point I found something out that was very interesting. Each place I cleaned had a house number that added up to a five. That has always been the number that has steered my life. There were five of us siblings, I had five kids, I was born on December 14, 1955 at 7:52 p.m., which adds up to a five. When I looked 5's up in numerology it said "Hold on to your seatbelt baby, you're going on a ride!" That has always pretty much summed up my life.

CHAPTER 43

Soul Exchanges

BETWEEN CLEANING AND my healing practice, I started an 18-month ordination class to become an Interfaith Minister. The classes were a mix between a Mystery School, studying the Masters, Universal Laws, the Seven Rays, Essene teachings, and so much more. It also covered more traditional ministerial topics like counseling, prayer work, meditation, and how to do services and ceremonies. I didn't figure it would be such a big deal. I had already studied all those tapes earlier on Interfaith Ministry. Boy, was I wrong! It was a really hard class that took a massive amount of time and effort. There were ten of us in the class and we melded into a very close group. This is where I met several friends that would become paramount in my life.

One day at lunchtime, everyone got up to have their break except one. She just sat there with a funny look on her face. As I watched her, I saw a white cloud-like energy come out of the crown of her head and hover. Then I saw a different stream of energy go in through the crown of her head. The hovering energy then left through the ceiling.

I had never seen anything like it before. I wondered if it was a Soul exchange. After a while, the woman who was wrapped up in a sleeping bag looked down at her lap. She looked at it long and hard, as if she was trying to figure out what was around her. Then she grabbed the end of the zipper. Over and over, she zipped it up and down as she stared at it. Then she looked at me and said, "You humans make the most curious things!" I retorted "Hmm, I'm guessing you're not from here?" She asked how I knew. I told her it was just a lucky guess and then asked her where she was from. She said that she was from Arcturus and had come here on a mission. Then she told me that Arcturus was a water planet, quite similar to Earth. I asked her how Arcturians differed in looks. She explained that they were much taller, had a greyish-blue tinge to their skin, and wore grey suits or uniforms. She then looked at me and asked if I had any chocolate. Well, I have to say I wasn't expecting that to be one of the first questions asked by an extraterrestrial. I told her that I did and would share some with her. She said that she had heard a lot about chocolate. It was one of the two things she most looked forward to experiencing when she finally got here. I asked her what the other was and she responded with feeling air up her nose. Well, ok then! That's when I got up and alerted the teacher to what was happening.

At the end of the weekend, we all helped to clean the building up and left. As I was leaving, I noticed the lady that had gone through the Soul exchange sitting in her car. Come to think of it, I had noticed her sitting there twenty minutes previous to that. I figured she was having some problems, so went over and knocked on the window. She rolled down the window and I asked her if she needed some help. She assured me that she was just waiting. I asked her if she knew how to drive a five speed. She said she didn't, and was waiting for a download so that she could. Then I asked her if she knew how to get home, and she said that all the information was coming to her with the download. I gave her my business card and told her to call me if she had anything go wrong. With that, I left. I noticed her drive by as I stopped to pick up a few groceries before heading home. I guess she received the download.

CHAPTER 44

The Hummingbird and Mischievous Beings

SEVERAL TIMES WHEN I got home from my ordination classes, I noticed that the curtains at the back of the house had been shut tight with clothespins so there were no gaps anywhere. I figured Linden was getting scared with those big windows open. I guess at his age, I probably would have too.

That night we had a talk and I asked him what was going on. He told me that there were Beings from the ravine that kept throwing small pebbles at the house and it scared him. I didn't know what to say. Of course, I thought it was his imagination. I told him if it ever happened again to call me and I would come right home. With that, I sent him off to school.

A little later that morning, I went out to meditate before working with my first client. I loved to sit on the swing and meditate a bit in the morning. It always cleared my head and helped me to feel more connected and aligned. It felt like it helped me to get an overview for the day. As I sat there with my eyes closed, I heard a humming bird come right up to my face and hover. I could feel the wind from its wings brushing me. Then I felt a little shot of liquid spill down the front of my shirt. I opened my eyes and said, "Did you just pee on me?" The humming bird backed away without breaking eye contact, and then came right up to my face again. Once more I felt a shot of liquid squirt down the front of me. I laughed and said, "Oh my God, you did pee on me!" It hovered a while longer and shot off. What the heck? Well, I didn't know what that was all about, but at least it was a humming bird and not an eagle. I decided that I had better go in and change clothes. After all, it wouldn't be very professional to work on someone with streaks of humming bird poo down the front of my shirt.

As I turned to go in, I noticed little rocks lying all over the patio. What the heck? There were piles of small stones laying everywhere! We were on a one-hundred-foot cliff, and had a fenced in yard with a locked gate. It would be a pretty big feat for a person to play a prank of this magnitude. I got a broom and a dust pan and cleaned up as many piles as I could. The rocks got thrown back over the cliff.

When Linden came home from school, we talked about the pebble situation again. He told me that there were these Beings from down in the ravine that would look in the windows. Sometimes they would throw small stones to get his attention. It scared him, so he closed the curtains. I asked him why he thought they would do that. He told me that he and his friends had been down in the ravine with flashlights, and maybe that bothered them. I asked what they looked like and all the other questions I could think of, but I have to admit there was still part of me that was a bit skeptical. I'm not sure why. It wasn't as if nothing weird ever happened to me. Why wouldn't he have similar things happen as well?

Many mornings when I went out to meditate or water the plants, the rocks would be there again. It was beginning to be a daily thing. I didn't really know what to do to help Linden, or how to get it to stop. I didn't have the tools yet to figure out how to take care of it.

CHAPTER 45

Wild Dreams, Spaceships & Star Beings

OVER THE NEXT several months, a lot of things started happening. First, I started hearing a low hum during the night. Often it was as I was just drifting off to sleep. Frequently, I would wake up and walk around the house to see if I could figure out where it was coming from. I could never find anything that I could attribute it to. After a while, I figured it was actually coming from outside. I would go out and look, but there was never anything that I could connect the noise to. While the humming was going on, a different feel would flow through me, almost like my body was being fed energy of some sort. I could feel tingling in my body, especially my extremities and it felt like my core was vibrating at a faster rate of speed. It wasn't an unpleasant feeling, just a different feeling.

The energy seemed to bring on vivid dreams about being with whales and dolphins. In one of my dreams, I was on a small boat with all five of my children. We were in the middle of the ocean with several dolphins swimming around us. I decided it would be fun to jump in and swim with them. Then I could show my kids that they didn't need to be afraid. The dolphins were our friends. I shared that we could even hold on to their top fin and they would gladly pull us along. As one came close, I grabbed ahold of its fin and we started surfing the top of the water. I got a little nervous when I figured out the dolphin was going to take me on a dive. My newfound friend slowly pulled me way down to the ocean floor. He was trying to show me a giant bubble that had a city nestled within it. I couldn't believe my eyes!

I held on with everything I had as the dolphin picked up pace. We hit the bubble head-on as we pushed our way through the thick transparent outside wall. Both of us were suspended for a second, then fell into a crystal-clear aquamarine pool of water located at the bottom tier of the city. Where in the world was I? After popping to the surface, I began to take a look around. The dolphin took off and swam through a doorway on the side of a building that was built into the water. By the looks of it, he'd been here a time or two.

From the pool, there were many walkways veering off in different directions. Each pathway led to another level and looked to be made of seamless polished white marble. The stairways led to garden landings lush with exotic flowers and vibrant greenery. The beautiful shimmering off-white buildings looked to be made of crystal. Each was exquisitely ornate with high carved doorways adorned with two carved pillars to each side. Everything felt ethereal.

I saw a man walking down a stairway from one of the higher buildings. He wore a long white tunic tied at the waist, sandals, and a robe hooked with a short chain at the collar. A beautiful shimmery embroidered pattern lined the hem of his robe, which looked to be more like Roman attire. He felt to be very high vibrating, and I wasn't afraid at all.

As I started to climb out of the pool, he welcomed me to the city. I asked him how this was all possible even though somewhere deep inside me I felt I already knew. This trip to the bottom of the ocean was to awaken some remembrance in me. He asked if I would like a tour, but I was really worried about my children who had been left alone in the boat on top of the water. I needed to get back as soon as possible. I didn't want them to think I was dead. He assured me that he understood. To get back up to the top of the ocean where my kids were, I needed to get back into the pool. He explained that I would need to swim through the small doorway that was slightly under the waterline. It led into the same building the dolphin had swum into. Once inside, I would be instructed on what to do. With that, he said his goodbyes and told me I was welcome to come back any time. After telling him thank you, I got back into the pool. It was time to make the journey back to the top of the ocean.

The doorway was easy to swim through, and on the other side of it I saw a big machine that seemed to encompass the long outside wall of the room. I was instructed to swim to the middle of the pool and wait. The machine fired up as I floated in the water. Within a minute, I was encapsulated in a massive bubble. The water began to flood the room and when it reached the ceiling, the roof opened. The bubble started its assent and broke free from the outer wall of the city. From there, it quickly rose to the surface where it popped. I was right back where I had started. You could see the questions and relief in the kid's eyes as they helped me back into the boat.

There were many other dreams about the ocean with dolphins and whales, along with Star Beings that felt more real than the life I was waking up to. More often than not, I would wake up with the word "Arcturian" in my consciousness. It felt like I was being mentored in my sleep. I would wake with a remembrance that I had just been in contact with a particular Star Being who was teaching me.

Then, I started sensing a spaceship above the house. I believe it was parked there. It didn't move around, it just sat over the top of the house. I couldn't see it with my physical eyes, but when I tuned in, I could see it with my inner vision. The ship was round and several times bigger than the house. Before long, I was feeling the occupants of the ship inside the house.

For several weeks straight, I felt that work was being done on my physical body at night, both inside and out. Sometimes it seemed to go on all night long. I could literally feel hands and energies sinking into my body. When I would ask what was going on, I would hear that I was getting work done on the energy pathways of my body. They were healing parts of my body that needed a little help. Mostly, it seemed to target the organs. Since I had already experienced this when listening to a Tom Kenyon meditation, it didn't really scare me. It actually felt like I was being taken care of, and it was always done with a feeling of love as I was being worked on.

After that, I started having strange interactions with electricity. At first, I noticed that TVs were beginning to bother me a lot. It was like they interfered with my energy field. When the TV was on, I would get really anxious and feel extremely out of sorts. Maybe scrambled is a good word to describe it. I decided that I needed to quit watching TV. It wasn't that hard for me, because I thought it was all pretty much a waste of time. I didn't like the constant bombardment of negativity and violence it projected through news, let alone the programs that were being showcased. I also knew there was a lot of subliminal programming that went along with watching it. (In many of the spiritual circles, the TV is called mind masturbation.)

Soon after, the microwave above the stove blew up, along with its replacement. I guess I wasn't supposed to use those either. Radios and TVs started fading in and out whenever I walked near them. I would back away and they would sound fine, but if I came near them again, they would scramble and barely make a sound. Sometimes the CD player drive would go out and in several times without being touched. Light bulbs began blowing in the house a lot, and as I drove down the streets there would be street lights that would make a popping sound and then dim or go out.

After a while, it started affecting where I did my cleaning jobs. I blew several vacuum cleaners and circuits began overloading. One time it happened three times, within two hours, in the same house. The guy kept asking me if I was putting too many things on at the same time, but I knew that wasn't the case. All I could do was shrug my shoulders and say I wasn't sure what was going on.

One morning, I had a lady cleaning with me. We were in an upstairs bedroom of a house. This lady had an expensive vacuum and I was half afraid to touch it. I figured my helper had better do the vacuuming. At one point, I was going to carry it down the stairs because her back was sore. I asked her to unplug it from the wall so I could get it ready to take down, but as she was going to do it, I saw a spot that had been missed. I quickly turned it back on to get it. Her face went white when she saw me vacuuming while she held the unplugged cord in her hand. I remember muttering something like, "Wow, it must have had a little bit of stored up electricity in it." I shrugged my shoulders as I wound it up and put it away.

I went home that day and said out loud that I didn't like what was going on. It was getting expensive replacing all the broken things. Whatever was going on, needed to be regulated so it didn't cause so much damage. Speaking it out loud seemed to work. I still knocked out street lights pretty often, but at least the objects in our homes quit breaking, for the most part.

Once, I took advantage of it in a fun way. Might as well, right? I was visiting my daughter and we went to the grocery store to get a few things. It was night time and as she drove into the parking lot, I could see that the lights were gas instead of electric. I knew that those were especially susceptible to being affected by my energy. I was certain that within a minute they would pop off. As we got out of the car, I took my hand and whisked it at one of the lights while commanding "Out you go, light!" It couldn't have been timed more perfectly. As my index finger lined up with the light, it made a popping noise and went out. I didn't know it, but there was a woman sitting in the car right in front of us. The car tore out backwards and sped out of the parking lot. The lady driving looked like she'd just seen a ghost. Paige looked at me in that "how could you" way and yelled, "Mom!"

CHAPTER 46

The Neighborhood Ghost & Helping Others Transition

THINGS SEEMED TO be a bit more open-minded in this town. I also figured that a town of this size would support me in my healing practice, as well as beginning to teach. There could be endless opportunities if I chose to put time and effort into creating what I wanted. Being in a bigger town was attractive in the sense that I could do what I wanted, without being the center of gossip. In bigger towns, people don't seem to care as much. At least, I thought that was the case.

I ran into my neighbor, Clay, one day and we struck up a conversation. He told me he was a teacher and coached basketball and other sports. I told him I did energy work and had a cleaning business. He seemed genuinely interested and asked me to tell him about what energy work consisted of.

At one point he confided that he had a problem at home with a ghost that wouldn't go away. He had even caught it on film, which he was only more than willing to show me. In the pictures, he and his buddies were toasting a beer outside his house. You could plainly see an area near them that looked like condensed smoke about the size of a man. He also had that same white smoke across his upper body. I told him that I had worked with releasing ghosts before and offered to help him out if he thought he needed it. He felt a little nervous, so I let it go and gave him my number, just in case he decided he was in over his head.

That night, I got a frantic call from his wife. She just kept pleading for me to please come down and help her. I have to admit, I was more than a little worried about what I was going to walk in on, but a promise is a promise. I called in my Angels and went.

When I knocked on the door, she yelled at me to come back to the bedroom. When I opened the door to the bedroom, I saw her husband standing in the middle of the room with a strange look on his face. It was obvious that he was extremely intoxicated. The wife kept telling me that she saw the ghost go in through his chest. She was frantic, and didn't know what to do. When I looked into his eyes, I knew she was telling the truth.

I started talking to the ghost, and asked who he was, and why he had gone into Clay's body. He told me that he knew Clay because he had been his teacher. The ghost told me that he was lost, and wanted to find his way home. He had tried to get Clay to help him, but he couldn't hear him. That's why he went inside. He wanted to see if he could make him understand. I told him that he needed to get out of his body because it wasn't his to use, and that I would help him to find his way home. With that, Clay swayed and stumbled to the bed as he exited his body. I can't say I had ever seen that before!

I could see now that the ghost was a teenager. I talked to him for a while to help him understand that he was dead. Then I told him that if he came back tomorrow when this man was sober, we would help him find where he was supposed to be. I said that I would be back the next day at 5 p.m. to help him. With that information, he thanked me, and disappeared.

The next day, I went back at 4:30 p.m. as promised so we could talk. Clay apologized for his condition the night before, and told me that his wife had explained everything. He then promised he hadn't had any liquor that day. He felt he now knew who the young boy was who was showing up as the ghost. Several years ago, a dad and his son had gotten into a car accident on a slippery road not far from there. The car lost control and flipped upside down in the creek, killing father and son. Clay had actually coached the boy in wrestling. I told him that he was right, and that because the boy had come to him, I felt it was his responsibility to help me cross him to the other side. He and his wife were more than open to it. A few minutes later, I started calling the ghost in. It wasn't long before he was standing right in front of us. Even though the couple couldn't see him, they could feel him.

I explained how we were going to help the young man get ready for the tunnel of light to open, so he could follow it to the other side. We helped him to realize that he had gotten stuck here after the car accident. He also understood he had been wandering for several years looking for his dad. After he listened to it all, we told him that his family was waiting for him on the other side. When he was comfortable with it, we called in his Angels, and the Arch Angels, then asked them to open the tunnel of light to the other side. We could all feel the joy and wonder as he was lifted by the Angels to go through the tunnel. As he began to follow it, I could see those who had died before him waiting to welcome him home. I have to say, it felt pretty good to be able to help a trapped Soul cross over to the other side. For the next several months, it seemed like whenever I went somewhere and was asked my name, there would be a hesitation. Then they would come back with "Oh, you're that lady who can get rid of ghosts!" I guess this town wasn't as big as I thought.

Not long after I moved to Mankato, the voice came through and asked if I would consider helping with a mass crossover for Souls that were caught in this area. It talked about the thirty-eight Native Americans who were captured and hung from the rounding up of the Santee Sioux by the government. They had been forced from their land and put onto reservations. The government had failed to honor the treaties that were struck, and the food that was to be given to the reservations had been sold to white settlers instead. Our government labeled it an uprising. Three hundred and three males were scheduled to be hung because they were accused of stealing eggs from a farm. (Never mind the deception used to steal their land and they had no choice if they were to not die of starvation.) For some reason, 38 were chosen to be hung, and the others were imprisoned, making it the largest mass hanging in our history. It has always made me very sad the way our forefathers have taken the land from the Indigenous in the name of progress. There has been a very unbalanced account of history when it comes to the Indigenous in America, as well as the history of the Americas. If you really want to know the truth, start digging, it's out there.

I have always been very connected to the Native way of life and was glad to be of service. I agreed to help, but I said I would need to be guided, because I had no idea what to do. That next night I was to go to the river near where the hangings had occurred and collect wood to make a big bonfire. I had to admit, I was a little scared. A fire that big and visible could definitely cause a lot of unwanted attention. I also didn't think it was legal right in the middle of town. But again, I said I would do it, so I wasn't going to back out. Once I got the fire going, a man with an accordion kept walking back and forth playing music on the walkway above the river. I found it very odd, and surreal, yet in other ways incredibly calming. It felt like he was there holding space for me like a guardian.

Once the fire was going really well, I was told how to open up the directions. Next, I was to call in the Arch Angels who would help open a portal. A bunch of Angels were called in to help each individual cross over to where their families would be greeting them. As soon as the portal was fully open, I started calling out to all the Souls in the area that were ready to cross over. I couldn't believe all the people who started coming towards the fire! There were definitely a lot of Natives, but there were other people as well. Men, women and children of all ages, races, and colors came walking into the fire. As their Angels greeted them to escort them home, they nodded their appreciation. It was so beautiful to see their joy as they connected to what was there for them on the other side. When the last person walked into the fire, it was time to close the portal and all the directions down. I was to thank and release all who helped, and make sure that the fire was completely out. Having that experience of service for the Souls that still roamed this area was an experience I am forever grateful for and will never forget. It opened my eyes to things I didn't understand or know before, and I was glad to do something for the Native people who have always held a very special place in my heart.

There are so many facets of life that we really don't think about or understand. I had often wondered about ghosts and why they are here roaming the Earth instead of crossing over. What I found through my practice is that it can happen many ways. It can be caused by someone that cannot accept that their loved one has died and won't let go, which produces an energetic tether. It can be that the deceased loved one decides to stay to watch over the family and gets caught in a limbo of sorts. It can also happen when the one that is deceased loves someone so much that they can't bear to leave the living partner. I've also seen confusion when someone dies in an accident, or from a blunt trauma, and doesn't understand that they're dead. I've experienced someone who is mad because they died, and to spite God they choose to stay. I've also seen where someone

has died and felt deep regret towards someone, or something. They stayed because they felt they needed to right it. I've worked to clear places where there has been a mass slaying and a mass grieving such as one of the civil wars, or Indigenous genocides. Often when the grieving goes into a reenactment of sorts, there is a constant calling to the energy which keeps a Soul here. I'm sure there are an endless number of reasons why they get stuck on the Earth plane.

CHAPTER 47

The Buddhist Nun, & The Shoshone Elder

SEVERAL PEOPLE THAT would become profoundly significant in my life started showing up. First, was a beautiful Buddhist Nun, who I met at a local market in town. We seemed to be pulled together by an invisible force the minute we were in the same vicinity. Her name was Aunie Pema Psultra, and she was visiting from India. I was quite taken with her playful spirit and we became fast friends. She would often come and stay for a week or two at a time.

I loved Pema's deep respect and honor for all things. She had a ceremony and an offering for everything you could imagine. I especially loved her beautiful chants of devotion before retiring and first thing in the morning. There was something so soothing about listening to such beautiful gratitude as you woke for the day. I learned a lot about Buddhism and she was eager to learn about what I knew. It was an absolute pleasure to spend time with her.

Pema was conceived in Tibet. The Chinese government orchestrated massive killings of the Tibetan monks, as well as the Tibetan people. They say that 10,000 to 15,000 people were killed in three days. Her family was one of the many that fled into India in 1959 to take refuge. It was there that she was born. At the age of 13, Pema knew she wanted to be a Buddhist nun. Her family dropped her off at a temple to be trained.

Her biggest dream was to meet Native people while here in America. She felt very connected to their culture and ways of life. She also felt that Tibetans were their ancestors. At this point, I only knew a handful of Native people and none of them were close by. Even so, they didn't feel like the right match.

I had heard that there would be a Shoshone Elder named Bennie Le Beau talking about his work at a nunnery in a town nearby, so I offered to take her. It was a fascinating talk about how emotions, thoughts and actions cause the harsh weather patterns and discord in nature. He urged us to all take a look at healing our lives and take right action to clear the collective consciousness, as well as the Earth. These were concepts I had been teaching already, but the way he explained it was a lot more from a nature perspective. He also talked about massive medicine wheels that he was being guided to make to heal the Earth and the weather patterns. He said that often he would go into different places that were in severe drought and perform ceremonies to bring the water back in the form of snow or rain.

We both found him to be a fascinating man, but I have to say, I was getting irritated at how many times he said things like "And you white men did this, and you white people did that." Finally, I couldn't take it anymore. I raised my hand to speak and he gave me acknowledgement to go ahead. I asked him if he believed in rein-carnation to which he replied, "yes." I told him that I was told that I had been Native American 56 times. Even though I was white now, I still felt very connected to that culture. Hypothetically, if that was the case, could it be possible that a lot of the Natives that were in reser-vations now were the white people who had massacred and forced the Natives into reservations from the beginning? Perhaps they were there to clear off their karma from that life-time. And what if there are a lot of white people here now that were the Natives that had been so horribly treated? Of course, I didn't believe it was that way in all cases because I believe that many were chosen to carry on the codes of their genealogy to keep in their Native tribes. But hypothetically, if that were true, couldn't it mean that we have been all things and now we all held parts of each culture?

I have to say, I thought that he would be really upset with me, but instead he listened and was open to feeling into what I said. I don't know that he agreed with me, but he didn't argue and shove it back down my throat either. Even after that, Bennie and I became friends, and I decided I would help him get his message out by hosting him at a few gatherings. It was very strange how quickly we meshed. I could feel that we had shared several lifetimes together. I didn't see them at this time. It was more an inner knowing. There was way too much energy running between the two of us to not have been the case. When we would sit to talk, hours would go by without either of us catching it.

CHAPTER 48

Israel

THERE WAS A trip coming up to Israel with the same group that I had traveled with to California. I was feeling the call to go. The Interfaith Center was going there on a mission for planetary peace. A few times, I thought it was going to be canceled because we heard there was so much unrest. We were told by those who would be guiding us that it was all made-up hype from the press to keep people away. There was no question that it was war torn, but they said the war had been over for a long time. They assured us there was no way they would be putting the trip out there if it was unsafe.

My mom and Randy were very upset that I was going. They tried their hardest to talk me out of it, but I really felt I needed to go. If there was one thing I was learning, it was that it was important to listen to the guiding of the heart and to follow where your Soul was pulling you. If you don't follow those promptings, you can miss out on life changing experiences.

After a lot of volleying back and forth, the group took a vote and decided to go for it. The flight was 16 hours, and I was thankful to finally land in Tel Aviv. Once there, we still had a three-hour bus ride down the Mediterranean coastline to Galilee and Nazareth. I was exhausted, but it was all worth it when I stepped off the bus for a break at the Mediterranean Sea. While standing at the edge of the water, I saw a cloud that looked like a mushroom covering a massive portion of the sky. I could feel it was a ship. I had already had experiences with this before. I could feel its energy was more cosmic in nature. We all waded into the water to get grounded into the land. Of course, I looked for rocks to bring back home. It seems to be a compulsion for me to carry rocks back from where ever I travel. Just as it is a compulsion for me to bring rocks and crystals to leave wherever I go.

The next morning, we finally got to see what Israel looked like. I have to say, it was a bit of a shock to see the war-torn land around us. There were perfectly beautiful buildings which were mostly hotels for the tourists. Yet, many of them had visible bomb damage. Other hotels were brand new and shut down. There was great poverty, as often is found in places that had been touched by war.

Everywhere we went, we would get propositioned with every-thing you could think of. People of all ages were selling a variety of items like water, maps and jewelry, out in the open streets. It was very hard to see the amount of begging and the poor conditions that the people lived in. We couldn't go anywhere without at least twenty people approaching us to buy something. It would even happen when we were in meditation. Many times, it felt as if the kids were being used as pawns. It was easy to see that they had been taught very well. You couldn't blame them. They were just trying to survive. More often than not, it felt to be invasive, inappropriate, and overwhelming.

On the first day, we visited Mount Precipice, where Jesus was run out of town and they decided they would push him off the mountain. Then we traveled to Mary of Nazareth's house, as well as the tomb of

St. Joseph, where Jesus was taught and preached at. Lastly, we visited Cana, and the Church of Annunciation. The Church of Annunciation was an amazingly beautiful place. We were all beginning our group meditation as two young men came up to the altar and began to sing. I was confused as it sounded like there was a choir of voices. As they gifted us with their song, tears of cleansing went through each of us. I kept on cracking an eye open to find where the other voices were coming from. There was no one else there, just the two of them. I had never heard or felt anything quite like it before. We all nodded our deep appreciation for their beautiful songs as they left.

The second day, we sailed in a big wooden boat. It was recreated to look like it would in the time of Christ on the Sea of Galilee. I was a little taken aback on how Galilee was actually only a little bigger than an average lake in the United States. It was beautiful, although small in stature, just as the compactness of the land dictated. As you sailed, you could imagine the story of how Christ spoke to the fisher-men to follow him. You could imagine where he walked out to them on the water while they were calling out for help. His energy was permeable there.

Being on the water after so much desert felt really good. The cool breeze blowing across you felt like a gift when you were so hot and tired. The men who were manning the boat couldn't have been sweeter. At the end of the trip, they raised the American flag and sang the national anthem to honor us. That was when I noticed that most of us on board were actually embarrassed, maybe even ashamed of our own country. I could only assume that they had similar experiences of uncomfortable run-ins with people from other countries. They look at the U.S. as being a big bully. I have heard that from people who come from other lands. They tell how the U.S. has forced their laws and beliefs onto their country. And how we use up so many of the resources meant for all. Since my traveling abroad, it has always both-ered me.

As we traveled to different places, I began to understand the pic-ture of what is truly going on in this part of the world. First of all, Israel is not a very big place. It is 1/15 the size of the state of Minnesota, yet it holds approximately 8.5 million people. Minnesota, on the other hand, holds around 5.7 million people. In Israel, there are at least four major religions, as well as several minor ones, and they are often at war with one another over the land and resources. One could understand because of its population and size, that the land was very important to its people.

I think one of the hardest things for me while I was there was the apparent contempt between the different nationalities and religions. There were many times when I saw an argument erupt between two or more men. In one hotel where we stayed, signs were posted on the different elevators, each stating that a particular religion of people was not allowed on it.

We were having breakfast and a man walked up to me. I was surprised when he asked me why our group was there. I told him that we came to walk the path of the biblical times. He looked into my eyes and asked "Are you here to help us?" I told him we were there to plant a peace pole. He then asked "Why do you pray for us? We are very bad people." I didn't know what to say. I could see in his eyes that he truly believed what he said. I told him that I didn't think they were bad people at all. I just thought everyone was sad from so much fighting. He gave me a nod and a smile, and walked back to his table. I wondered how it must feel to people who are in such conflict, fighting for the right to live their life in peace.

In Israel, there were young people everywhere with M-16's slung over their backs. After they graduate it is mandatory for young adults to put three to four years into the service. One time on a hotel elevator, I accidently opened the door to a wrong floor. I walked into at least a hundred young men and women crammed into the hallway with their guns either being held or slung up on their backs. I spouted off an" oops" as I backed up into the elevator to try another floor. It made me wonder. What exactly would it take to justify one of them using their gun? It was a thought that ran through my mind for pretty much the entire trip.

CHAPTER 49

The Power of Meditation

Many of the places that we traveled I noticed a wall around the city. I never asked why, but I assumed that it was to keep an eye on who was coming and going, as well as controlling who entered and left. Sometimes we would go into a town and many of the hotels and shops would only open when there were groups to accommodate. I guess the war news had kept everyone away. It showed in their economy. I could tell our guide, Kitty, was very sympathetic to what was going on. She made sure that we knew that our visit may be the only time these places would make some money.

The days were packed as we wove our way through Israel. We also traveled to where it was said St. Paul started the foundation of Christianity. We visited the Wailing Wall in the old town of Jerusalem. There I watched as Jews pried their prayers into the blocks of the wall, while reciting their sacred text. Then we visited Bethlehem, and where Jesus walked the Crucifixion. **I always shy away from the crucifixion story. It all seems so cruel and senseless to keep reliving it over and over again. It has always been a sore spot to me to keep our minds on torturous things, when there was so much beauty in his life to bring into our teachings. Why is it that there are so many teachings around suffering, pain, and sin? It always felt to me that there was too much focus around fear of God. Perhaps it was to create a control of sorts. If you fear God, you would follow his ways. You would make sure not to incur the wrath bestowed on those who didn't believe, or who would break one of the commandments and commit sin.**

The churches in Israel were amazingly beautiful! It was seldom that we actually saw people there. We went during times when most people weren't around. That way, we were able to explore the insides with all the beautiful paintings, carvings, and stained glass. I loved seeing all the different architecture and could only imagine the stories each church held.

We also traveled to the Dead Sea and spent a long time floating in the water and scrubbing mud all over our bodies. From there, we traveled to Jericho, and were baptized in the Jordan river where Jesus was baptized by John the Baptist. At the end of that day, we visited the Valley of Doves. It was more peaceful than anywhere else we had gone so far. I could almost feel Christ and the disciples walking beside me as I explored the land.

The next day, we visited an orphanage. In Israel, they say that sometimes children were left outside in orange crates near the churches and orphanages. It didn't seem to lean towards one sex or the other. There was an equal number of both being raised here. It was wonderful getting to spend some time holding and playing with the children because they were so appreciative of the attention. They loved being lavished on. We couldn't speak their language, but there was no need for words. Love is a universal language. We all felt very privileged to be able to spend time with such precious little Souls!

I think my favorite visits were the Magdalene church, the place they believed Mary Magdalene's house was, and the Garden of Gethsemane where Christ sat among the olive trees. I could feel those trees from blocks away. When I got in front of the fence to get a closer look, I literally dropped to my knees. The energy that came from those ancient trees was phenomenal! I felt humbled to be in their presence.

At one point we were led to a special place where we could sit in meditation. Each of us connected to an olive tree that we felt pulled to and began a group meditation for peace. Before we got very far into it, a commotion erupted outside the gates to the old walled city of Jerusalem. There was a rumor that a bomb could go off. Several weeks earlier, six men had been killed by a blast in one of the temples inside the city. Many people were upset that they were being barred from their place of worship during a very special holy time. The yelling became louder and louder as more people joined in. Soon it turned in to a full-fledged riot. People were shoving and pounding on the locked doors to the old city.

We all started our meditation for peace knowing that it was the only thing we could contribute to try and help calm things down. I prayed and meditated, but then I felt I was to open my eyes and watch what was going on. There were several low flying fighter jets beginning to fly over in formation. I also saw a blimp hovering that seemed to be used as a vantage point to see what was transpiring. The young soldiers were beginning to show up in large numbers, as well as more seasoned military that were dressed in darker uniforms. I figured they were ones who worked with riot situations. They wore helmets and shields and carried batons, as well as guns. It was easy to see that things were starting to get out of control.

Sitting in silence, we each began to visualize and emanate peace. As I sat there, I began to see two doves flying around the riot in the flight pattern of an eight. They circled the riot, then counter circled us. They kept a vigil flying this same pattern over and over. After about ten minutes, the charge around the riot seemed to lessen. Within fifteen minutes, the tension began to break apart. Within twenty minutes, the riot had lost its charge and people were beginning to leave. The doors were finally opened, and people were allowed in.

The doves flew away, and we kept meditating until everyone felt it was time to stop. I was so glad that I had been able to watch the whole experience and see the power of meditation at work. I was also amazed at the part the doves played. Aside from my cat, and my experiences with the hawk, I had never seen animals doing anything like this before. I wasn't surprised, just in awe. I was beginning to see that animals were far more in tune with things than I had given them credit for. I had a feeling that I was going to understand a lot more about that in the future.

On the trip home, we were rerouted to Vienna for an overnight stay. The tab was to be picked up by a very rich person who wanted to thank us for the energy and peace we brought to Israel. He must have been pretty well off because there were around 26 of us. He put us up in one of the fanciest hotels I've ever stayed at, with by far, the most amazing breakfast spread I had ever seen. It was a buffet with over a hundred high quality entrées to pick from. It was outstanding!

We were free to do as we wished for the night, but come eleven the next morning, it was time to take off again. I was exhausted and stayed behind to rest. Most of the group went to a famous restaurant where Mozart had eaten and had a fun night out. On the way back to the hotel, they said they saw two low flying space ships with their physical eyes. Everyone was pretty excited!

When you go on a pilgrimage with a group of people, things change within you, as I am sure that you also change the very ground you walk on as a group. They often say there is more power in numbers. One could understand how the unified meditation for peace could dismantle a riot. We are far more powerful than we believe ourselves to be. I knew deep down that there was a lot of change happening within me because of this trip. Part of me hoped that we had made a difference for Israel. I couldn't help but feel that Israel was a representation of all the division that we have created within ourselves and our world. Perhaps when we, as a whole, have more peace in our lives, Israel will finally come to find the peace that has been so elusive for them.

Getting back to "normal" after a pilgrimage like that takes time. Besides all the jet lag and time differences, there is a lot of integrating that goes on. The frequencies are held in the field around us until we transmit them to where we are to share them. Or, it's integrated into our cells. I know this to be true because I can hear different frequencies, as well as feel them. I also know when I am sharing frequencies, as well as receiving them. I think you become more sensitive to energy once you take notice of it. The more you feel it, the easier it is to sense it. When you are called to travel, it is like the collecting of bones. As we walk, we collect energy and information from the land. We also pick up energies from different incarnations that we've held there. In turn, we share frequencies that would be beneficial to the land and people.

CHAPTER 50

Crazy Dreams

AFTER COMING HOME from Israel, I started having a lot of strange dreams. Usually I don't remember my dreams, but at this point, they were very vivid. The White Brotherhood visited my dreams several times. **The White Brotherhood is a collective of highly evolved Beings who have gained enlightenment. They are here as a group to oversee humanity in their evolution. They work within the Universal laws.** In my dream, there were five of them standing shoulder to shoulder wearing long white tunics and robes. They seemed to emanate light through their skin. In the dream, they would always show up at a certain waterfall. They felt very familiar, like I knew them. For some reason, they were waiting for me at the waterfall so we could talk. Not long after, my son, Randy, showed me a place that we could go mushroom hunting. I was in shock when we got out of the car and I saw the same three-tiered waterfall that was in my dream! The place felt incredibly holy and became my favorite place to go.

Another dream I often had was about a human male body with the head of a dog. **They call this Being an Anubis. He is often referred to as the God of Death, or the God of the Afterlife**. In this dream, he would always follow me as I walked through a town. The Anubis looked to be dressed in Egyptian attire from the time of Osiris and Isis. I instinctively knew that he wrote inscriptions on the inside of pyramids. In the dream, I had stopped in front of a store. As I opened the door to go in, the Anubis came up behind me and tapped me on my shoulder. I turned around to look at him, but he didn't say anything. It felt like he was trying to talk to me telepathically. I just couldn't hear what he had to say. He felt so familiar. I sensed he was trying to remind me of something, but I could never figure it out. The dream would always end at the same place.

The third dream I dreamt over and over again, only with a little different variation each time. In each dream, I would be at my sister's house and would hear a knock on the door. I would open it to find two men and a woman on the other side. They looked to be pretty ragged and poor, and I would always invite them in for a cup of tea, and something to eat. Each time after eating, I would look at them deeper and say "I know who you are!" They would smile and turn into Mother Mary, Jesus and Maytreia. After visiting for a bit, they would start training me to teleport. They would say "Okay Barbara, there will be a plane crashing in exactly ten minutes. When you know that it has happened, we want you to teleport there to help out. Once there, we will give you your next instructions." They would then disappear.

I would wait for the plane crash, then take off teleporting. Unfortunately, I would always end up a mile or two away from the crash. I was never able to make it there on the first try. As soon as I gave it another try, I would make it. Each time there were flames and people everywhere, but that was all the farther it went. That was where I woke up every single time.

I was beginning to see that each stage of dreaming that I went through seemed to follow my inner turmoil, or inner peace. It also followed what I was allowing into my conscious and subconscious awareness. Dreams can give you so much information if you can write them down and dive into understanding what they mean. They can teach you a lot. If it is something you are interested in, I would recommend placing a notepad and pencil on your nightstand. Otherwise, use a recorder of some sort. Make sure to write, or speak your dream out as soon as you wake up. You may think you could never forget it, but within a minute, you begin to lose important details. The longer you wait, the more the chances are that you will forget.

As a child, my dreams were often full of fear and stress. I was in a house being chased by a white horse with wings who was trying to bite me. Other times, I was sitting in a rocking chair that was tied to the top of a crop duster plane. The chair was tied, but I wasn't. I was holding on for dear life as it did loop-de-loops. Oftentimes hanging on by a thread. I had numerous dreams where I was in my pajamas and hadn't had breakfast yet knowing that the bus was right outside the door honking. Other times, I was being chased by a bad guy or a vampire who was trying to kill me. They were always very traumatic and I would wake up in a panic.

In my mid-to-late-teens, I still had those dreams but they weren't as frequent. In this part of my life, I was having prophetic dreams. I would dream of something, and the next day or two they would come true.

As an adult going through marriage, divorce, and raising children, they were full of serial killers trying to get my children, and me needing to protect them. Or, they were about me working myself to a frazzle. After my divorce, I had more holy and Soul awakening dreams. These were more about spaceships, the Masters, beautiful animal encounters, and world changes.

CHAPTER 51

Conversing with the Masters

FOR A TIME, I was intrigued by the Universal Laws which are the laws that govern our Universe. And the Seven Rays, which are the seven color rays of the pure white light emanating from the heart of God as it descends. I found that each of us are born on certain rays that align with our birthdates. I also looked into the Masters and their retreats. These are specific places around the world that are used as retreat centers for specific Masters and the energy that they hold. It was incredibly fascinating to me. There was all this information that most people knew nothing about. Why was it that this stuff was hidden and had to be searched for? To me, it should have been more accessible, like any religion or belief was. I guess that is one of the reasons that I was so glad to study at more of a mystery school through the ministry program. What I was learning, was more of a cosmic/universal understanding and history of our world. It opened up so much more than I could have ever imagined. And, if there was one thing that I knew, it was that **you can only open up your mind when you learn how to stretch beyond its perimeters.**

I went through a period of really wanting to understand each Master. I wanted to know who he or she was, and what they were like. I decided that I was going to make large copies of each Master and put them around the ceiling in my bedroom. **When I say Master, I mean people who have reached enlightenment or self-realization. People like Christ, Buddha, Quan Yin, and Mother Mary.** Each night, I would call one Master in and ask to be downloaded with their energy so that I could know what they were about. Perhaps even talk to them. It was like a meditation shared with their individual energy. Often, I would ask questions and write down the answers that I heard. I guess in a way I was channeling and enjoyed it immensely.

Often times, they would share information about themselves and the times in which they lived. Many times, they would share wisdom for my life and what I was going through. When I asked how it was that their energy could come to me, **I was told that no one's energy ever dies, it only changes form. We could call on anyone and their energy would be there. But one must have the desire and belief, to be able to hear and receive, the information.** I'm really glad that I took the time to experience it. These channelings opened up a vast amount of information about what is really happening on the planet, our capabilities, as well as what the Masters are really about.

CHAPTER 52

A Past Life During the Holocaust

I GOT A call from one of the women who worked for me in my cleaning business. She explained that she had talked about me to her sister and niece. When she did, her niece had felt very strongly that she needed to meet me. She was wondering if it would be possible to meet with her alone over tea.

A few days later, she came to visit. Carlie was a beautiful, curly-haired thirty-year-old woman, with the most beautiful brown eyes I had ever seen. I really enjoyed her bubbly and optimistic personality, but was at a loss as to why she felt so pulled to meet me. As we talked, I noticed her eyes always going to my feet. I thought it a little odd, but people seem to be attracted to all types of things. After a while, it made me a little self-conscious, so I got up to get some tea and cookies in the kitchen. Before I could bring it in, she came over to stand by me. There was an awkward silence and I noticed tears falling down her face. As she looked into my eyes she asked, "Don't you remember who I am?" I said, "I'm sorry sweetie, but I don't know what you're trying to get at." She started sobbing and threw her arms around my waist as she laid her head on my chest.

Through her tears she said "You were my mother in Germany at the time of the Holocaust!" As she said it, I was thrown into a vision of her as a little girl around ten years old. She had light brown hair with big brown eyes. Her dad and brother had been torn away from us earlier when we were forced at gunpoint to another facility. They took our clothes and shoes. Then prodded us like cattle into a holding area with high fences. That's where the women, girls, and young children were being held. Both of us were wracked with fear as we stood naked in a line that was guarded by many armed soldiers.

I didn't want her to see what was going on, so I kept her head by my chest telling her to look at the ground. I shielded her eyes with my hand the best I could to keep her from seeing the horror that lie ahead. I knew we were in a line to be gassed. As we waited our turn, we could hear the screams of the others as they were being forced into the chamber. Not long after, there would be carts and trucks stacked with dead bodies driving past us. The smell of death was everywhere.

I knew what was coming, and didn't want my daughter to have to go through it. I told her I loved her, and would see her soon. Then

I smothered her to death between my breasts. No wonder she was so captivated by my feet, it was the last thing she saw before she died. The vision then faded.

I held and rocked her as we both cried releasing the hurt and trauma that had been caused by that lifetime. After the tears subsided, it was as if the charge of that past life experience went away. We spent a few more times together, but it wasn't necessary to do more than that. I knew without a doubt that we were brought together to be able to heal that lifetime. I was so grateful to have had the chance.

That was the second time that I had been shown a past life while awake. Each time had been equally traumatic. It made me wonder what happens when something horrific happens in a life without being resolved, healed or processed before death. Is it then carried over through the DNA into the next incarnation? If that is the case, then most of us are probably carrying things that affect our lives from our past life experiences.

For myself, I had always had an incredible dislike for Hitler. When we studied the Holocaust in high school, I had a very hard time reading about it. Not in the "this is disgusting" way, but in a horrified in the pit of my stomach way. And with the Native lifetime I was shown, it made sense why I had always been so attracted to the Native culture, even as a child. I was always looking for them. I was looking for my people. I felt more connected to them heart-wise than to the settlers. Even when I was watching old cowboy shows, I always cheered for the Natives.

I have also always felt a deep connection to biblical days. It was like I personally knew certain characters of the Bible. Perhaps we gravitate to that which we once experienced. Perhaps we gravitate to the kinds of foods we loved. Maybe we are attracted to different styles of clothing and architecture. Or gravitate to the values that we held so dear in past lifetimes. If that is true, then maybe we also get clues to our past lives by what we are intrigued by or attracted to in this lifetime.

CHAPTER 53

Connecting to the Animals

The property surrounding my house was so magical! I found an amazing spot at the top of the cliff that I could sit lotus style and let the wind blow over me as I meditated. When that happened, it was like the ancestors were whispering to me. I could be gone for hours in that state. For me personally, meditation practiced indoors was a fraction as powerful and easy, as it was out in nature. Often, as I meditated at the top of the cliff, a mated pair of hawks would fly in this beautiful formation that reminded me of the double helix DNA. The grace that they flew with as they spiraled took my breath away.

One time while meditating, I thought I felt Jasper climb onto my lap. Anytime I was in prayer or meditation he was like a moth to a candle. It didn't surprise me he had come to visit. Unfortunately, it could be a bit of a distraction. If I didn't acknowledge him, he would often give my arm or nearest body part a nibble to get my attention. I softly laid my hand on top of him so he would feel acknowledged, and I wouldn't get the dreaded bite. I knew it wasn't Jasper the minute my hand landed. The hair I was now smoothing was wiry, and closer to the body. When I peeked my eyes open, I saw a full-grown possum looking up at me. I have to admit, it was really cute, but what if now that I was out of meditation it would bite me? I started to go into a bit of fear. I gently told the possum that it had better get back to its family. Finally, it lumbered off my lap, and scurried away. I felt bad that I couldn't stay out of fear to see how it could have played out. We've been so programmed to be fearful of wild animals.

I've been told that when you are in a really true heart space, full of love and gratitude, you attract animals to you. I think it is because when you are in that space, it naturally opens a connection to a higher state of consciousness where everything is one. Animals can feel when a human is in the right heart space, and when they are, they have no fear of being near them.

CHAPTER 54

Working Through the Fear of Darkness

AT A RETREAT one weekend, we were discussing something similar. It was that if one could walk through a forest in pitch darkness with no fear, that the animals would guide you. Of course, most of us have a fear of the dark. We have been programmed from childhood that there are things in the night that are out to get us. Regardless, I wanted to try going out onto the retreat property to see if I could stay out of fear. I talked my friend, Denise, into joining me for the endeavor.

The property was more a lake acreage, than woods. We were pretty proud of ourselves for how far we were getting. Then, we came to a place where the underbrush blocked the way. It was so dark that we couldn't see our hands in front of our faces, but we made our way through. That's when we began to hear snorting. It was long, deep snorts, as if it came from a big animal. Then we heard a pawing at the ground, like a bull before it charges. We were scared shitless, as whatever it was, came charging straight at us!

Denise jumped behind me and grabbed ahold as if she were using me as a human shield. (What are friends for?) The animal stopped just short of mowing me over, while blowing warm, wet steam across my face and chest. I almost peed my pants! I quietly urged Denise to back up. We kept backing up until we were far enough away that we could run back to the retreat center. Whatever it was didn't come after us, thank God! We ran back as fast as our legs would take us without falling. I decided that was the last time I needed to try out something like that.

The next morning my curiosity got the best of me. I needed to know what had happened. Retracing our footprints to where the incident had taken place was pretty easy. The reality of what had happened that night was far different than what I had perceived it to be. As I walked through the woods, I came to a fenced in pasture. Had we kept going, we would have walked straight into an electric fence. The beautiful white horse penned within it was what had made all the noise last night. She was trying to warn us that we were going to get hurt if we kept walking forward. She was protecting us from getting shocked by the fence. That was why the horse charged! I thanked her over and over again. I guess we had been guided by an animal after all!

CHAPTER 55

The Native Understandings of Nature & The Beautiful Chief

I HAD CALLED out to the Universe to show me different kinds of men other than what I had known growing up and in my two marriages. I knew I needed to heal the anger I had towards men. I didn't realize how much anger I had, until one day my youngest son told me that he felt it projected towards him, and encouraged me to take a look at it. As hard as it was to hear, I was glad to be lovingly called out on it so that I was aware. You can't heal what you don't know.

A few weeks later, Bennie called to ask if he could come to visit for a bit. It was nice spending time with a man who was so in touch with his spiritual nature and the Earth. I felt a deep Soul connection between the two of us and always looked forward to his visits. When Bennie got there, I could tell something was bothering him. Later, he asked me why I had taken off the lower branches of a tree that was growing in the side yard. I told him that I had made a small meditation and honoring place there.

I was hoping to eventually place a medicine wheel around the bottom. He asked if I had communicated with the tree to see if it wanted its branches cut. I looked at him like he was crazy and said, "No, do people talk to trees and ask permission to do things to them?" He then asked if I had sealed the cuts from taking the branches off. Again, I didn't know what he was talking about, so how would I know how to do that? He told me that the tree was crying and leaking energy from the cuts I had made, and that I needed to honor the tree and be a good steward of the land. That meant that I needed to seal the energy leaks by painting the cut, or holding it with my hand. I also needed to tell the tree that I was sorry I hadn't asked permission.

Evidently, by trying to create a peaceful place for a medicine wheel, I had unknowingly thrown the whole property out of whack. **He explained that this very thing was an example of what was causing distress within nature. So many people just do things with no thought to anything but what they wanted. If they would be more in tune with the land and nature, there wouldn't be so much damage to the Earth. He said that people have forgotten that the Earth is their mother. The Earth is a living, breathing, Being, and she gives us everything we need to live. He told me that because of the disregard we have shown her, she is now sick and polluted. People being out of balance, was creating a world out of balance, and nature was being adversely affected. We then talked for hours about the Earth and how all the elements of nature worked together to keep things in balance. He explained this at a very deep level and I am ever grateful for the information he shared.**

The Indigenous people have always understood nature and the way to connect to it. They know that if they honor, and listen to the whispers of the land and animals, the guidance of the Creator, and their ancestors, that nature would provide them with everything they needed. They are taught from a young age how to communicate with it, and were given the ceremonies, keys and codes to keep the Earth in balance. I think it's imperative that we understand that

they have been given the ability and task as keepers of the Earth since their inception on this planet.

They understand why places are sacred. They know that those places are to be honored, not exploited for the precious natural resources that lay under and within. Those resources need to be there to hold, and amplify the energy each spot represents for the planet, and humanity.

They know the sacredness of forests as the lungs of Earth. The rivers as the veins of Earth. The swamps as the liver of Earth. They understand that water is the sacred giver of life, and all things are born of it. They know and respect the natural order of all different land types and understand to honor, respect, and live in harmony with it.

Indigenous know that plants are here to gift us with nourishment and their healing properties. They learned how to hear them, and can ask for guidance in how to cultivate and process them for the healing required. They understand that animals are here as respected brothers and sisters, and are often guided by their wisdom. They give sacred prayer before hunting, knowing animals that show up are offering their life for the good of the whole.

They understand the sacredness of life, knowing that every action creates a ripple in all directions, affecting the whole. They are taught the rhythms, cycles, and spirals of nature, and have a deep connection to the land. Connection to nature is their inherent blueprint.

Once you have that kind of information opened to you, you're never the same. How could you be? It opens up a whole new understanding of the world. I made a promise to myself that I would explore it deeper and share it forward wherever I could. Then I went out to talk to the tree and seal the cuts.

It made me really sad that I had been so unconscious about the tree. I would never intentionally hurt anything. It made me wonder how I had become so disconnected, especially since I enjoyed nature so much. How could I have not known this stuff? I finally quit beating myself up and gave myself compassion. **If it was not ever taught, then how would one know? I believe most people don't know. Indigenous people are brought up with this innate understanding. It is their way of life. How did we become so oblivious and separate from this connection and knowledge? And why? I now understood that everything holds a consciousness, and that we could interact with anything if we choose to do so. But one has to open their mind and expand its perimeters. It's also important to know that we need to be in our hearts instead of our minds while interacting.**

CHAPTER 56

The Medicine Wheel, The Chief & Bleed-Throughs

AFTER BENNIE LEFT, and I had made amends with the tree, I went out to start creating the medicine wheel. **A medicine wheel is a circle made of stones. Usually the colors are red, yellow, white and black which represents a specific direction or doorway. It is used for insight into health, healing, and connection to one's own spiritual essence. It creates insight and understanding through opening doorways to different directions, seasons, animals, life cycles and spirit, to answer questions about life.**

The medicine wheel took several days to complete. As I began to lay it out under the tree, I began to feel what the Earth was asking of me. Each stone was to be cleared, as I prayed for them to hold a pure intent and frequency for the wheel. I had already collected rocks from different places that I had visited, so there wasn't much that needed to be gathered. Even though they weren't bright colored rocks, I felt they were perfect. I also placed special crystals and stones from around the world that I'd picked up or had been gifted to me into the center of the wheel. I guess you'd have to say that it was a specialized wheel built uniquely for me. My Soul Brother, Craig, and I activated it once completed with honor and prayer. He brought his channupa (an Indigenous prayer pipe) over and we smoked tobacco together to honor it being activated.

Not long after the dedication of the wheel, I started having experiences where I would be in bed and I could hear a boy and his dad right outside my bedroom window playing catch. I'd get up and look out the door, but there was never anyone there. I'd lie back down, and it would happen again. Each time I'd check, but no one was ever there.

A few nights later, I started hearing splashing in the bathtub. I could distinctly hear two elderly women's voices talking, and they would end up in fits of laughter. I would get up to look in the bathroom but there was no one there. The tub was always as dry as a bone. It was bizarre! That happened five nights in a row. I felt it must have been some sort of bleed-through into other dimensions.

Several nights later, I was awakened by the most beautiful masculine singing I had ever heard. It was a Native tongue, and incredibly soothing to my Soul. I got up to see if I could find its source, but once up, the singing stopped.

The next night it happened again. This time, I remained still for quite a while so I could listen to his song. I was afraid that if I moved, it would disappear again. For some reason, listening to his voice made me feel so safe and protected. Instead of getting up, I decided to close my eyes and see if I could locate where it was coming from. When I did, I could see an incredibly handsome Native man dressed in white fringed buckskin. Even his headdress was pure white with many feathers lining the outside like a chief's bonnet. His black hair was hanging loose to his waist. There was beautiful, intricate, beadwork on his clothes and moccasins that was absolutely stunning! He was dancing around the medicine wheel shaking a rattle in one hand, while singing with a voice as pure as I had ever heard. I knew that he could feel and see me, because he kept motioning for me to come out and join him in the wheel.

The same thing happened for several more nights, but still, I couldn't get enough courage to go out and join him. After the fourth time he disappeared, as though it had never happened. I was sad that I couldn't work through my fear to go out there. I had never experienced something like this before. I kept telling him that I was sorry that I wasn't brave enough to meet him. Hopefully someday I'd get another chance. Evidently, I had a lot more fear of the unknown than I realized.

CHAPTER 57

The Flying Car

MY FRIEND, JO, came to visit on a regular basis. She still teases me about my insistence on making her come outside to swing with me in the backyard, even when there was snow on the ground. I always tease her that at least we did it with a cup of hot tea to counteract the cold. She was a good sport, and I really enjoyed our time together.

We were out walking around the neighborhood one night when we saw a pair of headlights coming at us in the sky about 50 feet off the ground. We kept staring as it came closer, trying to figure out what it could be. When it got close enough for us to see clearly, we both couldn't believe our eyes. It looked to be a darker colored Model T with the skinny wheels. It was a convertible, and there was an older white-haired gentleman driving it with crazy white hair like Albert Einstein, with a younger boy in the front seat beside him. They were smiling and waving at us. There were no wings; it was a plain car just as if it were driving on a road. Only, of course, this one was flying! It made a little noise, but only slight compared to it being driven down a road.

We just stood there with our mouths dropped open while it went by, turned around, and came back past us. After it was out of sight, we jumped up and down screaming "Oh my God! Can you believe we just saw that?" Of course, once we calmed down, we were wondering what it was all about. How was it even possible? I love it when I get to see these kinds of things with another person. That way it can be validated by someone other than me. What I wouldn't have given to have had a phone that took videos back then!

What are you supposed to think when you see something like this, and why was it shown to us? I could only guess. Was it because we both wanted to have more experiences with spaceships? Maybe this was a way they could come near us without us going into fear. Was it to expand our mind and show us that there is far more out there than the experiences we normally have as a human? Was it to show us that anything is possible? I can tell you that I was definitely up for more experiences.

Later that night, I sat in my swing reflecting on the experience. It was then that I noticed something out of the corner of my eye. As I turned to look, I saw six furry black Beings on the other side of the fence staring at me. They were about five-feet-tall with white faces. They looked like what I would imagine a humanoid panda bear to be, only these didn't have round bellies, and their faces were different. I just sat there looking at them, wondering what they were, and why they were standing there staring at me. I wondered if these were the Beings that were throwing the stones at the house when Linden was here alone. They definitely felt a bit mischievous. I never heard any noise and couldn't understand if they were trying to tell me something. Perhaps I was a little scared so it blocked my ability to hear. I got up and backed my way into the house. It was an uncomfortable situation and I was glad to get away from them. I guess Linden didn't just have an overactive imagination after all! He confirmed that they were the ones who came and looked into the windows, but they weren't the ones throwing the stones against the house. Huh?

For the rest of the time that I lived in that house, I sensed spaceships coming and going often. Several times, I saw some come really close to the house. Other times, they took the place of the one that had been stationed above the house. I wasn't sure why they were coming here, but it didn't scare me. I always felt they were here for our benefit. Often times, I would feel them at night when I was half asleep. More than once, I was woken up during the night with several Beings in the room working on my physical body. Sometimes, I was lulled awake and asked to empty my bladder. Other times, I was asked to lay in a certain position as they worked on me. Writing this out now, it all sounds so surreal, and yet, it seemed so natural as it was occurring. I was never afraid when I woke up with them in my room; they felt familiar, like they were the maintenance crew of my vessel. I didn't share what I was experiencing with very many people. It was hard for even me to wrap my head around at times. I didn't think that people would be open to it. It can be a lonely when you have a lot of experiences you feel you can't talk about for fear of being judged. Sometimes I felt like I didn't fit in. My experiences certainly didn't fit into what I felt normal people talked about.

CHAPTER 58

Dr. Emoto

I KNEW MY cleaning days were coming to an end because the healing and counseling was taking off. I decided to cut back to six houses. They were the ones that felt like family. One client became one of my closest friends. I could share anything about myself and my life with her and always felt heard and accepted for who I was.

Jane was interested in a man named Dr. Emoto. He was a holistic doctor and scientist who had been doing teaching around the world about water. His work was to show how water carried intent and could be programmed. In his studies, he would gather water and have people pray and say nice things into it. Then he would watch as the structure of the water changed. He would do so by freezing it at high temperature until it formed an ice crystal or flake. Then he'd take pictures and document it to prove his theory.

Dr. Emoto did a study with some families in Japan. Each family was given three jars with freshly cooked rice in them. One jar they were told to daily say "thank you," another "you fool," and the other jar was ignored. At the end of a month, the jars were checked. The jar that had been told "thank you," had turned a soft yellow and was starting to smell like fragrant malt. The jar that was told "you fool," smelled rotten and was turning black. The jar that was ignored, had rotted even worse. It showed how important interaction, connection, and love are in our lives. His work showed how our words affect everything around us in a positive or negative way. He also did studies to show that water holds intent. That was shown by the clearing of water. People went to a body of polluted water to pray for clearing and infuse love through their words. Then they drew samples every day to test. The water slowly cleared day by day.

Since we are basically 85% water, it shows us that we are programming our bodies through emotion, thoughts, and self-talk. If we could take that a step further, we could conceive that we are a body of water consciously creating our reality, through our words, thoughts, and emotions.

Jane was very interested in flying to Wyoming to take a class with Dr. Emoto. She didn't want to go by herself and asked if I would like to come along. I had never been to Wyoming before and was definitely up for an experience. As I started packing for the trip, my attention got pulled away to some pictures that I had just gotten from my sister. The pictures were of my Grandpa Evans. Because he had died when I was five, I never really got to know him very well. When I started looking through them, one energetically grabbed me. It was a picture of him standing next to a sign that said continental divide. I felt that I was supposed to bring it along so I stuck it in my journal and finished packing.

The landing at Jackson Hole Wyoming, with the Tetons as the backsplash of a lush blue lake, was incredible! I could feel the energy of the Grandmother Mountains as we flew over for the descent. Hopefully, at some point in the trip, I could get near them.

It was wonderful to see Jane in her element and be able to support her. I had no agenda as far as the classes and study went. I was feeling the need to let the Universe direct me to who would be most beneficial to meet, and where would be most beneficial to go. I left myself wide open.

The first day, I had a long talk with a beautiful woman who loved rocks as much as I did. I was excited when she invited me to her room to see the ones she had brought along. At the end of our visit, she told me that she was guided to gift me with a serpentine heart. It had been placed on Dr. Emotos heart as she gave him a massage. She was told it would help to heal my heart. I was very taken because I knew the heart meant a lot to her. I felt really honored that she could so easily give it up to someone she barely knew, and accepted it with gratitude.

Because I had overshot my stay with her, I missed a class that I had wanted to attend. I didn't want to walk in late, so I sat in the lobby for a bit to regroup. There I ran into a voluptuous, vivacious woman named, Choné, and her boyfriend, Robert, who were singer/songwriters from Sedona, Arizona. We were drawn together like magnets to a refrigerator. There was a definite energetic flow that was running between Choné and myself. I definitely felt we were going to have a connection in the future. We exchanged contact information when it was time to gather for a rafting trip down the Snake River. The Shoshoni people were in charge of being our guides. I didn't put it together until then, but Bennie was Shoshoni. I wondered if he would be there as well.

The ride down the river was slow and meandering. Perfect for seeing wildlife and centering your energy. I kept feeling an elderly Japanese woman who was sitting across the raft from me. She felt so much like my grandmother who had died a few years back. I noticed that she kept feeling into me as well. Finally, she motioned for me to come over to her. The raft was crowded, but there was a place near her feet that I could sit comfortably. As I did so, she slid down onto the raft floor next to me. It didn't take long to figure out that she didn't know a stitch of English. She picked up each foot one by one and began rubbing them and my legs while doing pressure points. Then she'd say a certain word to me as she put her hand on her heart.

After the raft docked, she kept coming over to me and repeating the same word. Regrettably, I didn't understand a word she was trying to say. Finally, she brought over an interpreter. The interpreter told me that she kept saying that I was her granddaughter. I thought that was very interesting. I told her that she felt just like my grandmother. She asked me what my grandmothers name was, and I told her it was Margret.

The elderly woman got all excited and began talking very loudly. The interpreter told me that when she was born, her mom wanted to name her Margret, but her dad wouldn't agree to the western name. I guess her mom adored an actress from the U.S. named Margret who became famous in Japan. All her life she was told by her mother "This is the name we gave you, but your real name is Margret." We had a very special moment in time that I will forever cherish. I was filled with the love of my deceased grandmother once again. And she, was filled by the love of her granddaughter who she had not seen in a long time. It was a priceless experience.

When we had wrapped everything up, we all got into vans to go to the Wind River Reservation. That was where Bennie lived. Too bad I hadn't known all of this so I could have made arrangements to meet up with him. On the way to the reservation, the van driver put in a CD that Robert had recorded. I'm not sure how, but it started opening up visions of past lives as I looked out the window. In the first vision, I was a Native man just standing there waving, on the top of a ledge, watching as we drove by. A little further down the road, it happened again. This time I was a Native woman. She too, just stood there waving at the van as it went by. While driving past them, I heard my grandfather's voice came through as it said; "Barbara, always walk the path of the peaceful warrior. Only through the energy of love will you change the world for the better. Always walk in peace and love."

Just as his voice faded out, the driver said "Hey look, we just crossed the continental divide! There's the sign." I grinned from ear to ear as I thought about the picture I had slipped into my journal. The words from my grandfather were the first I had ever heard from him. How amazing that everything on this trip had come together in such an organized fashion to provide validation and give me so many beautiful Soul messages.

Once to the reservation, the Shoshoni shared their beautiful dance and talked about their culture. Then we traveled to Yellowstone Park to visit Old Faithful. To my surprise, Bennie and Dr. Emoto were doing a ceremony with the water there. I decided to stay and get a ride back into town with him so we could visit. On our drive back, I helped him tear down and clean up a medicine wheel site that he had put together. It was not being used in an honoring way, so he had gotten the message to take it apart. I was more than happy to help out and we soon had the wheel dismantled. I got to see how he put the different stones and crystals together to do ceremony through the wheel. It was fascinating! It was also the first time that I heard a crystal talk and show me a vision.

The crystal explained why they are so important for humanity right now. It told me that as the Earth ascends to higher frequencies, those energies are energetically held by the crystal beds buried in the Earth. Each crystal bed shares their frequencies with one another. They in turn, send their frequencies to the crystals that are held on the surface. Each person who wears, or sleeps near a crystal, is being helped to raise their vibration through the crystals they carry, or are nearby. Crystals also carry information that when tapped into, can help those who carry them. They also can be programmed to hold certain frequencies, or radiate intention. Of course, there is far more things we can do with crystals. A really good book to help you understand crystals and stones, is "Love is in the Earth" by Melody.

The trip concluded without me visiting the Tetons, which was what I was most attracted to in Wyoming. It was one of the places that I had studied about in the book, "The Masters and Their Retreats."

However, the first night back home, I was taken into the mountain. I awoke from a dream that I knew was far more than a dream. There, the Masters met with both Bennie and me. We were facing one another on our knees, with our left hands on each other's heart, and holding our right hands together. I remember saying we would do something together. Then they showed us libraries with rolled papers and rooms that were filled with light used for healing. I didn't remember what it was all about, nor what I had agreed to, but I had a feeling it would all come clear when I needed to know.

CHAPTER 59

Good & Ill Intent

BENNIE CAME TO stay again shortly after that. This time he stayed for a week. We had two events scheduled. One was in Rochester, Minnesota, and the other in Northfield, Minnesota. When everyone came together for these ceremonial circles, and put their energy into the one unified intent, it was incredibly powerful. While doing these medicine wheel ceremonies, the energy of our focus would steadily escalate. When almost ready to hit the apex, you could see bugs and worms coming out of the ground as they made their way into the circle. Animals would show up and the birds would fly in from all over. Especially the crows, hawks, vultures, and eagles. When Bennie would drum and sing the songs in his Native tongue, it was as if a remembrance opened up in me. I could sing it with him verbatim. I didn't know how I knew the songs and the language, but I did. Perhaps from the memory I held of past lives that are stored in my cells.

This was also the second time that I experienced how ill intent and thought could cause physical pain to another person. There was a Native woman who I could tell was very jealous of my relationship with Bennie. Halfway through the ceremony, she joined in the circle directly behind me. At one point, I screamed out in pain because it felt as if an arrow had been shot into the middle of my back. As I tuned in, I could see a black arrow, and knew it had come from her jealousy and intent to harm me. Because of that experience, I vowed to carefully monitor my thoughts. Thankfully, Bennie was able to energetically remove the arrow. **I learned that even if we don't physically say or do something mean to someone, our thoughts are just as hurtful, and can affect others at a deep level.**

The rest of the time Bennie was there was spent getting to know one another better, and I enjoyed it very much. He was teaching me so much about Indigenous ways and how the Earth works. It was fascinating to listen to his knowledge about nature. He taught me how to listen and create balance through ceremony with the Earth. He also talked about how the Star Beings taught the Indigenous people songs and ceremonies to keep the world in balance. I gained so much respect for what the Indigenous people around the world knew. I couldn't imagine being taught from a very young age how to connect with nature and the elements. How different our world would be, had we all been taught like this.

I also felt like Bennie was helping me to heal my heart towards the masculine. Maybe even see that I could open up to a relationship again, if with a different type of person. We were both pretty free spirits, and it was just nice to have his company.

During this visit, Bennie told me that he could feel the ravine that lay below the house needed clearing. He said it felt to be out of balance and misaligned from all the people who had used it as a golf course in the past years. He also thought that maybe the boys going down there and having paintball wars had caused some disruption. The Beings that were down there didn't like it. He explained various ways that were used to clear large areas, and I remembered a lot about how he put his ceremonial wheels together. I decided to call some friends together to help with it.

I knew Bennie had to leave late morning that day. I decided to get up extra early to make sure that everything was ready. I took for granted that Bennie was going to do the ceremony with me, but he told me that it was my responsibility. It was important for me to do it on my own so I understood how to do the work. He didn't want to take my power away. I was upset, and didn't understand. After all the promoting and setting up groups for him, I took it for granted that he would help me with this. After the ceremony, I understood why he was so adamant that I do it on my own.

As I descended the ravine, I could almost feel the anticipation the land held for this ceremony. There were crows sitting in trees and flying above me like sentinels holding space for what was to come. Their calls were filtering through from every direction. It filled my heart knowing nature was there to help. The air was heavy with mist, and when I started burning sage, it hung in the air over a hundred-foot radius. I sat and ground into the Earth while asking the area what it needed to come back into balance. As I listened, the people that I had asked to help started showing up. I had created a very nice crystal center point for the middle of the altar. Then we all gathered things from the surrounding land that wanted to be represented on the altar. We drummed and used our rattles to open up all the directions. Simultaneously, we called out for their guardians to help support the ceremony nature was guiding us to do to help restore balance. As the crescendo hit, I could feel a rippling of energy wash over the land. I have to admit, the land felt really good when we were done. I could also see that it was good that Bennie had me do it alone. Otherwise, I would have handed it over to him. I would have given my power away, just as he had indicated. It's easy to take a back seat when someone else is a master at what they do. Climbing back up the ravine, I noticed several of my neighbors peering over the side. I'm sure they were trying to figure out what the heck was going on. Had I heard it, I would have been right there with them.

CHAPTER 60

My Walk In: What the Hell is This?

SEVERAL MONTHS LATER, I was driving from one cleaning job to the next and had a very strange thing happen to me. I figured I had gone out of my body because nothing looked familiar. I didn't know where I was. I didn't even know what town I was in. I pulled over to the side of the road and just sat there for a while trying to get my bearings and figure out what to do.

I wondered if this was the same kind of thing that had happened to me before. Several times in the past I had been driving and had a realization that I had no idea where I was. I had driven those roads my whole life, but all of a sudden, nothing looked familiar. It was like I was in the Twilight Zone. Thank God for my sister! I'm not sure how many times I had to call her so she could help me figure out where the heck I was. I'm sure she wondered about me sometimes, but she never made me feel bad about it.

This time something felt different. I was disoriented, and felt incredibly vulnerable. I decided to close my eyes and rest awhile. Maybe if I rested, a thought would come through to jar my memory. Unfortunately, nothing surfaced, so after sitting there for about ten minutes, I decided to just drive and see if anything looked familiar.

A few minutes into driving, I came to the end of the road at the edge of a town. Hopefully it was my town. I decided to turn around and headed back on the same road. After a bit, I figured I would cut to the east. That is when I saw something that sparked some remembrance. I was finally able to remember that I was close to a house I had been on my way to clean. It is so hard to describe what was going through my mind. It was like fragments were there to help me put a puzzle together, but I only got a glimpse of the picture I was so desperately trying to see. I didn't know what was going to happen, but I was here.

In my mind I knew who I was, and that I was supposed to clean a house, but there was also a very disconnected piece that was very confused. I felt I was me, but yet I didn't. I remembered enough to maneuver around, but for the most part, I was faking it. Maybe going inside would help me understand what this was all about.

When I walked in, Lois looked at me funny and asked if I was feeling alright. Thank God, I remembered her! I explained that I felt a little off, but I'd start in and see what happened. She smiled and told me that she already had the vacuum out and it was on the stairway. I went over to the stairway and looked down. I had no idea what that strange object was that was sitting there. If that was what she was talking about, I was in trouble. I hadn't a clue what it was, or how to work it. As I looked it over, I saw a long round rope like thing so I picked it up and studied the end. I just stood there trying to figure out what to do with it.

Lois came over and said, "Barb, you need to plug that into the outlet in order to get it to work. You know that, right? Are you sure you're okay?" I shook my head and told her I didn't think I was. She just said "It's going to be okay, Barb, I've got you. Everything's going to be ok." I thought it a very strange thing to say, yet it was profoundly comforting. It was as if it was coming from someone else through her. I told her I thought it was best that I go home and lie down. I'd call and reschedule the cleaning for another time, gave my apologies, and left.

I didn't receive any information on what had happened, but I felt that there had been some kind of a change out in who I was. I didn't notice a lot of differences as far as my core information and knowledge. I did, however, know that I was void of a lot of information from previous experiences and people that I knew. For example, one day a very old friend called. She was thrilled that she had run into my son's fiancé and was given my phone number. We talked for a bit about our kids and what they were up to and then I asked how her husband was doing. There was silence for a while and finally she said, "Barb, he died four years ago. Don't you remember? You were at the funeral right next to me helping me through it!" Those kinds of interactions weren't fun. I would just have to be mindful and know that there were things I wasn't going to remember anymore.

CHAPTER 61

The Pixies

FOR ABOUT A month, these little white Beings would come into my bedroom at night. They were about six inches high with pointy heads and wore no clothes. At times there were ten to fifteen of them and they would run all over my bed as I tried to go to sleep. They reminded me of what a pixie would look like, and seemed to be very mischievous. The more I would ignore them, the more rambunctious they became. I was having a horrible time getting a full night's sleep. One time I'd had all I could take. I gave my bedspread a heave-ho and they all went flying. They were driving me crazy, and I didn't know what to do! It's not like you could get advice about this kind of stuff from just anybody. Most people would think you were off your rocker.

Finally, I broke down and talked to a friend about it. She asked me if I knew what they wanted. Hmmm, now that's a revelation I hadn't thought about. I needed to ask why they were here. She thought that maybe they had something to share with me, and if that was taken care of, they would leave.

That night when they came, I finally asked them what they wanted. They told me that they had work to do on my energy field but needed my permission before they could do it. It seems funny to me now that I didn't ask them who they were, let alone why they were here. But I guess that was the way things seemed to roll with me. I told them that they had 30 minutes. After that, they needed to leave me alone so I could finally get some sleep. They agreed and as I lay there, they worked on every part of my body.

They were as efficient as a well-oiled machine. Nothing hurt, I just felt energy running through from them to me everywhere that they put their little hands. It was actually quite a pleasurable experience. I told them that I was sorry that I had been so grumpy to them, and that it had taken me so long to come around. I made sure to say that I appreciated the work they were doing, and then I fell fast asleep, never to see them again.

CHAPTER 62

Sedona: The Staff & The Bishop

I HAD TALKED to Choné several times since we met in Wyoming. She kept inviting me to Sedona to spend some time with her. She told me she was living in a mansion where there was plenty of room. I had never taken off to visit someone I really didn't know all that well, but sometimes you just know it is meant to be. I decided to buy a ticket and go.

The plan was that she would pick me up from the airport, but I waited over an hour with no sign of her. I tried calling several times, but there was no answer. Unfortunately, it was too late to rent a car, so I guess I just had to wait it out and have faith she would show up. Finally, she drove up with a man who looked to be around 70. Choné apologized for being so late, and explained that she had misplaced her phone. She had just moved and lost it in the process. Choné, and the man she had been living with, had gotten into an argument and he kicked her out. Now, she was staying with the man driving her car, whose name was Stanley.

Instead of driving to a mansion, we pulled up to a trailer park. I was a little surprised, but I'm a go with the flow kind of gal. As long as there was a clean bed to sleep in, I was good. Well, there was one extra bed so Choné and I shared it. We talked late into the night as she explained what was going on. Choné was a beautiful, sensual, sexy woman with a huge heart. She was a very complex person that I sensed was full of opposing energies. Even with all the differences, I felt as connected to her as a sister.

She and Stanley were both recovering Mormons. Choné had been shunned by her faith and her family. She was kept from having any contact with her four children by her husband and father-in-law. As could be expected, it weighed heavy on her heart. Stanley had been a Mormon minister, and decided that he wasn't feeling aligned with their ways anymore. They were old friends, and often times he had a place here for her when she was in need.

Choné shyly told me that 73-year-old Stanley had just had surgery to help him with his love life. Evidently things were all healed up and working, because there was a constant chorus of moaning coming from his bedroom. It was pretty hard to dispute that he was having a go at it. I didn't know that people his age even had sex, but obviously I was wrong.

We spent the next day meeting up with various friends of hers, all men, and that night we visited a house where her boyfriend and a woman were recording some music. It was a beautiful place full of high-end Egyptian paintings and statues. Every room was decorated to the max.

The music they were recording really resonated with me. I could have listened to them all night. It was music Robert had created for a DVD that he was putting together about water. He claimed that when he would go into ceremony and walk into water, he could phase through to different dimensions. Often, he could capture faces and Beings that lived in the water with his camera. He showed me some of the pictures and they were amazing! I could definitely see animals, human faces, and bodies that he had captured in the pictures.

We spent the next night there as well. At the end of my time with Robert, I was walking to the door and noticed what looked like a Native American staff leaning against it. The staff was a beautiful natural piece of diamond willow with a hawk and a crow feather dangling from the top. They were woven into black braided leather with beading. You could tell it was a woman's ceremonial staff. It reminded me of a snake or dragon, and it had a heart and yonis, with in the natural shapes the diamond willow is famous for. I exclaimed over its exquisiteness, and Haden said, "Good, I'm glad you like it, because it's yours." I told him I knew it was a Native piece and I couldn't possibly take it. He answered "I don't think you understand. It really is yours!" I told him I had no idea what he was talking about, so he explained.

Five years previously, he was hiking on a trail in Sedona. A Cherokee woman appeared out of nowhere and came up to him with the staff. As she handed it to him, she told him that it was not his, and he was not to use it. One day he would meet the woman that it belonged to. When he did, he was to give it to her. He asked her how he would know who that was, and she answered that he would know. She turned and walked off, never to be seen again. I found the story incredulous, but things like this seem to happen in Sedona.

I looked at him and asked "Well, how do you know?" He told me that he had a dream that first night that I had come there. In the dream, there was a very old medicine woman with the staff doing ceremony by a fire. When he looked at her closer, she turned her face and it was me. Haden told me that I was to be very careful with the staff because it was very powerful. He was warned to tell me that I was not to use it until I understood it better. I gave him a hug, thanked him, and off we went. I didn't know how I was going to get it on the plane, but I was going to at least try. I was a bit confused about it all, but grateful for the beautiful gift.

Choné and my days were packed with getting to know different people in the community. We definitely had a synergy of energy that seemed to attracted people wherever we went. Choné definitely attracted a lot of male admirers. She was like sex in a bottle. I would watch with curiosity as men turned into putty around her. She always had them eating out of her hand. I didn't feel it was always a healthy thing. It was easy for me to see within the dynamics of it all.

I felt her being cast out by her husband and father-in-law had created a hurt so deep that she began to use her charm to create unhealthy energetic cords of attachment on the men that she met. On one side, she was regaining her worth by energetically manipulating men into wanting to do things, and to take care of her. She had been callously thrown away by the men who were supposed to love and protect her. Now she was in control. She was also setting them up consciously or unconsciously for a broken heart by promising things she could never deliver.

As far as the other side goes, the men were getting their egos fed. A lot of the time, she insinuated hope of a future and more intimate connection. Her sensuality was like crack to a drug addict. That being said, none of us are perfect. We are all using or working through our little energetic games. I loved her all the same. She had a beautiful caring heart, and I accepted her as she was.

At one point, she invited a man we had just spent a day with to come and stay at Stanley's. He was in Sedona visiting, and hadn't found a place to stay yet. Now mind you, this man was a retired bishop, and there was definitely no more room at the Love-inn. I shuddered at the thought of our host and his fairly loud sexual escapades as a bishop slept on the couch in the living room! I decided I would pay for a night in a hotel for the three of us. Choné and I could have one bed, and he could sleep in the other. Everyone seemed to be on board, and we talked well into the night. It is weird to hear it now, but back at the time, it all felt perfectly natural. There was never a thought about anything being inappropriate. I didn't seem to have any problem opening up to whatever presented itself while in Sedona. There, synchronicities and out of the ordinary things happened all the time.

Sedona is an incredibly beautiful place. It is said to be a spiritual mecca and is full of healers, readers, and everything you can think of including UFO tours. Although they are all intriguing, and can be very helpful and fun, what I am most attracted to are the beautiful red mountains that surround this beautiful town. You can tell that the mountains hold very special energy. I had heard that before it became a spiritual mecca, it was a very sacred place where the Natives used to come and do their ceremonies. There were tribes that had settled in several places around it, but they were outside of the main part of where the town now lies. It wasn't until the mining boom that people decided to split off and find new places to establish homesteads with their families. Sedona was one of those places.

In some ways, it was sad to see the population explosion with roads and houses taking such precious land. But evolution, or perhaps what I felt as de-evolution, seems to find a way. The town was to become a place where people travel from all over the world to connect to nature. Or, to find spiritual guidance and healing in whatever way suited them best. There is a saying that Sedona calls her children home.

CHAPTER 63

Meeting My First Humanoid Star Being & The Codes from Isis

CHONÉ WAS NOT much of a hiker, which was easy to tell with her high platform shoes and frilly she-she clothes. Regardless, I did have to give her credit for taking me up to the Buddhist stupa. At least we got somewhere out on the land. I loved all the beautiful sparkly rocks that lay everywhere! I picked some up to share with people back home.

Afterword, we made a quick pitstop to McDonald's. Choné's stomach was upset, and she needed a bathroom ASAP. I decided to take the rocks out and look at each of them as I waited. The rocks here were virtually crystalline sparkles with iron ore in between. As I sat there, I began to feel a very strong and strange energy come in through the front door. While looking around to see who it could be, I saw a man peek around the corner trying to get a look at me! He definitely had a different look about him. With a sweet smile on his face, he walked back to me and asked if my pile on the table was rocks. Chuckling, I told him they were, then asked if he would like one. He replied "Oh, no thank you, I have a big rock of my own, I don't need anymore. Would you like to see it?" Nodding my head yes, he proceeded to pull a huge crystal out of his pocket. It was about ten inches long and looked like an icicle with a strange white coating on the outside. I had seen a lot of crystals, but nothing remotely close to what he was showing me.

I gave him a look over, and noticed that his face didn't seem real. It looked like he was wearing a mask. A very good one at that. His eyes were an incredible shade of blue that I had never seen the likes of before. I looked deeply into them and said, "You aren't from here, are you?" He chuckled and said "No, I'm from a star system a very long ways from here. I asked him what he was using the crystal for, and he told me he was holding grid lines at different quadrants on the planet so that the Earth changes didn't cause a lot of damage. I thanked him for all he was doing, and told him I was very thankful for all the Star Beings were doing to help us. He gave me a big smile and said "You are quite welcome! I was told that there was someone in here who would understand me and could see who I was!" We continued to talk until Choné was feeling better. Who'd have thought at the beginning of this day that I'd be talking to a Star Being in McDonald's!

The next day, we went to visit a woman who Choné knew. While we were in her kitchen talking about Egypt, a bunch of things fell off a wall in her bathroom. The lady took that to mean that she was supposed to bring us to where she worked at a retreat center. There was a picture of Isis hanging there that a deceased local artist had painted. She had been told that the picture energetically held codes to share with people. If she was given a sign when with someone, it meant they were one of the people the codes were meant for. She was to offer them the chance to meditate with it so the energetic download could happen. It took an hour to get there, but it was sure worth the drive. The retreat center was built on a beautiful creek and was absolutely amazing! You could tell that the land held a very sacred and high energy. The lady told us that it was created by several intersecting lay lines that ran through the property. The ranch also raised horses and alpacas. Much to my delight, I got to spend time with them before seeing the grounds. Finally, she took us to the house. That is where she brought us to the painting that she felt we were being called to meditate with. As we sat lotus style below it, you could feel a lot of energy begin to run through our bodies. We had been sitting there for around an hour when the lady quietly came over to us and said "I'm really sorry, but I forgot to tell you something. I was told to warn whoever meditated with this picture to be very choosy on who they made love to next. A spell would be placed on them, and they'd be bound to love you the rest of their life."

Well shit! That would have been a nice thing to know before we started! Had we been told that beforehand, I don't think I would have chosen to meditate with it. I guess it was too late now. I simply chose to not give it any power.

CHAPTER 64

The Cherokee Healing Staff

MY TRIP CAME to an end, and I was a little worried about what was going to happen as I tried to bring my staff on the plane. I slung it over my back and walked through the airport asking for help from the Universe to make sure it was allowed on. A voice came in and said to envision a fuchsia cape being slung over me and then it would become invisible. Well, it was worth a try!

Surprisingly, not one word was said. Not when I went through security, or while waiting to board the plane. In fact, I only heard one thing mentioned as I walked to my seat. There was a man who touted "Holy crap!

That thing could knock someone out!" Dang, my cape must have slipped. I hurried and sat next to the window, and wedged my staff to the side of me. It rode there the whole way home without another word.

When I got ready for bed that night, I placed the staff in the farthest corner of the bedroom about twenty feet away from my bed. I didn't really know how I felt about it yet. I felt it was best to keep some distance until I understood it a little better. My sleep was very fitful that night. I dreamt about walking around with the staff in a big crowded house. A friend walked up and knelt in front of me to stop me from moving forward. I asked her what she was doing. She just pulled the front of my pants down and started sucking right below my belly button. I was embarrassed and pushed her away asking what the heck she thought she was doing. She said "Our teacher told me you have some dark energy there that needs to be released." I told her I didn't think she knew what she was talking about and needed to stop.

I got away from her after she tried once again and sat on a couch nearby. As I leaned back on the couch, I put my staff on my lap to rest. The end of the staff rested between my legs and right away a grey cloud of matter started coming out. Oh, my God, she was right! I did have some dark energy that needed to come out! I startled awake from the dream and realized that the staff was lying on top of me exactly like in the dream. I was so freaked out that I threw it! Holy crap! How was this possible? Obviously, there was more to this staff than I could have imagined.

CHAPTER 65

An Embarrassing Neighborhood Party with Bennie

BENNIE CAME TO visit again. We were becoming a lot closer, but he traveled so much that I couldn't see us being in a steady relationship.

I knew he had very specific work he was being guided to do and I wasn't supposed to piggyback off from it. I had my own work that was being asked of me, and couldn't afford to lose myself. We each needed to follow our own paths and we both knew it.

On his second night there, I was contacted by a group who called themselves the Thunder Beings. They came in to talk to me about who and what they were to Bennie. Often times they would come in what I call the "tween" states. That is right before waking up or going to sleep. I could feel and hear them, but couldn't see them. They would talk to me telepathically and felt very familiar to me. Again, there was no fear; only an openness to experience their energy and words. I believed these to be the Beings that I had connected to as a child during the storms. When I asked Bennie about them, he told me that they had been guiding him for a long time, and were very sacred to the Native people.

On this visit, the neighbors invited us over for a cookout. I declined several times because I knew how Bennie could talk a blue streak, and some people weren't ready to hear what he had to share. The neighbors kept assuring me that they would love to meet him and so we went. Before leaving, he promised that he would behave. He would just talk general stuff so as not to get anyone upset.

It didn't take more than twenty minutes of formalities and he started in. He let the teacher know how school was brainwashing our children with things that weren't even true, like our real history. That school just teaches kids to be subservient and how to follow directions. He told the contractor that he was ignorant because he didn't do ceremony and ask the Earth if it was okay to dig a hole or build where he did. He then told the doctor that western medicine was bought off by the pharmaceutical companies and they pushed drugs to cure everything. Then he ended the night by telling the pharmaceutical salesman that he sold poison and because of that he would have to clear up karma for him and his family around the pharmaceutical companies' greed, deception, and control. I'm pretty sure he made an impression because everyone's bottom jaw was hitting the table. I guess I should have listened to my inner voice. Bennie was banned from any more neighborhood get-togethers!

CHAPTER 66

Sedona Garage Sales & Meeting Dana

AFTER COMING BACK from my last trip to Sedona, people started asking if I would consider taking a group there. After it happened several times, I decided it was the Universe's way of telling me that the energy was right for me to do so. **That often seemed to be the way I was alerted to a door opening, or to find information I was looking for. I would hear or see something three or more times. Then I knew that it was something important to tune into.** Setting up a tour might be a lot of fun, but there was a lot I needed to know in order to create an awesome experience for the people who would be attracted to come. I guess it was time for an exploratory trip. This time I was going to figure out the hiking trails and vortexes that Sedona was so famous for.

Because I knew it would be more of a physical trip, I asked if Choné could set me up with people who might want to share what they knew with the groups. She introduced me to a Mongolian Shaman who could do a sweat lodge and ceremony, as well as a beautiful black man named, Sao, who was a Shamanic Astrologer. She also introduced me to a goddess painter whose work was amazing, and a lady that made incredible jewelry, plus sold stones and crystals for a fair price. I was meeting lots of interesting people, but I wasn't finding anyone who wanted to get out on the land.

The third to last morning there, I called out to the Universe. I asked to be shown someone who was knowledgeable about the land, the trails, sacred sites, vortexes, and petroglyphs. As well as someone with a medicine wheel, teepee and a sweat lodge. That's what I felt I needed to put my tours together. If either was a massage therapist, it would be the icing on the cake.

Immediately, the voice came through and told us to go to the first garage sale that we saw. We did, and I was really glad. You wouldn't believe the garage sales in Sedona. They're like going to a metaphysical store. There's everything you could possibly imagine. I'm sure it is because so many people come from all over the world, then at some point, they're directed elsewhere and want to unload their stuff.

Susan, the woman who was putting on the sale, was beautiful and we had a very strong connection from the start. We talked for hours. After a bit, I walked through to see if there was anything I liked. Sometimes I would pick something up and hear nothing, other times I was told to put it down because it wasn't for me. I thought it odd, but I knew better than to not listen to that guidance.

It was an extremely hot day and we waited around for almost four hours. It was time to move on. Evidently, it had been a bum steer. Even so, it wasn't a total waste of time. I got some pretty awesome things, and we met Susan. We were getting ready to leave when a purple van showed up and a man got out. I told Choné that maybe we should wait for a few minutes because it could be one of the people that I had asked for.

I decided to just watch him for a while. As he went through the sale, I noticed him pick up literally everything that I had been told to put back down. Finally, they gave me a shove to go and talk to him. I asked him what he was going to do with all the stuff he had since there were good sized rocks and some Native things. He told me that he was finishing up a medicine wheel at his house. The rocks were just what he was looking for. The other items were going to help decorate the new teepee he had just put up.

I guess he was one of the people I was looking for! I asked him what he did in Sedona and he told me he was retired now, but had been a jeep tour driver. He drove people to the sacred sites, vortexes, petroglyphs and trails. As a jeep tour guide, he shared information about the land and a lot of the Native wisdom. He was also a massage therapist and had taught it at a college in California.

Oh my God, he was the whole enchilada! I asked him if I could come over the next day and see his place. He told me he was having the second day of his garage sale. He suggested that I come between ten and two and we could talk. I guess that explained why he got to this garage sale so late.

His place was amazing! He had several stone wheels on the property, and everything was decorated beautifully. I had never seen anything like it. He talked about each wheel, then showed me his teepee. He told me that he was getting ready to put up a sweat lodge within the next few months. There was no question; this was the person I was to work with.

The next day we went on several hikes, then out to eat and to talk things over. He invited me to stay in his teepee for the night so I could experience it. That I took him up on, and it was a wonderful experience! His name was Dana, and he had one of the most gentle and beautiful hearts I had ever felt in a man. I'd found everything I needed on this trip to create a beautiful experience for those who wished to come. I flew home completely at peace with the tour I would be giving. **And I will never forget that I don't have to do anything alone. One simply needs to ask, and be open to receive.**

It seemed every time I flew to Sedona on one of these trips, I would get seated next to someone who needed help. There were several times, when after an hour into the conversation, they would confide they had just tried or were contemplating committing suicide. One time, I was put by a man who was a national skate board champion and the doctors had just given him the news that he was going blind. Once, I was being guided to teach about energy and advanced spiritual teachings. Another time, I was seated next to a pilot trying to save his marriage from a divorce. I didn't mind helping, but often times it was exhausting. I really just wanted to be quiet and left alone. Once again, I asked the Universe to not do it anymore. I needed to take better care of me, and it stopped. When things felt differently for me, I could always open it back up again.

CHAPTER 67

Hawaii: Swimming with the Pleiadians

WHALES AND DOLPHINS started coming into my bedroom at night. It seemed to be a sort of an in-between sleep state, like a dream. Most of the time, it felt more real than the life I was currently living. In the dream, we were swimming and playing together and they spoke to me telepathically. I was acutely aware that they came from Sirius and that representatives from that planet were there in the room with us as we interacted. It seemed to last for many hours and as I started to wake up, and ground into my body, it felt as if I was being ripped away from them. I didn't want to leave the beauty and serenity I was experiencing. From then on, I felt a tremendous pulling of the heart and Soul to go to Hawaii and swim with the whales and dolphins. It was like they were calling me there.

I knew the trip would be expensive and didn't really think I could afford it at the time. I was also afraid to go by myself, so I waited. It felt like part of me was dying every month I delayed. I was being called to Hawaii and could feel it with every fiber of my being.

People often ask me how one knows something is being directed from their Soul verses their own wants and needs. I would tell them when it was such a strong feeling or knowing within, that to do other than what was being guided would feel as if they were turning against themselves. It continually haunts them until they take the steps to make it happen. That is exactly how I felt about this trip.

Finally, my friend, Mary, decided she wanted to come with. We bought the tickets and secured the trip. The next piece was figuring out how I was going to be in the water with the whales and dolphins. My friend, Jane, showed me a website on a lady named Joan Ocean who had been studying dolphins for decades. She actually took people out on a boat to swim with them. I guess I didn't have to jump off a whale tour boat like I thought I would have to!

Often, when I go places, my Soul directs me to it. **What I mean by my Soul is my Higher Self. Your Higher Self is a part of yourself that resides with you and yet in a higher frequency, or dimension. It has a broader view of your life and what is supposed to happen within it. Because of that, it has a lot of information that would be helpful if you could learn how to tune into it. I feel a lot of people do tune into it without knowing what it is. Many times, it is that still, soft voice of reason and insight that comes through to help guide you on your path. Guides often do the same, but for me it has mostly been my Higher Self. That's your direct connection to your God Self**. Sometimes I am asked to do some work like clearing places with sound and energy in a group. Sometimes I would be asked to do things not meant for another person, and needed to do it alone. I wasn't sure what was going to happen in Hawaii. I was a little nervous bringing another person along for that very reason. I have had experiences where another person can be pretty shaken by the energetics of the work as it was being done. Often, a lot of opposing energetics can come up for them causing a meltdown of sorts. I loved my friend who was coming with and didn't want to cause any discomfort for her. All I could do was explain, and let it unfold.

Hawaii was an interesting place. The ocean and the sky seem to go on forever and the land is filled with greenery and live food everywhere you look. You can feel the high energy from the land in all its lushness. You can also feel the weariness of the Native people with the constant stream of travelers invading their paradise. I guess I couldn't blame them. The Hawaiians long to save their ways and culture just as the Native Americans do. I could feel their pain, sadness, and discomfort at non-Native people buying their land, and influencing their children further away from their traditional way of life.

I'm not sure what was going on when we arrived there. We seemed to be stuck going back and forth on the same highway over and over again. It was the weirdest thing! We just wanted to get to the water. Two days in a row we drove the same stretch of highway. We got out once in a while, and visited a shop or two, but it was like the ocean was being kept at bay. Neither of us could figure it out. It was like we were in a weird dream and couldn't wake up. Finally, I called my go-to Cynthia, and asked her if she could check into what was going on.

She told us there was a rip in the **continuum which is a normal succession or sequencing of events that create a forward movement** and to be patient. By the end of the day, it would be fixed. Then we should be able to go to the water by the day after. We were to make sure to not go near it until it was done. True to her words, by the next morning, we were able to finally visit the ocean.

We kayaked, swam, and visited a lot of the normal vacation spots mostly staying at bed and breakfasts. We were having a really nice time. Then we went to stay at a place called Sky Ranch. It is where we were to connect with Joan Ocean, the dolphin expert, and her partner Jean Luc, who was a futuristic painter of dolphins and whales. It was an interesting mix between the two of them. She had been studying and swimming with the dolphins for decades. What I didn't know about her was that she was also really into Bigfoot, like me. She told me that she had met them several times, and that they had left her gifts and notes. (Yup, evidently, they can write.) They were both fascinating people to talk to.

Neither Mary nor I had experience with snorkeling at all, so we were glad to have hired Joan to teach us. We were super excited as the dingy took off the next morning. It couldn't have been a more beautiful day to be out on the ocean. Right away we saw pods of up to thirty dolphins. Unfortunately, they were where no swimming was allowed. I guess we were to connect to the whales first. Not far offshore there were several Mamas with their babies. You could see their water spouts from far away. Although I would have liked to have gotten closer to the whales, there is a law in the Hawaiian Islands that prohibits anyone from going in the water with them. A distance of 100 feet also has to be maintained so as not to disturb them.

The driver was careful to stay farther away than the law stated, but the moms would keep bringing their babies over and nudge them up to the boat. It was really sweet! There seemed to be no fear whatsoever, and it felt as if they were excited to connect. It happened several times and it was amazing to be able to make eye contact with them. So much was shown through their eyes. The driver was extremely nervous. I'm sure he was afraid he'd get reported and fined so he only allowed us to connect for a few minutes before he took off again.

Ten minutes further out on the ocean, we found a pod of dolphins, and he finally let us go in. It took the two of us a bit to get going because Joan basically got in the water and took off without saying a word. The lady who was helping everyone else on the boat was the one who helped us to get started. We were both pretty put off, but who could stay mad long when you're in the water with a pod of dolphins who wanted to play?

Once in, you could hear their mesmerizing clicks and tones as they raced their beautiful sleek bodies through the water. What was interesting, was that wherever they swam, I could see a pink hue. Often, they would encircle us. Some would literally come face-to-face and make eye contact. As they made contact, I could feel my heart opening farther than it ever had before. I was amazed at how long the pod of dolphins played with our group. I was also happy to see that Mary was really enjoying herself. I was so captivated by the whole experience! It deeply embedded me into each moment and I was fully present.

At some point, I began to notice that no one was around me anymore. I couldn't see another snorkeler or dolphin anywhere. I just kept looking around trying to see if I could see anyone. Finally, I spotted some forms swimming towards me. They were definitely not people, or dolphins, because they were around 10 feet across. As they swam closer, I could make out what looked to be see-through manta rays. I could see their outline with their organs visible and pumping, but the rest of their body was completely see-through. It was fascinating! I could actually see the ocean water through them! I kept thinking how incredibly odd it was, but then I was no expert in marine biology. Was there such a thing as see-through manta rays?

As they swam nearer still, I saw they had very strange eyes that were in the shape of an eight. When they came within 10 to 15 feet, the eyes began to pop up on top of their heads like antennas. Then a humanoid head started to emerge from between its wings. It had only two holes where the nose would be and the same went for the ears. I kept rubbing my goggles, but it didn't alter a thing. The transformation continued. Next a neck and shoulders emerged with long arms and skinny long fingers. The fingers were followed by the torso, legs, and finally the feet. By the time the morphing was finished, they looked to have whitish skin, were about eight feet tall, and there were around ten of them.

They seemed to be very drawn to me. Not just as a curiosity, but it was like they wanted to feel my energy. They kept swimming very close around me. Each looked into my eyes as they took turns placing their fingers on my heart. I could see no expression on their part, and I can't fathom why, but I felt no fear.

I don't know how long I had been there with them, reveling in what was going on, when I began to hear yelling. The yelling jarred me and I popped my head out of the water. I could see the snorkeling boat was pretty far away. The captain was pointing at me as they drove the dingy over to pick me up. Everyone was in the boat and he was visibly upset with me for going off on my own. We were to stay together as a group, and he felt we should stop for the day. I told him I was terribly sorry, but the current had taken me. I asked him to please not punish the group for what I had done, and promised I wouldn't do it again. He begrudgingly decided to let us try one more time.

We found our next pod of dolphins and went in for the second time. I tried very hard to stay with the group, but there were other plans afoot that I had no control over. Once again, the current took me far away from the others. This time there were around 30 of the see-through manta rays that showed up. Again, they morphed into these tall whitish humanoid Beings that would swim around me and touch my heart as they looked closely at me. I don't understand why I never tried to talk to them. Perhaps I was too transfixed in the whole morphing process. I just know there was no fear on my part. I could feel the love emanating from them and knew they would not hurt me.

I had only spent minutes with them when I saw three huge fish swimming directly below us. As I looked closer, I saw they were hammer head sharks. I started to panic. To be honest, being eaten by a shark was one of my biggest fears. But then I could feel that these Beings, whoever they were, would not let anything happen to me, and came to a profound place of peace.

I began to hear people screaming "Shark! Get out of the water!" and popped my head up once again. People in the group were hurrying to the safety of the boat. Then I heard my name being called as they searched the water. I was a lot farther out then I had realized. Once again, the boat came to get me. It was obvious that after this there would not be another time in the ocean. I had messed it up for the rest of them. The dirty looks I got from the captain said everything. I asked if anyone had seen anything weird in the ocean, but they all just stared at me. I took that to mean it was all I was supposed to say. The Beings had only showed themselves to me.

As we settled into Sky Ranch for the night, I was asked by Jean Luc if Mary and I would consider critiquing his new meditation DVD he had just finished. About halfway through, the same see-through manta rays with the crazy eight eyes were floating in his visual meditation. I could hardly believe it! He had met them as well. Jean Luke felt they were Pleiadians. He had also seen them in the ocean while snorkeling and they had been teaching him in his dreams for years. How amazing it was to be able to share our common experiences!

CHAPTER 68

Iris & The Ankh

I CHOSE TO be outside and connect with the incredible land at Sky Ranch that evening. I am always a person who would rather be outside than sitting around inside. A new guest from Holland, named Iris, was just showing up and I could feel that we were supposed to get to know one another. I found out she was writing a book on the divine feminine and had just come from Sedona. Iris was only in Sedona a day when her guides told her she needed to pack up and go to Hawaii. She was specifically told to stay at Sky Ranch. Iris bought her tickets and was off for Hawaii within 24 hours. Holy cow, what a whirlwind!

I invited her to supper with us, but she was tired and wanted to go to her room to settle in. As we were finishing up our meal, Iris decided to join us. She felt she was supposed to show us her **Ankh, which is an ancient Egyptian object meaning eternal life**, and pulled it out from its carefully wrapped case. It looked like a cross except the top of the cross was a circle instead of the straight line we are used to seeing. I really didn't know what an Ankh was, but I could feel it held the highest vibration of an inanimate object I had ever experienced. She also had these beautiful diamond-cut stones called **Andaras. They were said to be solidified water and held the energy of the feminine diamond**. Then she explained that she was working with the diamond light. I think my friend felt out of place, because she excused herself. I guess this was to be one of the things I was supposed to experience alone.

After Mary left, everything started to open up. Iris told me she had been on this quest of finding out about the diamond light. Jesus was teaching her all about it. I could feel her love for him. It would sneak into her conversation sometimes in almost a possessive manner. Iris explained the diamond energy was information that was energetically brought in by Mary Magdalene. She was told that after she had retained the information, she would be guided to do Diamond Light Activations. Sometimes she felt pulled to activate a certain person, other times she was asked for an activation by a person.

I could feel her impatience at how long everything seemed to take in the gathering of information to complete a book about it. I strongly felt to share that perhaps it was her need to hurry and get it out there that was actually causing it to take longer. I told her that it wasn't about her, it was about the consciousness of humankind and their evolution forward. Sometimes when we need to take ownership of our projects, our egos and personalities can put a halt on things. I told her I didn't think many of us could see the whole picture. It may be time for her to let go and get in the passenger's seat. It was time to let the Universe be in charge and show her what to do.

I really admired this young woman's trust and faith. At 34 years old she had sold her house to travel and do the work that spirit was leading her to do. What a powerhouse she was! By the end of our conversation, I was getting a strong pull to have the diamond light energy downloaded into me and asked her if she would be willing to facilitate it.

She told me that usually she felt Mary Magdalene was to do the download through her, but this time it would be Christ. She sat me in a kitchen chair facing the door, then moved to the back of the room to center herself. When she felt things were ready, she moved to stand behind me. As she lay her hands on each of my shoulders, I felt complete unconditional love running through me. It felt similar to when I was in the bathtub on the farm and first saw the visions of Jesus and Mary. Once again, I could feel Christ's energy through Iris's touch. It was as if my heart was being surrounded with his love. He spoke to me with such tenderness as I felt his energy begin to merge with mine, like a sacred union. I had never felt anything like it before or since.

I had one vision after another pass through my mind. It was as if I was watching a movie with the film slowed down. There were hundreds of picture frames flowing past. I figured they were future events, because I hadn't experienced any of them as far as I knew. There was no way that I could keep track of, let alone remember them, because there were so many. The first were waves of lots and lots of people's faces as they lived their lives. Then, a lot of chaos and Earth changes.

I was overtaken with waves of orgasmic energy that began to run through my body and was embarrassed because I assumed Iris could probably feel what I was experiencing. The energy that was running through me felt to be stretching me up and down at the same time. When she was done, she took her hands away and quietly went to the back of the room. It took many minutes of sitting still before the energy finally stopped. I can't say I had ever felt anything as powerful as the work she shared with me that night.

The two pictures that I had bought a few days previously, while stuck on the highway, made a lot more sense now. One was a picture called sacred union which had a man and woman intertwined. It was full of sacred geometry and roses. The other was one of Isis with her Ankh. I had battled between two pictures, but only bought the sacred union one first and left the store. The Isis picture kept showing itself to me. It wouldn't leave me alone. I had to go back and purchase it a few days later. It is so interesting to see the synchronicities and how everything comes together in experience. I knew Iris and I would keep in contact with one another. I could feel there were things that we were meant to do together.

Mary and I used the last two days visiting Pele, exploring the beaches, snorkeling, swimming, kayaking and getting a few mementos to bring home. There were a few tense moments between us, but we were able to work it through. I was incredibly grateful for our experiences together on this beautiful island. I was also grateful for her ability to listen to the guidance she was given to go on this trip. Had she not, I'm sure it would have taken me far longer to go.

At the airport, I noticed a Native Hawaiian man and knew he was in a lot of physical and emotional pain. I could feel I was supposed to help him. So, when he sat by me at the gate, I started a conversation with him. I asked him what was going on because his feet were so swollen that he couldn't wear his shoes. He said that he had just found out that he had congenital heart failure. He told me that he was in a lot of pain and had forgotten his medications at home.

I told him that I was a healer and asked if he would like me to run some energy through him. He looked into my eyes and said, "I would like that very much, thank you." I ran energy through his heart, back, legs and feet and when I was done, I said, "You have a beautiful heart. Have you decided whether you want to stay or not?" As I looked up, he was crying. He told me that he had left his island and no one knew where he was. He just needed to get away. He was contemplating that very question and didn't know the answer yet. He felt like no one cared and he didn't like what he'd seen and felt within his experience here. He didn't know if he wanted to stay or not.

I told him that I had felt the same way once, but things changed and it could happen for him, too. I was sure there were people who would love for him to stay, but it was up to him. He was the only one that could choose.

There was no right or wrong choice, only what he felt was right for him. I gave him my card in case he ever needed someone to talk to, gave him a hug full of love, and left for the plane.

Again, it took a lot of time to integrate all the things that had happened, and the energies that had come to me on this very special trip. I finally asked my friend, Eita, if she could do a massage to help set all the new energies in. When she started, I knew that she was in complete surrender for my best and highest good. As she stood there, I saw an orb go into her through the top of her head. I could feel Jesus' energy through the touch of her hands as they infused love into my cells. Eita said that many Natives were standing around me and they kept dropping breast feathers on top of my body. They called me Little Feather because they said that I can now blow in the wind wherever I choose to go. Then a voice whispered to me "Little Feather, don't grab onto the sides of the river, float to the middle and keep your head above water. See who's there and unite." Confirmation of my Spirit name came a week later when Jane gifted me some jewelry after her trip to Colorado. It was a necklace and earring set, each was a little feather carved out of bone and painted to look real. She had absolutely no way of knowing that I had been given that name. To this day, little feathers show up for me everywhere I go.

CHAPTER 69

The Tom Kenyon Retreat & Denver's Underground Alien Airport

FOR EASTER, THE kids were going to go to spend some time with their dad. I was really glad, because I was being pulled to go to Washington with one of my friends to do a workshop with Tom Kenyon and his wife, Judy Zion. As stated before, he was one of the people I felt most pulled to in this lifetime. I could feel his toning work reverberating through my cells to change and heal things within me. His music has been a very instrumental part of my awakening, and is probably the reason I took up sound healing as well.

I drove to Jan's place in Stillwater to stay overnight. Her sister, Jill, was going to pick us up in the morning and drive us to the airport. I never sleep well when I know I have to get up early to catch a plane. I think I am just too nervous that the alarm won't go off. I'm not sure if I dreamt it, or the Universe was trying to get my attention, but I saw Jill come in the house and knew the alarm had failed. We were going to be late for the plane. Just as I saw it, Jill came in yelling that we had overslept and were going to be late for the plane. We threw on our clothes and took off.

I couldn't believe it! We were late, and she wasn't even going the speed limit! No amount of prodding seemed to make any difference so I just kept praying everything would work out. When we got there, the gate for the plane had just closed. We got chewed out, but they held the plane. We literally begged people to let us go through the long lines. Wouldn't you know, Jan's bag was held up to be searched. What were the chances? It definitely felt like something was trying to stop us from going on this trip. Thankfully, we made it.

Being in the same room with Tom as he sang was life-altering. His music pierces you to the depth of your Soul. We were told that the reason we were all brought together was because there was a wave of darkness that was coming to the planet. We were there to counteract it. Over four hundred beautiful people from all around the world felt the calling to be there.

It was wonderful being with like-minded people and making connections. When you attend these types of events, you meet really interesting people. There were way more women there than men. But that seems to be the norm for a gathering with a spiritual nature. I guess men didn't feel as pulled or comfortable in these types of gatherings. The conference was several days of intense work and both of us loved every minute of it. It was all about clearing our hearts and healing the hurts from our lineages seven generations behind and ahead. When we left for the airport, we were definitely holding a pretty high vibration.

This time, there were no issues or worries about catching the plane on time. Everything went off without a hitch, until our layover in Denver, Colorado. It was early afternoon and we wanted to catch a quick lunch before the next plane was ready to take off. McDonald's was the first fast food restaurant we came to, so we both ordered something and sat down.

Both of us were enjoying our meal and watching the people go by when the floor started shaking. It was a very strong shaking like an earthquake had hit. We both looked at one another and acknowledged what was going on. What was strange was that as we looked around, no one else was reacting. They were all acting normal. Pretty soon everything started to blur. A white cloud came up like a wall. When the shaking stopped and the white cloud receded, I saw that we had been transported somewhere else. We were now standing in a room looking out into a population of Greys. At least I think they were Greys! They were greyish white Beings with long skinny arms, big heads and huge eyes, but these were taller. Many were dressed in a uniform. It seemed like we were in another airport that was for them. We started freaking out and I kept telling Jan that we had to be quiet so that they didn't see us. Greys are a race of Beings from another star system that came to Earth after destroying their own world. They are the ones that people talk about when they say they have been abducted and experimented on.

I didn't know what was going on, or what to do, so I took a chance and called Cynthia at work. Thank God she picked up the phone! Right away she asked us what was going on. She had felt something was wrong. I whispered to her that we had been transported into another dimension with the Greys. She kept telling us to pull our chakras in all the way and to hurry. If we were seen, we may get stuck there. Believe me, neither of us wanted to get stuck there! Just as we were finished pulling in our chakras, a couple came by pushing a stroller. The dad was carrying their baby. I knew that the baby had seen us, because it was trying to get his parents attention. He was pointing our way and trying to get them to look when the shaking started again and everything went blurry. The white cloud came up once again, and as it re-ceded, we were back at McDonald's. We were so grateful to be back where we started! McDonald's never felt, or looked, so darn good!

Cindy told us to keep our chakras in as close to the body as we could on the plane ride home. She also told us not to make eye contact or talk to anyone on the way home or it could happen again. I was so glad that Jan had the experience with me. I don't know how it would have turned out had I been taken to the under-ground alien airport by myself.

I am sure that there are people who have off the wall experiences and feel all alone in them. Sometimes I wondered why I had them. I've felt to be a misfit a lot. My life didn't exactly cookie cut into what people perceive as a normal world. There have been so many experiences that I can't explain. And yet I'm glad that I have been able to experience things outside this reality. I think that it is part of my mission here. I am predestined to have out of the ordinary experiences, so that I can share and help the other self-perceived misfits to feel their way through what is happening to them. I also feel that sharing my experiences can help others to open to their own unique experiences. Or, help them to know that they aren't alone, and they definitely are not crazy.

And besides, who's to say that the out of the ordinary things that I see and experience aren't the real normal, and everything else is us all being stuck in a programmed reality? I mean, what do we really know about what is our normal, and what isn't? It's definitely something to ponder.

CHAPTER 70

The War Chief & Our Human Experience

I WENT BACK to Sedona to make some final arrangements for hotel accommodations and line up people who would do some work with my first group. This time, I spent a lot of time with Dana exploring the land. I also wanted to know him better so we could make an effective team. I knew there was a connection between us because I had been shown some past lives that we shared. I felt incredibly comfortable with him. Before long, we were exploring a relationship. I knew that if I chose this relationship, it would help heal the abuse from the men that I had experienced. He would help me feel safe again. A part of me was scared, but I decided to dive in.

On our hikes, Dana took me to different places where I knew without a doubt in my mind, I had lived in a previous lifetime. One was at a place called Polenki. There I was guided through my inner voice right to the house that was mine. I was shown me as a woman in my 20's with a husband and children. The other was at a place called Montezuma's Well. I instinctively knew which house was mine there as well. I saw myself as a little girl around six years old who fell to her death while playing with friends. At times it was a bit traumatic to see the things that I saw. But, as it was being shown to me, it felt as if I was literally picking up my energy from that particular lifetime and bringing it back into my body.

They say that Sedona calls her children home and I believe it. Some people are called there to learn what they need to know. Then the doors close and she boots them out. For some, the doors never open and you're only allowed to stay for a visit. Others are invited to come and are pulled to live there forever. You know if you are welcome or not, and when your time is up, it's up. She either welcomes you in, or spits you out. Through the years, I have seen it happen over and over again.

One night, Dana and I decided to sleep in the teepee. I wanted to know how it felt because each night two of our group would be sharing it. That night as I slept there, I had a wild dream that this crazy Indian Chief had come to me. He was dragging me all over the place to do work with him. It was nonstop, and I was exhausted when I woke up.

When I went home, I felt totally unbalanced and ungrounded. It reminded me of the time I couldn't remember where I was in the car, and finally got information around a Soul fusion, **which is when a specific energy comes in and merges with you to add its energy. It's there to help you move through an area in your life that would be too difficult on your own. It doesn't always stay. Once its piece is finished, it usually leaves**. This time, I didn't lose core information, but my personality changed. I felt very confrontive, almost warrior-like. I finally figured out several days later that while I was in the teepee that the Chief/Warrior had come to help me get into my warrior energy for the next leg of my journey. It was like he was sharing his energy to help me become emotionally and mentally stronger. I wondered if the chief was someone I knew in another lifetime. Or was he me from another lifetime?

Everything had once again shifted. A grieving process began as I let go of all I thought I would be doing, making way for the new and unknown. I felt strength in me that I had not felt before. There were several people who commented that I had changed in looks, as well as energetically. I have thought about this a lot. I suppose since it had happened to me several times, and I had witnessed it happening to others, I wanted to figure out what it was all about. At one point, I received this information around it.

The human is much more than they believe themselves to be. They are multi-dimensional, multi-faceted diamonds, and Universal Citizens. Each has had many life experiences by choosing different times and timelines, dimensions, and realities at different places around the world and even on different planets. Each time you incarnate you choose a new role, gender, culture and experiences. Sometimes we are the good guy, sometimes we are the bad one. We have been all things. Our Soul is eternal and never dies; it only changes form.

In between our human lives, we go to a place that many call heaven and meet with our Soul group. Soul groups are people we reincarnate with over and over. At the time of our death, we have what is called a life review. In the life review, we get to see our current life experience and all that it encompassed. We see where we excelled and where we had problems. We get to see how our acquired love and light has touched others, and how it spread from one person to another. We also get to see where we have consciously or unconsciously hurt others and the effect it had. You're shown how the negative act rippled out in different patterns and directions.

All of it is being done with a Guardian who is holding unconditional love so you can heal the places that you have incurred shame or judgement towards yourself. There is no judgement from God/Goddess/Source or your Guardians. This process is done in a blink of time, and after it is shown, you are brought to a state of remembrance of your true perfect and eternal Soul, where once again you remember you are one with everything. The experience is only a matter of knowing so that you can heal what needs to be healed. Then you can choose the next incarnation with a greater understanding of what you would like to accomplish and expand upon.

Perhaps you didn't get as far on patience as you would have liked. Well, then you may choose a life where you have a chance to master it. You could choose being a mom with lots of children. Or, having a mentally and behaviorally challenged child. If that doesn't help you to master patience, nothing will. Maybe you hurt a large group of people by conning them out of money. In your next life, you could choose to be a spiritual teacher, and teach those who you feel you have misled. In the next lifetime you vow to mentor them to a state of enlightenment, to clear the karma. Maybe, you came to help open people's minds and set them free. Whatever one chooses, all the experiences will be used to strengthen your eternal Soul, and those that you incarnate with. As you heal and strengthen yourself, you also help to do the same for your Soul group and lineage, as well as those around you. Sometimes you are being asked by one of your Soul family to play a hard role so they can experience forgiveness at a deep level. Maybe you want another time of being in love with a person you only had a short time with in the previous life. Perhaps you would like to feel what it is like to be rich, or famous? There is no right or wrong, good or bad, there is only experience. Usually, you come to master several things in one lifetime. Each lifetime you pick a different expertise like a lawyer, engineer, activist, ditch digger, nun, nurse, medicine woman, guru, pilot, or soldier. The list of course goes on and on.

What if all past, present, future, and parallel lives are being played out at the same time? What if you could jump timelines and visit different incarnations? If you have had all experiences, then perhaps you can call on one or more of these lifetimes to help you through your current one. Maybe you could download certain parts of their energy or mastery that would be helpful for what things you are facing and need help with in this life.

There is so much that we don't know, and so many possibilities for what could be the truth. Maybe there are even multiple possibilities of truth depending on what we believe, or if we've broken through the programming around it.

Take what feels true for you and leave the rest. Sometimes you come back and revisit information when you've have had more experience in life. As is often the case, more of the information then becomes understood and valid. Other times, it's totally irrelevant for you and needs to be thrown out.

CHAPTER 71

Mt Shasta & The Knight

CYNTHIA AND I were feeling that there was a trip coming up to California. Five women including me, were being guided to camp on Mt Shasta for the 7-7-2007 gateway. **Energetically, triple number dates bring in new energies from the cosmos onto the planet to help humanity come into higher states of consciousness. Many people go to power places to better tune into the energies and do ceremony.**

On the trip there, I kept noticing semis going past with the logo "Knight Trucking." It seemed every time I began to daydream out the window there was another one driving by. **I knew that when something keeps coming to my attention that it's a sign. It's telling me that something is happening or about to happen and I need to pay attention**. I tucked the word "knight," into my memory bank and let it go. After all, my mind couldn't figure out how that would relate to anything. It's not like there are knights running around anymore, right?

The land in California was breathtaking! I loved being near the ocean and having the diversity of the mountains and big trees that California has to offer. I have to admit, I was the most excited to get to the Redwoods, but first we were scheduled to camp on Mt. Shasta. Unfortunately, you couldn't make reservations, because it was a first-come, first-served basis. There was no way of knowing how many people would be called to come there on the 7-7-2007 gateway. We could only hope enough spaces would be open for us. I had read that Panther Meadows was the place to go. The article I read said that St. Germaine, who is a spiritual Master of the violet flame of transmutation, often showed up there. There were many stories of people having mystical experiences while visiting.

The drive to Mt. Shasta was long. The closer we got, the higher the frequencies became. Soon we were seeing lenticular clouds forming and I could see orbs with my physical eyes flying around. The clouds felt very different. I could tell that they were being used to camouflage spaceships. **After being around ships for a while, you can feel the difference of the frequencies that they carry. You get attuned to feeling them. It's the same way with Star Beings.**

On the way past Mt. Shasta Lake, I saw a bright ball of light bouncing across the water from one side to the other. I was so happy and surprised that my camera had captured it. I also took a picture of a very bright ball of light in the sky that I felt to be a spaceship. I didn't know if the two were related, but I had a feeling they were.

We were a little worried because we were getting to the mountain later than we had anticipated. At this rate, there were only a few hours left before the sun was going to set. Much to our surprise, there were several conjoined spots open as if they were waiting for us. A group of gentlemen who were camping nearby helped carry things from our car to the campsite. It all flowed like it was divinely appointed.

After everything was up and secured, it was time to find the outhouse. I found a huge rock sitting near the pathway that would be perfect to sit on while I checked in with Dana. He'd asked me to let him know when we had made it there safe and sound. We hadn't been talking more than a minute when I began to hear a weird clanking sound in sync with heavy footsteps coming toward me. I could hear and sense it, but I couldn't see what it was. All of a sudden there was a huge clang and I could literally feel the rock shake as whatever it was took a seat right next to me. I hung up the phone and sat there trying to figure out what was happening. All I could sense was a very strong male energy. After my inner vision finally came into focus, I could see a huge knight. He was about six and a half feet tall, dressed in full armor, and carried a jagged red triangular flag.

I couldn't hear a thing, so decided to go and get Cindy to see if she could figure it out. She said he was indeed a knight and his name was Lerado. He was sent to protect us and make sure our missions were completed. Lerado said he was one of many on the mountain at our service and would be with us throughout our stay. Evidentially this is what the semis were pointing to.

Sometimes I wondered if my imagination was going haywire. But then I don't know if I could even think up half of the things that continue to happen around me. After a while, it all just seems irrelevant, and I ride with the flow of what shows up. I begin to feel in my body whether something is okay or not, and listen to the guiding of its innate knowing. If I feel scared, I throw protection around me and leave. If I don't sense danger, I open up to experience what is there for me. I try not to close experiences down. I know that if I never open up to what is presented, I create a barrier that is hard to move past. If I move through the barrier, I receive more and more opportunities to experience what is on the other side of the veil. The veil consists of places, objects, and Beings from other dimensions and realities that we are not able to see or access with normal sight because

they vibrate at a higher or lower frequency than what we vibrate at. I've learned that in order to be able to access these things you need to strengthen and use all of your senses. Opening up to feeling energy is the fastest way I know to start tuning into other realities.

Experiences like this are one of the reasons I sometimes feel that other dimensions and realities are simply overlays. I think that we all share the same physical space; it is just a matter of living in different frequencies. If this is true, then at times when you raise or lower frequencies, you can shift into another reality and have experiences.

CHAPTER 72

Going to Middle Earth with Grandmother Willow

WE MET SO many people on Mt. Shasta the first few days. Groups of people seemed to be gathering all over the mountain to do ceremony together. Someone recently asked me why people do ceremony. She wanted to know what it was all about. What I could share with her is what my experiences had been thus far. Whenever I was being guided to do a ceremony somewhere, it was usually to help the land lift and clear an energy imprint such as warring, or negativity. Sometimes it was bringing in higher frequencies to upgrade for a higher consciousness, or to set something in place.

If I was asked to do ceremony, it always felt to be guided by a higher part of me, or a group of Beings that I was working with. Usually, they were from other planets or Native American Elders. When I perform ceremony, there is a bringing together of Spirit, nature, the elements, along with all parts of myself. I am talking about me in my expanded state of consciousness with nature, Earth and the Cosmos that is needed to shift something not working on the planet. I remember hearing that humans are the stewards of the Earth. It was through them that all change needed to happen. I believe I came in with contracts to connect to different parts of the planet and do work that is beneficial for the ascension process. When one is in ceremony, especially with others, their combined energy creates a powerful transformation.

That being said, there are also those who are here with ulterior motives and choose to create and spread darkness. Some, are here to stop the spread of light on the planet. They are here to keep the world controlled. One has to be discerning and make sure that they are not being used by the wrong side. Discernment should always be used for everything. Always seek your inner guidance and tune into your gut feelings in all that you open to. If you are unclear, ask that your Higher-self and/or your I Am presence for guidance. Also ask them to be the gatekeeper of your work for the planet. It is also wise to say a prayer of clearing, or energetically clear the space you are working on.

On the day before the 7-7-2007 gateway, I was told through my guidance to find the place where we were to do ceremony. I was shown the spot in my sleep. That morning, I led eight women and six men to the place that I was shown. It was pretty far from the campsite and I later found out a Native man often used that spot for his sweat lodges.

The ceremony was a beautiful process of burning sage, sweet grass, and using holy water to cleanse our energy fields. Then we all gathered things from nature that asked to be present to create an altar. One person called the opening of the directions and another called in the spirits and the ancestors. We were ready to honor the Earth, elements, and Elementals of this beautiful mountain, and all that nature was there to share with us.

Once everything was ready, a voice came in and said that I was to go lie in the middle of the circle. The ceremony was being done for me. I was really embarrassed to take it upon myself. I didn't want anyone to think I was trying to be the center of attention, so I refused to do it. Then Cynthia came over and whispered to me that the Guardians of the mountain were calling me Grandmother Willow. They were asking me to lie in the center of the circle while they did ceremony around me. They asked me to put my fears aside and just surrender into it.

And so, the ceremony began. Each shared the love that they carried as they drummed, chanted, channeled and sang. I quickly went into an altered state of consciousness, which propelled me into a journey to the beginning of Creation. I was shown an endless black hole of darkness. There, worlds and galaxies were birthed by the spark of divine inspiration and sound, through the intent of pure conscious light. That light I felt to be God/ Creator/the Universal Consciousness.

The next thing I knew I was standing on Earth next to a big tree. There I met with the Beings that lived on the Earth's surface. I talked to our Star Brothers and Sisters, as well as the Beings who lived in the mountains. I then was guided to observe the Devic Realms called the Forest Beings. I started sinking into the ground as I followed roots down to the star seed of Earth which was named Middle Earth. There I saw how nothing is extinct and all things we believe to be myths were real. They had relocated to Middle Earth for protection. Examples were the Mayans, Aboriginals, Unicorns, Giants, Pegasus and Cyclops. It was endless. They were all alive and well and they greeted me as they crossed my path.

I felt that there was no warring here of any kind. I could only feel great amounts of heart energy. Even the animals seemed to be at complete peace. I didn't feel they ate one another because everything was intermingled. What we would consider a great predator was next to what would be considered its prey and they seemed to be companions. It was so totally different than the outer Earth that we live on.

As I looked around at the grass, flowers, and trees, I could see a light emanating from them. I could sense and feel their consciousness. Their colors were very different from the outer Earth in that they were much more vibrant. I'd never seen colors that were so alive! Everything had a very faint, but beautiful sound it emitted, and yet, all consciousness came together into one beautiful, peaceful, tone. It was barely audible, but always there. The water sparkled as patterns danced across its surface. It emitted its beautiful frequency as its consciousness swirled into my field and flooded me with its essence.

Then my consciousness went into a tree that I knew was me and I became the Grandmother of Willows. I loved the feeling of my branches moving in the wind. It was so fluid and freeing. Through the embodiment, I knew that trees held vast knowledge and consciousness. It was fascinating to see how interconnected and entwined trees are to the planet and all that inhibit her. I was shown how their roots interlink and send information to one another through them. I also saw how they hold a field of love like a grid, within and around the Earth.

I knew that I was sought after for my wisdom and shared my knowledge freely with those who would ask and take the time to listen with honor and respect. I taught the Indigenous people that willows were one of the trees that hold the most water which could be programmed with intent. I taught them how to use my branches with respect and in ceremony for powerful healing and clearing by making sweat and prayer lodges for the people. Then I was shown that the diamond willow staff that was given to me in Sedona was actually one of my own branches.

I had an awareness that I was talking out loud in a language that I had no reference for. I heard drumming coming from every direction as I was told my purpose, why I am here, and what I was to do with that knowledge. Part of me was scared because I felt too unqualified for what was being asked of me. I was reassured that I would be guided every step of the way and didn't need to worry about anything. I would always be taken care of.

I began the assent back to the surface and felt like I had been gone for days. In reality, it had only been around 20 minutes. It was hard for me to leave the loving energy that I had just experienced. I lie there with my eyes closed and shook as I worked at coming fully back into my body. As I opened my eyes, I saw that the circle had expanded. People must have traveled down from the mountains to see where the drumming was coming from. I was glad that I had listened to the guidance about this ceremony and was grateful for this beautiful tribe of people who were there to hold sacred space. Tears shamelessly streamed down my face. I was in so much gratitude for this journey. It was an incredibly loving experience that I would never forget.

There were many other amazing things that we experienced on Mt. Shasta. One was finding a big white mushroom the size of a small basketball with diamond patterns all over it. Several of the other women who said they didn't have inner vision also saw our knight, Lerado. We literally had a beautiful young man, named Raven run into us and become part of our tribe. The men who camped near us kept in touch with me until the day they died. And one day, after hiking and getting too much sun, Cynthia did some healing work on me that had me in awe. As she began, I could feel her call in the elements. Even though there was not as much as a slight breeze, the tent filled with wind to the point that had we not been anchoring it down with our bodies, it would have taken off.

As we left this magical place, I was given one last gift. While bringing the last load from the campsite to the car, I was told that I would be shown where the spaceships flew in and out of Mount Shasta. I kept trying to figure it out while I was there, but couldn't see it. Now, as I looked where I was being directed, I saw the top of the mountain begin to glow gold. It perfectly outlined the doorway the spaceships used to access the mountain. I can say for certain that this was one of the most magical places that I had ever been!

CHAPTER 73

The Talking Trees & Pan

ONE CANNOT IMAGINE how gigantic and magnificent a Redwood tree truly is. The size and energy they hold is unlike anything I had ever experienced. I could feel the excitement in the air as we drove through the massive trees and I was anxious to get out and actually touch one. Of all the places I had ever been, this place felt the most like home.

Our visit to the Redwoods was done in a state of awe. We were all like small children full of wonder. How could one not be, when you were next to these gentle giants? Some were so big it would take 18 people holding hands to encircle it. Most of our days there were spent walking, connecting, and exploring the beauty that comes from an ancient ecosystem. I could only wonder what it must have been like before the endless stream of cars and people everywhere.

It was there that I began to deeper understand the consciousness of nature as a whole. As I walked through the forests, I began to see faces show up on the trees. I could also hear them talk to me. One of the faces showed up in a burl on the side of a tree and called himself the Green Man. He told me that there were many different Beings that lived within nature and that at some point, I would get to know them better. It was surreal walking through the forest seeing these faces show up on different parts of the tree. How was any of this even possible?

That was also when my camera started to change. We went into a hollow tree that had been hit by lightning and I was guided to point the camera up and take a picture. As I did, all that I could see was molecules moving very quickly like static electricity and orbs of light bouncing around. When I took the picture hundreds of orbs showed up. From then on, every time I used the camera, all I could see was static energy. I let others use the camera so they could see with their own eyes how everything is energy. It was such a gift. People who couldn't see energy could now experience it through the use of my camera.

We only did one ceremony while in the Redwoods. Before setting up the altar, we were asked if we would be willing to clean up the area. It was sad to see how much garbage had been strewn around by people. Within minutes, we each had garbage bags full. I just can't fathom how someone can defile nature in such a way. Why dirty something that you traveled so far to visit? Weeks before, I had been told that I was to be gifted a new hawk feather for my staff. While picking up trash, I felt to go in a certain area and came across a perfect hawk and raven feather lying side-by-side. I was told that the hawk feather was for me and I was to gift the raven feather to the young man named, Raven, who had come with us. I love these gifts from nature!

This time we did a short ceremony and were given information that each of us needed to go out and connect to one of the redwood trees. We were to go off on our own and see which tree called out to us. As we sat with it, we were to connect and ask if it had any information to share with us. I was told to ask my friend, Jan, to go with me, but I didn't want to interfere with her process, so I refused to. She must have gotten the same message because she came over and told me that we were supposed to go together. I seem to have a problem with listening when I am told something that I feel would infringe on someone else. I'm glad that others get the message, as well, to make sure that it happens. As we walked through the giant trees, we were both called to the same grouping. There were three of them clumped together to form a perfect triangle. They had been hit by lightning so there was a hollow in the middle of the grouping. It took some effort to get the barrier that had grown around the trees worked away enough to go inside, but once we did, it was totally worth it. The hole was the perfect size for the two of us to sit comfortably and because of all the overgrowth, it was like being in a womb.

I could tell that Jan was off in her own process as I began to quiet my mind. I wanted to be available if the tree was going to talk to me. It didn't take long before I began to hear a whisper of a voice into my left ear that was next to the tree. It was definitely male and he told me that we were in a grouping of trees called the Great Trinity. He welcomed me and told me his name was Venegue, which meant Speaker of Truth.

Venegue taught me more about the Beings of the forest called Elementals. He told me that they were the builders of form. Their work was to bring 3D objects into form by using energy. **I felt he meant the energy that is always around us. The energy like I saw when looking through the camera.** He told me that we could create things easier if only we would ask for the help of nature. I was told that I could call on them at any time. He also told me how nature was saddened by the split off from the human race. We had forgotten the importance of nature, and that in all actuality, we were nature just as much as the trees and animals.

Venegue told me a lot about myself and my mission and directed me to always follow my heart. **The heart is the true compass to the path we are all here to follow.** He also said that **love is the glue that holds everything together,** and that I should learn to connect better to the Mother. I took it that he referred to the Earth as Mother.

He told me that I would be called to many places around the world and that I needn't worry. That everything would be taken care of. I would always have a place to stay and the money that I needed. He proceeded to give me the names of the places I would travel to. He also said that I could call on nature at any time to help bring things into alignment for my trips. Doing so would help to create a clear pathway as I went out to do my work. The energies of the trees and my lineage were here to help guide me. **Infusing prayer with nature could move mountains.**

Venegue talked for a very long time and I wrote as fast as I could so I wouldn't forget what he told me. When I began to feel the energy dwindling, I looked over to the left from where my head had been resting. I couldn't believe it when I saw a face raised out of the wood in the tree. Its mouth was exactly where my ear had been. How incredible! I saw Jan stirring and knew that she was also at the end of her experience. We gave great appreciation and gratitude to the tree, then put the wall back in place, just as we had found it. I would never forget that trip with those beautiful women, meeting up with so many special people, and the priceless gifts nature had given me.

CHAPTER 74

The Shaman & the Protector Stone

A FRIEND CALLED to tell me that she had learned of a man, named Wayne, who was in possession of a stone they called the Protector. Evidently, he and a friend were out walking in a forest when he tripped and fell right on top of it. Supposedly, people came from all over the world to be in the presence of this rock. She felt that I was supposed to see it as well. I told her to go ahead and talk to Wayne the next time she was in contact with him and, for some reason, she was to tell him hello from Grandmother. Why, I didn't know, it had just blurted out of my mouth. I guess we would see if I was supposed to meet him or not.

She called back later to tell me he had been out on the land for seven days doing a vision quest in Sedona. His guidance came in and told him he needed to go home. He was being contacted by Grandmother. He was confused. He didn't know a grandmother. Nor did he have one anymore. For him, it was a cue that we were supposed to meet. He had just come home and asked if we could meet up at my friend's house. Because it had all came together so easily, I felt that it was meant to be and took off to see what it was all about.

It felt a little awkward meeting him alone, so my friend sat in at my request while we began to figure out what the Universe had in store for us. He talked on and on about how he was a Lakota Shaman, medicine man, and chief. There was a distinct feeling that he was always trying to impress and best me. I felt myself speaking in defense mode through the words I chose to speak in response.

I didn't like what was going on with my rising protection mode, so I consciously realigned, and chose to only talk from the heart. I could feel a switch in the conversation almost immediately. I could see that he was a good person and cared for what was going on in humanity. He was really pulled to work with empowering women and felt he was called to share his gifts as a medicine man and Shaman with them. I had several women recently tell me that they were feeling pulled to work with a male Shaman to help heal what went on with them. I felt this could be who the Universe had brought forward to give assistance to those women. I told him that I thought perhaps that was what our meeting was about. He seemed pleased at the prospect, so we set up a date. He could work out of my home so I would be able to monitor what was going on. After all, I didn't really know him that well.

CHAPTER 75

Being Followed by the Onashwabi & Nature Fights Back

SHORTLY AFTER MEETING Wayne, strange unexplainable things started happening. I was at work cleaning a house and could feel and see three Native jungle men following me. They were around five feet tall, and wore only loin cloths that looked to be made of grasses. They also had their faces painted in various manners and had chopped off black hair that came to their jawline and wore bangs. Each one carried what looked to be a blow tube and wore a band around their left ankle.

I could only see them with my third eye vision, not through my physical eyes which is often the case. I believed them to be some form of Spirit even though they didn't feel good to me. This was one time I felt I needed to put protection up. **I surrounded myself with golden Christed light, and put full length mirrors all the way around me so that if they tried to throw a dart, or a spell, that it would be reflected back at them.** Everywhere I went they followed me at a distance, like they were trying not to be seen. I couldn't figure out who they were or what they wanted, except that they were called Onashwabi.

During this time, I had gotten a call from *Iris*, the lady from Holland that I had met in Hawaii. She was going to be visiting her host family in Michigan and wanted to know if I would be up for a visit. I was really glad. I felt we had things that we were meant to do together. I also wanted to get to know her better. We made plans for her to arrive two days into Wayne's work with the women and she would be staying for a week.

By the follow-up reports from the women, Wayne's work seemed to be helping them. It was nice having him there, but part of me was a bit untrusting and uncomfortable. I wasn't sure if that had to do with my first impression or not. I decided to work through it and to get to know him at a deeper level. That meant spending more time together.

One night we decided to take a walk and get some fresh air. That gave us the time to do a lot of talking. I had to admit the talking went way better than the first time when so much uncomfortable ego seemed to be in the way. We walked to the end of the subdivision and back, then sat on the curb by the house so we could enjoy the night a little longer. We were just going to go in when we heard screaming and the crashing of big branches coming from the ravine. I couldn't imagine what was going on! As I looked towards the ravine, Linden and two of his friends came running out screaming! They were visibly shaken and told us that something was throwing rocks at them. Whoever was chasing them was also tearing down big branches as they ran behind them.

Wayne tuned in and told them that they needed to apologize. He said that there was a race of Beings that lived down in the ravine that were interdimensional. The boys were not respecting their space and kept defiling where they were living. They wanted the boys to stop. They didn't like that they were shooting paintball guns down in the ravine, and didn't like the late-night escapades with flashlights and cameras going off. They wanted them to apologize and to stop disrespecting their space. That was the end of the rocks in the back of the house and the end of the night escapades to find what Linden could see and wanted the others to see as well. I'm pretty sure an apology was given because there was no more trouble after that.

I was planning to go out and meditate on the ledge of the cliff late the next morning and noticed Wayne taking a nap on my swing. As I settled in and went into deeper states of relaxation and connection, I heard a voice come through and say, "He's taken your pillow off your bed and is using it to follow you into your dreamtime." I didn't even know what that meant. I stopped the meditation and went into the house to see if one of my pillows was gone and it was.

When I came back in after resuming my meditation, the pillow was lying back on my bed, and Wayne was in with his last client for the day. I looked at the couch and he had his sleeping bag and the pillow I had given him all folded up and neat. Why did he feel he needed to use my pillow? Could it be true that he was doing what I was told? Before bed that night, I decided I was going to change the pillow case. Maybe that would take care of whatever he was planning.

Although I got really great validation from the women Wayne worked on, things were starting to feel more and more off. I started to feel that he wanted more than just a friendship. Of course, I had no intention whatsoever of that happening. I was beginning to notice possessiveness towards me in the days that he was there. It was nothing that he said, it was more of an energy that he thought I couldn't feel, but I definitely could.

CHAPTER 76

Invading my Body

I WAS EXCITED that Iris was coming to spend some time with me in my home as I felt a strong connection to her. Even though it had been a while since our meeting in Hawaii, it seemed like no time had passed at all. We had talked a lot on Skype, but it was going to be nice getting to spend some one-on-one time together. I asked Wayne to stick around after his last client so that he could meet Iris, but I was more interested in Iris meeting him to see what she felt. After a little breakfast and coffee, they had a chance to talk for a bit before Wayne was packed and off to his next adventure.

Iris and I had a lot to talk about and I decided that I wanted to take her out to eat. During our time out I could feel Wayne's energy coming into my body. It was wild! I even talked with a lisp just like his and started saying things like he would say them. It was as if his energy had invaded my body. I really wasn't sure what to do, but I thought I'd give it some time and see if it went away on its own.

When Iris and I talked back at the house, I could see fear and confusion in her eyes. I could tell she was really studying me. Several times she said she got the message that she should sleep with me that night. Well, that wasn't going to happen! I kept telling her that I needed my space and was going to sleep by myself. I don't know how many times she tried, and the more she did, the more perturbed I was getting. I couldn't understand why she was so insistent.

Each time after talking, she would go back to the room she was going to sleep in and call someone. After one of these phone calls, she came back and was talking fairly close to me. All of a sudden, she screamed "Hi Yah!" as she swung a forceful karate chop directed at me that stopped just short of hitting my left eye! I remember not even so much as flinching and looking at her while I said "Is that supposed to scare me?" Her eyes got huge and she quickly took off for her room again. This time she locked the door behind her. I could hear her on the phone, but I didn't know what she was saying because she was talking in Dutch. It was all way too much drama for me! I decided to go and sit in the swing until bedtime.

The next morning, I felt different. Wayne's energy wasn't influencing me anymore. I couldn't hear his voice when I spoke and I no longer felt his energy in my body. As I sat there checking into what had happened, I could see something like a huge spider web that was on the ceiling over my bed. Wayne had made an invisible web so he could enter my body energetically during my dreamtime. I was infuriated! Why would someone do that? Who even would know that something like that was possible?

Iris could feel things were back to normal as well. She asked me if I knew what had gone on and I told her what I had seen. I told her I was sorry if I had scared her. She was so relieved that things were back to normal and told me that she had been in contact with her teacher from the Netherlands about it. Her teacher said that I was being attacked by the Onaschwabi and that Wayne was a mindless pawn in the whole thing. I guess that validated the three short guys! She said she had gone into prayer for 24 hours nonstop to stop the attack and that is what she had started that night. Iris also told me that she didn't know how to protect me and that is why she kept insisting on sleeping with me. Instead, she had hidden things in my bedroom that she could direct her and her teacher's energy to protect me that night so he couldn't get further in through the web he had created.

She was told that at the next full moon they planned to attack me again and I started to go into a panic around it all. I called to get Bennie's advice and he told me to stand in my power and send them love. Then it would all fall apart. I felt that was a better option for me instead of going into mind-boggling fear over the whole thing. What it was all about, and why they were after me, was beyond my scope of understanding.

Shortly after I talked to Bennie, I got a call from Cynthia. She asked what was going on. How the hell did she always know? I told her all about it and she told me Jesus wanted to come through and talk to me. When he started in, he said, "Barbara, where are you playing?" I jumped in and told him everything about the three men and how they were following me everywhere. I was scared and didn't know why or what they wanted from me. He came back and said **"If you don't especially care to get attacked, or attached to by dark ones, and if you have learned all you need to learn about them, all you need to do is to simply shift your thoughts to another reality. Simply know and proclaim that they cannot come near you or your home. You can know they exist without having them be part of your reality."** Man, did I shift! Then I sent them a huge helping of love just to make sure! Nothing happened again after following his advice, and **I was extremely grateful for the advice about love and how to use it to dismantle the dark**.

Iris and I finally got to have fun after all the drama subsided. I found out during her stay that she had an amazing singing voice and she channeled very well. It felt like we were being drawn together to see if our energies worked well as a team. After she left, I knew that we would be doing things together in the future. I'm pretty sure the feeling was mutual.

CHAPTER 77

Being Honored by the Birds

BENNIE WAS GOING to have a long layover in Minneapolis on his flight to Georgia. He wanted to know if it would work to come spend some time with him. I told him I'd pack a picnic lunch and we could go out somewhere close by for a few hours.

It was a really beautiful day and we had four hours to kill until his next flight. We found a picnic grounds nearby where we could share a nice meal. Then we took a walk to check out the rest of the park. About halfway through, we sat on a bench to soak up the sun and catch up. As we sat there, a pair of mated hawks flew out of the tree in front of us screeching. They started circling the tree over and over. It was so beautiful to watch with the sun shining through their wings. Every time they dove, I could see the intricate patterns of their feathers shining through. Three more hawks flew over to join them. We were mesmerized as they circled and called out. Both of us raised our hands in gratitude for being able to share in the experience. A few minutes later, three crows flew into the mix and landed in the tree right where the hawks had been sitting. They started calling out and we again raised our hands in honor and gratitude.

Within minutes, a huge bald eagle landed in the same tree the crows were sitting in. The eagle was literally 20 foot in front us. It was up close and personal. We could see every feature from where we sat. Bennie started chanting and singing a Shoshoni song of gratitude, as a crow flew in and perched next to the eagle. As the five hawks continued circling the tree, they were joined by five turkey vultures to create a majestic feast for the eyes. I had never experienced anything quite so beautiful! It was surreal.

Bennie told me that they had come to honor us for the work we had done to heal the land in this lifetime. He said that the eagle was a messenger from Creator, as are the hawk and crow. The vultures were here to clear energies. His song went on for at least 10 minutes, and despite all that was going on, not one person came near. It was like we were in our own little world. It continued as he sang, and we stayed in a state of honoring our connection to these beautiful winged messengers.

As soon as he ended his song, people started coming out of the woodwork. Everyone was yelling about all the birds, pointing to others, and taking pictures. Despite all the commotion, the eagle was still there when we left to go back to the airport. What an amazing honoring we had that day with the birds! I could honestly say there was no one I would have rather had that experience with. Bennie was instrumental in my reconnection back to nature. And for that, I will always be eternally grateful.

CHAPTER 78

The Sedona Retreats

IT WAS FINALLY time to lead my first retreat in Sedona. There were eight people including Dana and myself. That would make it easy to manage for my first group. Dana was so much help. He picked us all up from the airport and was our driver, as well as storyteller, of the land. It was a magical experience exploring Sedona in all her beauty! There were many unforgettable moments like hiking West Fork Park, where five trees fell one at a time, as we walked the windy trail. During our outings, there was an Indigenous energy that kept following us. We often captured him in our pictures as a green blob of light.

When we went to see Montezuma's Castle, I told them that they should take pictures of the tree tops to see if they could catch the Fairies. They showed up as rainbow-colored bubbles in our pictures. Each person took turns sleeping in the teepee, and Dana shared his teachings of the medicine wheel. We got to experience a lot, but our highlight was definitely the sweat lodge run by a famous Sedona artist named Bear Cloud. There was nothing that could have prepared us for that experience. **That is often the way of magic. When you have no preconceived notions or ideas around something, it can open to more than one could conceive. On the other hand, when you have preconceived notions around an event, you create a box around it that doesn't allow for any kind of expansion or magic to unfold. You're more often than not left disappointed.**

The day of the sweat lodge we got our gifts of sage and tobacco ready, and the women put on their skirts. The ladies were a little late getting ready on time, and I was upset because you aren't supposed to be late to a sweat lodge. It was considered disrespectful. I have to admit, I often laugh about the whole time-thing. If any of you are friends with our Native brothers and sisters you know they run on what they call "Indian time." You can get somewhere 10 minutes early to make sure you are ready and on time. Then wait an hour or more for things to get going.

When we arrived at Bear Cloud's home, we were 10 minutes late. By the look on his face, he wasn't very happy about it. He showed us where we could change our clothes and told us the fire starter for the ceremony was going to be Chief Golden Eagle. No wonder he was curt! We had disrespected him, as well as the Chief.

The women were scared because they had never been to a sweat before. Some wanted to know if it would be okay to get out if they got scared. I told them we would talk to Bear Cloud about it once we got in. I'd let them know I had virgin sweaters. We had gone over the rules of the lodge and I had given them advice on how to stay cooler. Each was given a wet towel to put around their shoulders in case they needed to breathe through them if it got too hot or smoky. I also handed them fresh sage to smell. It would center them if they started getting scared.

After waiting for what seemed like an hour, he came to get us. We were all to leave our shoes, bras, glasses, and jewelry behind. As was customary, we gifted Chief Golden Eagle and Bear Cloud with sage and tobacco to honor them. Those were placed on the altar. Each of us crawled in, giving our thanks to the relatives, as we settled into the lodge. While we sat there waiting for the first round to begin, 21 red hot stones came into the fire pit. I was dumbstruck! A normal round was seven stones. Finally, I looked at Rod and said, "You know none of these women have done a sweat before right? What's going on?" He told me that Chief Golden Eagle had been given a message that this was the way it was to be done for this group. I figured he was blowing smoke and that this was part of the punishment for being late. I put on my best poker face because I didn't want to scare the others.

After the 21st stone was brought in, the Chief crawled into the lodge backwards to take his place. I'd never seen anyone come in backwards and figured it was because he was really upset with us. Even though he now sat facing us, he didn't open his eyes. I was so ashamed! He sat in silence with his eyes closed for what felt like forever. Finally, he opened them and looked at each of us one by one and said, "I am so honored to be here doing this sweat with you and feel to be unworthy." Huh? What was this all about? He went on "I know each and every one of you. We have walked this Earth together before. I know that each of you has played an important role back in the times when Jesus walked the Earth. We refer to him by the name

Emmanuel. He knows each of your hearts and loves you very much. His presence and the presence of Mother Mary are here with us tonight as we do this sacred lodge."

Chief Golden Eagle went on to tell us that Emmanuel worked with and taught the Native nations and was very honored and respected by them all. He continued "I know that you have fear of the heat being too great, but I was told that this group needed a lot of heat. I was instructed to place 21 stones in for the first round. I trust that it will be exactly what is needed. I invite you to become one with the fire. If you can do this, it will not bother you. Overcome your fear of the fire. It is here to help you burn through those places that need cleansing."

The flap went down to create the perfect circle and womb of the mother, and the first round began. The Chief got his drum and told us that he and Bear Cloud were going to sing the songs in the traditional Lakota tongue. He said that he knew each of us would remember and be able to sing every note and word. Of course, it sounded absurd, but I kept my mind open.

He started to sing and we all sang with him. Every word came to us and it was in perfect pitch. Not one note or word was missed. I couldn't believe it! All the songs went that way. The 10 of us blew the roof off that sweat lodge! About halfway through, a spirit eagle and bear came in and made themselves known. It was a crowded and amazingly beautiful experience, and those who were afraid of the fire became one with it.

I watched in awe as two of the women moved within inches of the fire pit. As the new red-hot rocks came in, I marveled at the smiles and look of serenity on their faces. I am sure it is an experience none of us will ever forget. It was, by far, the highlight of the trip. I loved watching these beautiful women and seeing how empowered they had become. They literally glowed! The sweat couldn't have been more perfect had we planned it that way.

The second trip was totally different. On this journey, there were six women and three men. Two in the group were nonstop talkers. Another one, collected rocks that she couldn't carry, and asked others if they would put them in their backpacks. She also had several falls while we were there, luckily with only minor injuries.

We did a lot of hiking, and it was apparent on this trip that it was to help people to slow down. It was hard for them to be in the moment so they could see all the miracles in front of them and within nature. It was also about being quiet so they could hear their guidance. Past lives seemed to be coming forward for several, as well.

In this group, there was a couple who was having a really hard time with one another. Their agitation began to affect the group and I wasn't quite sure what to do about it. The one thing she would keep repeating to him was, "Would you quit taking away my choices!" I thought that a very odd thing to say to another person. Finally, I was shown to put them in the teepee together. They were to put out a clear intention to unravel the tension that was going on between them to see where it came from.

That night it finally broke. She saw that they were reliving a Native lifetime where he was called White Owl and she was Red Berry, the chief's daughter. She was in love with White Owl and he loved her. One day he overheard the chief talking about Red Berry being promised to a chief's son from another tribe. Without telling her, he left and joined another tribe. He felt he should leave so she could marry the person who would be able to give her the most status. It broke her heart. Red Berry ended up marrying the man to whom she had been promised. She had his children and was his wife, but she never loved him the way she loved White Owl. She pined for him until the day she died.

Many times, there is a peek into past lives to see where a current situation stems from. It's always a clue for me when there is an irrational fear or circumstance that doesn't make any sense in a person's current life. It's amazing to me that this is possible. I feel it shows that we carry the energy of several, if not all of our lifetimes, in our DNA and cells. I also feel that at times we can meet up with people from a past life that needs healing, or clearing of some kind. It's quite amazing if you really think about it. Perhaps our lives are more guided than we could have ever imagined.

A sweat lodge didn't work out this time even though it was set up, but we did get to do a pipe ceremony. We also visited a farm that housed several white buffalos on the way to the Grand Canyon. It's not hard to see why it is called one of the seven wonders of the world. It's absolutely breathtaking! You could sit there for hours taking in the beauty. I had been there several times before, but it wasn't until this trip that I understood the Grand Canyon's connection to ancient Egypt, Isis, Osiris, Ra and the pyramids. You could feel the energy that still lingered there. I didn't understand it deeper until I randomly happened on an article on the internet. You may have to use an alternate browser such as duck-duck-go, but it's there. If it intrigues you, look up the Grand Canyon's connection to ancient Egypt.

The last day we did a short hike to the Buddhist Stupa where our elderly lady fell once again. Thankfully, she only had a minor scrape. We doctored it up and took off for the airport. When we finally got there, we were brought to the main entrance. Normally, the driver opens the door and puts a step stool down to exit. The elderly lady decided she didn't need to wait. When she opened the door to step out, she fell flat on her face onto the pavement in a full body slam! Of course, we were all upset and trying to help her. I thought for sure that we would need to call an ambulance. By the time we had smoothed everything over and got to ticketing, they had closed our gate. They agreed to let half of us board and the rest of us were going to have to come back the next day to catch a flight. I will be kind, and skip the story of the night in a motel room sharing the bed with our tumbler. Sometimes silence is the best course of action. I will tell you that during our sleep that night, the same floor shaking started, just like in the Denver Airport. I looked around as the white cloud started to form and make its way up to the ceiling. My friend, Eita, sat up in bed, looked at me, and went fast asleep again. The cloud left the room the same way it appeared, and everything went back to normal. I was never shown where we would have been taken.

CHAPTER 79

Mexico: Marriage & The Dolphin

MY NEXT TRIP was to Mexico where I would marry my niece and her fiancé on a quaint island called Isla Majeures, the Isle of Women. It was a gorgeous island with very humble and beautiful people. I really enjoyed helping my sister, Rhonda, set it up, decorate, and watch the whole thing unfold. It was one of the most beautiful weddings I had ever attended. There is just something about having a wedding outside in nature with the people you love.

I had never traveled like this with my family before. It was fun seeing Mom and Dad in their older mellowed out stage explore different places on the island. At one point, we all decided to get in the water and let the waves cool us off. It was so hot and humid, and the water looked so inviting. I kept watching to see where the waves were the biggest and would hurry out to them, only to have them dissipate. It happened over and over again. I was so perplexed!

Finally, I figured it out. I looked at my mom and my sister and asked which one was working on the waves dispersing? Mom looked guilty and said "I was afraid the waves were going to knock me over and I would lose my dentures in the water, so I asked my Guardian Angel to please make the waves be little." I had no idea Mom ever did things like that. I was speechless!

We rented a golf cart to show them the whole island. At the tip of the island there were amazing views backdropped with the most gorgeous aquamarine water I had ever seen. We all decided to get out and explore. I figured out that it was actually an old Mayan ruin site and I could feel the energies that were loose there. At one point, we went into an arch to cool off from the hot sun. I began to take pictures of everyone because I could feel there was a presence with us. In the photos, there was a blob of white energy that went from person to person almost like it was checking them out.

We were all having a wonderful time! I was excited because the day before the wedding, the bride and groom had rented a boat to take everyone out for a ride around the island. At some point, there would be a chance to snorkel if we wanted. I hadn't snorkeled since being with the dolphins in Hawaii. I couldn't wait to get in the water and explore the ocean there.

Once out on the water, I got an inkling to go to the top deck. I could feel a dolphin was near, and wanted to see if I could spot it. I was telling the group around me that I could feel a dolphin and the captain piped up and said, "That's impossible. I have been a captain in the waters around here for over 15 years and have never once seen a dolphin. They just don't come to this area." I said "Well, I feel a dolphin and I know there's one nearby." As soon as it came out of my mouth, a dolphin jumped right out of the water within 30 feet of the boat! I looked at the captain with his mouth gaping open and said, "See!" Everyone started hooting it up, as a bunch of us jumped in.

I often wondered. Did I create the dolphin with my certainty consciousness, manifesting it into form to create that experience? Or, was it that I was able to tune in and feel that the dolphin was there? How much power do we really have in creating what happens within our own perceived reality? What about manifesting thought into form? These are the type of questions I constantly pondered.

The wedding went off without a hitch and I loved every part of it. It started with the ceremony on the beach, being serenaded by the traditional Mexican band and ending with a beautiful sunset reception outside near the ocean. It couldn't have been more perfect. I was glad to get to spend this precious time with my family and all of the bride's and groom's friends.

CHAPTER 80

Into the Service

MY YOUNGEST SON was graduating, and we had been looking into colleges trying to see what the next step for him would be.

We thought things were pretty much settled and he would be going to a place closer to the Canadian border where he could take nature-based classes. Instead, he started talking about going into the service. I was devastated. I felt that most wars have been made up to make big money for the contractors and the government. I also felt they were to control other countries. It saddened me to think so many young men and women had lost their lives, or had experienced things that no one should have to go through. No parent wants to see their child's life put in danger, or to think that they could possibly be killed or have to kill someone. I have seen what it does to a person's psyche. It haunts them for the rest of their life. I have worked with, and known many men, who could never come to terms with what they were forced to do. They relived it nightly through their dreams creating a hell they couldn't seem to escape.

The more I tried to talk sense into him, the more he seemed to make sure it was going to happen. Finally, he broke. He told me that I didn't understand. This was something that he felt he was being directed to do. He would really like to have his parent's support, instead of feeling like he was all alone in it. I had to give it up, and trust that the Universe had his back. Whatever happened was meant to be, and I would support him in whatever way that I could. I just prayed that it would all work out for his highest good. I had to let my expectations go and hand this burden over to a higher power.

CHAPTER 81

Breaking it to the Kids

I GOT THE kids together and let them know that Dana and I had decided to move in together. I felt it was time for me to start my world service work. I had raised children for 33 years and loved every minute of it. Now it was time for me to do what I felt I was being guided to outside of being a mother.

I had been feeling it for some time, and knew things would change when everyone was out of school and settled in to where they needed to be. I feel that we all have pieces or contracts that we need to fulfill with God/the Universe. For me, I felt it was also with the Earth. My first piece was raising them. Now it was time to be more of a free spirit and go wherever I felt called so I could grow my spiritual aspect and do what I needed to for the Earth.

As soon as Linden was where he needed to be, I was going to move to Sedona and live with Dana. I would be selling the house and everything I owned. They could think about the things that they wanted and each would be responsible for their baby stuff and what was kept for them through the years. I'm pretty sure they were a little shocked, but they were very supportive as well. I think they were happy that I had found someone to love again. Besides, there are always trips both ways. I felt it would be hard at times, but I knew without a doubt in my mind that this move was essential for me.

CHAPTER 82

The Freedom of Letting Go

I SPENT THE next several months selling everything I had. I decided that I was going to move to Sedona with what my car could carry and no more. It wasn't worth bringing all my stuff because Dana had so much. I began a series of garage sales and Craigslist ads. Everything flew out the door. My kids could take whatever they wanted, a whatever was left would be given to charity.

In letting go of everything, I gained a sense of freedom that I had never experienced before. It seemed to propel me to another level of forward movement that I don't think I could have experienced without doing so. When we have a lot of possessions, we form an attachment to them. We worry about someone else hurting them, or taking them, and sometimes even using them. We form protectiveness around them, as well as ownership. More often than not, we collect and hoard things as a way to soothe what is not fulfilled within our self. It is used as a tool to distract the feelings of sadness or lack, and only fills you for a short time.

When you go through the moving process, you clean out every nook and cranny. You let go of anything that doesn't feel like you anymore. You release things that no longer feel relevant in your life. You shake up the energy to clear out what is old, outdated, and no longer a part of you. By doing so, you open up energetically for what is to come. As you release things, you free the energy for something new to come in. Often it is something you could never have imagined.

The day after my going away party, I took off for Sedona. It took two and a half days and I enjoyed every minute of it. I had a lot of time to think, and as I drove, I worked through the sadness of not being near my children. I just prayed they would all be looked after. I hoped that they'd be able to spread their wings and fly.

CHAPTER 83

Sedona: The Sirians & The Wormhole

MY START TO living in Sedona was anything but normal. The first night I was there, I went out by myself to take in the full moon. A minute later, two Sirians in blue uniforms came walking up to me. I don't know how to explain how I knew they were Sirians, I just knew. They were not fully solid in their bodies, but rather opaque like the Beings I had seen before. Both were masculine and had a plump wrinkled forehead with squinty piercing aquamarine eyes. They told me that we had work to do together and that they would be here with me until it was done. For several weeks, they accompanied me everywhere I went. Often, they would talk to me about energetics and sacred geometry during the day.

Most of the work we did together was in the "tween time' which is that place where one is almost awake, but not fully awake. This usually occurred as I was going to sleep or starting to wake up in the morning. Sometimes we would do work together in my dreamtime. We mostly talked about a bridge that we had agreed to build together that would span from Sedona to their planet.

The next day I was told to meet them at Thunder Mountain. It was time to activate a bridge from the base of the mountain to Sirius. The activation took several days to complete. As we combined our energies together, I could begin to see the bridge form and expand. It seemed to be structured out of crystal geometric shapes. When they clicked into place, they created soft prisms of rainbow etheric light that emanated through each joint. Shortly after it was finished, they let me know that our work together had been completed. A week later, I felt their ship fly by. Through telepathic communication, they thanked me and were gone. I often wondered why I had geometric prisms often radiating through my eyes the past several months. Was it in preparation for this bridge?

Dana and I were always outside looking at the stars. It was one of our favorite things to do. Sometimes we would even climb onto the roof to get a better view. The stars were so incredible there! It was kind of like the big skies of Montana. I loved that in Sedona it was against city ordinances to have your outside lights on at night. There were also no street lights lining the main road like in other towns. Star gazing was taken seriously. It was normal to hear a lot of talk about UFO sightings. Sedona's known for its UFO shops, tours, and a diner that is decorated with everything alien. I read once that because of Sedona's unique and high energy, it was one of the few places on the planet where spaceships could easily come in and out.

Almost everyone had a UFO story to share. I loved to hear other people's perspectives on the subject. I could never understand why people would even consider it not to be true. **To think that we are the only planet with intelligent life in this vast Universe seems pretty arrogant to me. But then, it really isn't talked about in the mainstream population. Even on the internet with its vast amount of information, one really has to dig to find much around the subject.**

As we were stargazing one night, I looked up to see where Venus was. Venus has always been my favorite thing in the sky, and she's the first thing I look for. This night she was exceptionally bright and beautiful. As I looked, I noticed another light the same size. It was just as bright as Venus, and in the same vicinity. Interestingly, it had not been there a minute before. I got Dana's attention and just as he looked, a hole started to open in the sky. It started out as a small pin hole and opened very slowly. As the circle grew, we could see it was outlined with a thick grey ring. The minute it stopped opening, the other light mimicking Venus shot through it, and the hole snapped shut again. We could hardly believe our eyes! As I stood there in contemplation, a voice came through and said it was **a wormhole, which is like a tunnel that shortens the distance between two points.**

CHAPTER 84

Sedona's Unique Makeup

DANA AND I got along so well. I have never laughed so hard or so much. We were best friends in a very loving relationship. Our neighbor lady, Jan, would always tell us she could hear us laughing way into the night. She said it would often set her and her husband, Clem, off and they'd start laughing, too. They just couldn't understand how two people could have so much to talk about and laugh over. It really was just that way for us. It was such a different way of being in a relationship for me. With Dana, I never felt I had to dumb down part of myself or hide the things that happened to me. It was all so natural and easy.

Living in Sedona was so different from anything I had ever experienced. Everywhere you go there are rock and crystal shops, or healing centers, and psychics are a dime a dozen. Everyone was gifted there, or so it seemed. People were full of flavor and eccentric by nature. One day you would go down the street and see a man in a pink frilly puffed out dress with a fancy feather hat, touting an old pair of cowboy boots, with a purse on his elbow, while smoking a cigar. The next day you'd see an elderly woman dressed like a duck with frizzed out bright red hair, green plastic boots up to her knees, and a frog umbrella prancing around. I've seen a guy who dresses like Merlin and walks down the street with his staff. And, a guy who wears a long white robe with a turban wrapped around his head. He has a white beard and mustache down to his waist with a sword stuck through his belt. I also can't forget the guy in a long leather coat who walks around with a parrot on his shoulder. There are so many characters in Sedona. It's actually hard to feel out of place because there is no standard to go by. It's pretty colorful and anything goes!

There is another component to living there. Sedona was covered by an ocean many times, so she holds a lot of water energy, which brings up emotion. It also carries a lot of fire energy, since it's a desert, which can be very transformative. **When you live in, or visit Sedona, there seems to be a phenomenon that occurs in which there is a constant awareness of things that are misaligned in your thoughts, words, actions, or reality. The energy there helps you to intimately look at your misaligned thoughts and actions so you can correct them. Being in Sedona is a wonderful catalyst for growth within your human and spiritual nature, but can also be very difficult to have things continually being shoved in your face.**

There are so many people there with immense drive and passion. It seems everyone is fighting for justice or a cause. It isn't hard to get a job unless you're not supposed to, because there are so many people who really don't want to work. They say they're able to see through the illusion of money. But on the flip side, many don't seem to be able to keep their toes grounded in reality. People can become ungrounded and reside mostly outside their bodies. **Sedona attracts great light, and equal darkness, and if you don't have good discernment skills, you will soon get them through the experiences you draw to you.**

Sedona is also known for her many vortexes. They say over 4.5 million people come to visit every year so it's a hot spot for tourism. It's beautiful scenery and hiking is unparalleled. She is a fast track to spiritual awakening and healing, and people travel from all over the world to experience some form of growth. Sometimes living there is a blessing, because you get to meet so many people from all over the globe. The downfall is that the roads don't handle the added traffic well. When tourist season is at its peak, it can take two or three times longer to get somewhere.

It seemed like clockwork, that three times a year, I would see a mass exodus of residents leaving, and a mass inflow of new people coming in to take their place. There are books about people's stories of how they ended up there. I have met many who felt called to come, stayed for a few days or weeks, then went home and sold everything. Two weeks later, they would be back to find a place to live with what they could pack in their car and no more.

CHAPTER 85

Doing Readings & The Runaway Alien

I DECIDED TO take a job doing readings out of a store called Crystal Magic. It was a good way to meet people and get myself out there. It was only part-time, but it helped to pay the bills. However, I found readings to be boring. People always want to know the same old things. When is my true love coming? Can you tell me what they look like? Where am I supposed to be living? What kind of work should I be doing? What is my purpose? What if I said something that was wrong? Would I lead them down the wrong path? I would never want to do that. I always tried to be very careful and tuned in, but nobody is perfect all the time. It felt like a lot of responsibility.

I was far better suited to be a spiritual counselor where I actually helped people to get their own answers. I guess it's the whole "give a fish, verses teaching to catch a fish" for me. Sometimes while doing readings, I would end up being paid to take them out on the land. Sometimes they asked for sound and energy work or spiritual counseling from the house. Those were the things that were my true passions.

I did readings for about four months when the voice came in and told me I was to quit doing them. When I asked why, I was told that they were disempowering to the people who got them. It could create a box around people and was explained with this example. Let's say a man comes in and asks about when he is going to find the person he is supposed to be with. You see a blonde lady with shoulder length hair who dresses all in black, and that it will happen in the next six to eight months. Ok, he leaves and four months later a woman with purple hair who wears all white clothing comes up to talk to him. He feels attracted to her, but remembers what I said so brushes the whole thing off. He listens to my words instead of letting his feelings guide him and asking for her number. She keeps coming into his thoughts and he can't understand why. But what he doesn't know is that the girl was the same girl. She was just one of those people who is flamboyant and likes to express through the way she dresses. He met her earlier than what was expected because she had taken a new job and would be moving out of town within the month.

Psychics see what is in a person's energy field, which is the energy that resides outside the physical body. They also feel the possibilities that are being held within it. Those possibilities can change through events that take place, or lessons learned sooner or later than expected. Everything is in constant fluctuation according to our actions and

reactions. Wouldn't it be more empowering to help a person get their own information through connecting to their own guidance, or by paying attention to how their body feels, as well as the propelling of the heart? Well, who could argue with that? I gave my two-week notice.

Now that being said, psychics have a purpose too. They can help you to see possibilities in places where you were not able to open up to on your own. They can also help confirm a lot of things that you already know, giving you more confidence in trusting your own intuition or knowing. I guess one just needs to remember that it is always important to trust your own inner guidance over anything someone else says.

Towards the end of my last day, an elderly lady with badly dyed orange hair ran through the door. She quickly slammed it shut and peeked through the blinds. I asked if I could help her, and she started talking without turning to look at me. "I just escaped from my spaceship and have been running for days. I finally jumped into this old body. Why I chose this one, I'm not sure. The least I could have done was gotten a prettier, younger woman. Well, guess now I'm stuck with this saggy old thing! I put blue ink on my implant so that they can't find me. Otherwise, they'd just locate me and pick me up again. I have a homing device right on the top of my head and they can find me anywhere I go. I outsmarted them this time!" With that she turned and spread her hair to show me where she proclaimed it to be placed.

I looked around to see if there were any cameras propped anywhere. This had to be a set up! Nope, it was clean. She turned to me and said, "You do know none of this is real, right? Life on this planet is just one big video game. You guys are downloaded and uploaded. People here are watched all the time. It's like everyone is asleep or in a trance. You don't really see what is going on. I've seen city blocks disappear and nobody even catches it. Reality is altered all the time, and no one's the wiser." They can play humanity however they want. I asked her why she decided to come in here to tell me this, and she replied "Because I could see that your mind was open to hear the truth." And with that she opened the door and left. If I didn't know any better, I would swear I'm the star of an Alien reality show, and they're wagering on how I react to their antics.

CHAPTER 86

Tuning in to the Mountain

A GROUP OF women triathlon athletes hired me to take them up the face of Cathedral Mountain. I told them that there were no marked trails for that hike. I couldn't guarantee that they would make it all the way to the top, but I could certainly get them close. We started early morning as it gets so hot later in the afternoon. I didn't think any of us would want to get stuck on the sunny side of the mountain dehydrated and burnt.

It was nice to have a group of women that were so positive. It was also nice because they were all in really good shape. I didn't need to worry about it physically being too much for someone. We all kept a good pace as we scrambled up the waterway on the front side of the mountain. It appeared as though we were going to make it up to the saddle. Unfortunately, things can look very different from one angle to the next. By the time we had put in three hours, we knew that there was no way we were going to be able to get where they wanted to go. We were close, but there was a deep canyon that would have been really dangerous to cross. It was a little disappointing, but it wasn't worth someone getting hurt. After a short rest, we headed back down the way we came up. I felt so bad that I wasn't able to give them the experience that they had wanted, but in my world, I know that everything happens just how it is meant to. About half way down, I told them that I thought it would be good to sit and tune in for a bit. Perhaps everyone could take 20 minutes or so and meditate. We could see if the mountain had anything to share with us. None of the women were meditators, but they seemed okay with giving it a shot. I started it out with breathing and relaxing exercises. Then I asked the spirit of the mountain to come in and share its knowledge with each of us. Afterward, I held space for them to begin their own tuning in.

A few minutes in, I began to hear faint, yet audible drumming. I opened my eyes and looked around. I was expecting to see one of the local guides with a group of people, but there was no one there. As I listened deeper, I could tell that the drumming sounded more like it was coming from inside the mountain. When I closed my eyes, I could see a lot of Native Americans gathered in a circle as if they were having a celebration and doing ceremony. They were wearing their beautiful ceremonial dress. As they drummed, I could hear their ankle bracelets jingling to add its unique sound. The men began to sing as the dancers danced their stories. Soon the women and children joined in with their beautiful voices, creating music that flooded the senses.

I opened my eyes to see if any of the women were hearing or seeing what was going on. One by one, each woman opened her eyes and looked around. They were hearing it, too! I just put a finger up to my mouth and closed my eyes hoping that they would give themselves more time. When the song stopped, I opened my eyes again. Each of the women had been able to experience the music. They didn't see what was going on, but they had heard it. We were all in a state of awe as we packed our backpacks and walked the rest of the way down the mountain. It was quiet, but that felt fitting as each person processed through their mountain experience.

CHAPTER 87

Sedona & Our Work with the Galactic Federation

I HAD ONLY been in Sedona for a few months when I got a call from Iris. She was told we had some work to do and felt Dana was to be part of it. She'd be flying there in a few weeks, and already had a place secured for the next two months. I have to say, I was a little surprised. I knew there would be more work to do with her, I just didn't think it would be so soon. I didn't know if it was a good time to put a lot of time into a project when I had only been living with Dana for a few months. I told her I would have to see how he felt about it. When she got here, we could all talk it over.

When she landed in Sedona, it took on a life of its own. We found out after she arrived that we were being asked to put a book together about the diamond light. I knew that this is what she had been talking about in Hawaii. I also knew she had done a lot of work around it already. I was curious of exactly what was going to be asked of us.

This is when I truly knew that Iris was a channeler, and that she worked with a group of Star Beings called the Galactic Federation. They talked to us a lot, but there was also a lot of information that came from Isis, who is an Egyptian Goddess, and Esea, Isis's daughter. **The Galactic Federation told us that they are a group of benevolent Beings that were here to oversee the planetary ascension process for humanity. They said that they and Star Beings from other planets were overseeing things on Earth. They were keeping watch as we began to herald in a new Golden Age. They were watching with great love and curiosity as we began the process of remembering our true knowledge and power. They were also being a watchdog for the Earth while monitoring our climb as a civilization to higher frequencies. They called it planetary ascension.**

We were told that each of us who live here was actually reincarnated from different planets. Some of us came from multiple places, and we were their brothers and sisters. They were not something to look up to, or thought of as more evolved, they were just in a different stage of evolution. They told us that humanity was at a precipice where there would be great change in our bodies and spiritual nature.

The book would carry important information for this change. I never felt any pressure on their part, only a very caring and loving nature with deep respect. They often talked about our free will and that it was important to say no, if and when, we felt the need. We were told that each of us would grow a lot if we chose to work with them on this book. My job was to hold the energy and ask questions. Iris was to channel, and Dana would add a bit of flavor to the mix as he gave a masculine perspective of the questions and views which would make it well-rounded. They encouraged us to not give them an answer until we really felt it through. Each of us had to do what we felt called to do and they honored that. I knew without a doubt in my mind that I was supposed to do it. Dana was ok with it, but said he was a little unsure, and of course Iris was a go.

I could have never guessed the extremity of the work we would be experiencing. It was harder and scarier than I could have ever imagined! Often, we would put in 10 to 12-hour days for weeks on end. There were times when I thought I was going to lose my mind as the perimeter of my understanding of life was stretched to its max. At other times my foundation and everything I thought to be true crumbled beneath me. It's a very scary place to be, having no foundation to build off from. I was finding out that **many things that I thought to be true was programmed into my belief system by someone else's programmed mind. I was able to understand clearly that I believed myself to be the sum total of everything that had ever been projected at me from every person I had crossed paths with. That being said, I had crossed paths with some pretty screwed up people in my life. If that was true for me, then I could only assume that it was true for the majority of people on this planet. The other thing that I was able to see is that more often than not, the projection from the other person was more about their hurt, insecurity, judging, or lashing out. It really had nothing to do with me.**

As my perception of truth collapsed, I began to see what was really going on individually and within humanity as a whole. It became the most freeing, mind-blowing experience I could have ever imagined! I could write a book just on this time that was spent with the three of us and all the beautiful Beings who came in to share their knowledge. Instead, I will share a few of the highlights that may be thought provoking for you.

-I gravitated more to the down-to-earth things like seeing how our reality is affected by our conscious and unconscious thoughts and actions.

-How looking deeply into someone's eyes will show you their soul.

-How love is the most important thing to master. That the more love you carry and give, the more your gifts will be opened. It is the energy with which all things are measured. I saw how when our bodies get to a certain love vibration more and more gifts start to open up for us. That love is also the glue that holds all things together.

-We learned that we have a pain body and when it is activated because of trauma, the person experiencing it can only see what has caused the pain. No matter how much someone was trying to make it right, the person they were talking to could only see the version of hurt that had activated the pain body. I'll give you an example. Have you ever been in a relationship, gotten into an argument, and you tried to apologize but the person was unable to hear your words or apology? And even if you say to them that you are trying to say nice things, they keep insisting you said something else? That's because the pain body has been activated. I didn't believe it myself until Iris was intentionally triggered and I could experience seeing it.

At one point, they asked me to be alone in a room. I had a table sitting in front of me and on it they had me place a big rock the size of a grapefruit. They told me that they wanted to show me one of my lifetimes that would be helpful for me to see at this time. They let me know it was entirely my choice. They just thought it would be helpful for me to understand it. Curiosity got the better of me. I picked the rock up to look under it. As I did so, it was if I was watching a movie. In it, I was a woman scientist with a crazy high-piled hairdo. I laughed because it reminded me of Marge Simpson in the animated cartoon program that the kids liked to watch. My hair was blue and I was wearing a long white lab coat that we all associate with scientists. In the movie, I was looking into a microscope to examine different petri dishes. I was watching things grow and evolve. They told me that in that lifetime, I was one of the top geneticists for creating humanoid life forms. I was shown that because of a choice I made in the altering of the human life form, the pain body was created. Whatever is created on the Earth energetically moves into the rest of the solar system around the Earth. Now it was affecting other planets and those who live on them.

I felt horrible! I took that in and carried it like dead weight on my shoulders. I was the one who created the pain body. How could I ever forgive myself? Days went by as I mulled it through, chewed on it a while, and then held it all in my field. Finally, they came back and said, "Barbara, why do you always do this to yourself? You take something and carry it around doing so much damage to your body and spirit. How do you know that your choice to fix the problem involved wasn't the best choice possible? Perhaps a different choice could have been far more disastrous. You are just assuming something and you don't even know all the facts."

It is so true, isn't it? We all assume so much. But those assumptions are only projections of what we think is the truth. In a sense, I had somehow been programmed to shame myself for making what I believed to be a wrong choice. My programmed response around right and wrong, and good and bad, had kicked in, creating a harsh judgement against myself. It seems to me that when an unresolved emotional charge is triggered, it often opens the pain body.

To get to a point of balance in our choices and decisions, we need to look into the charges of energy that we carry and work deeply to heal them. My emotional charge around this projection was from experiencing so many times of being told that I was stupid, or wrong. I felt that what I thought didn't matter, or make any difference to those who were supposed to love me. It had been creating havoc in my emotional body from childhood on, and I was glad to be able to see it. You can't heal what you can't see.

I would like to share a technique that I often use to work with the emotional charges that you come across. This should help you to release or transcend them. <u>The best time to work with emotional charges and programming is when you are triggered and know it.</u>

-Sit in a comfortable chair and ask for your higher self to work with you on clearing stuck negative energy in your body. Explain that you want to work with the charges carried in your cells around negative programming from yourself, or others.

-Begin to breathe deeply. Use long, deep inhales, and long exhales until you feel centered and calm. Three to five breaths should be sufficient.

-Ask for your body to show you where there is stuck energy in your cells from negative words spoken by yourself, or others, or negative programming. (You will be shown by seeing it, sensing it through a knowing, or feeling it. Often it will be through color, shadow, shapes, or symbols. Pay attention to the way it works for you. That is your unique way of tuning into your body.)

-Once you have figured that out, begin to tune in to what is being shown.

-When you have it pinpointed, ask to understand where it came from. (If you are supposed to know, it will become clear.) Feel into it and see where you hold it in your body. What emotions come up around it? What does it look like, feel like? The more you work with it, the better you get.

-Try to understand the age it happened, and see the energy behind the words and actions of the other as it was said or done to you. If you can, try to have compassion for the other person knowing that they also were programmed and were acting from that place. Forgive them, and send them love, to free yourself from their trauma. If you can't summon up compassion for them yet, tell them what you now feel to be your truth.

-Ask your body to transcend the stuck energy imprint in your body into a supportive energy to replace it. It is usually the stuck energies' polar opposite.

-See the energy begin to change from dark to light, or from one color, or shape to another. As it begins to do so, infuse love and a new statement into it. Replace it with a positive and support-ive affirmation.

Thank your Higher Self for helping hold the energy for you to see this clearly so that you could heal, clear, and transcend all past and present negative imprinting and programming.

An example could go like this. One day when you were 13, you were going downstairs to clean up your room. A first-grade friend of your brother was coming up the stairs at the same time. He looked at you and said he thought you were the ugliest girl he had ever seen. You didn't say anything, but internalized it and became very self-con-scious about your looks. You, after finding the programming, look into the body and find you carry it in your solar plexus. It looks like a dark globby mass with tendrils. After it shows you its story you can see your age, who's program you took on, and why. The first-grader had gone through a really rough day earlier because his sister had gotten mad at him for coloring in her favorite book. She told him he was the ugliest boy she had ever met, and she hated him. He was just passing on his anger and words to someone else. He was purging his own hurt on to another. Now you can see it, understand the energy behind the words, and forgive him for saying something to you because of his own hurt. You can even send him love to help heal his own pain. You can see it had nothing to do with you. That makes it easier to forgive. You're able to forgive him and send love, then reprogram with a new statement of affirmation, watching as the color changes into a beautiful bright gold.

The fact that my choice from another lifetime had helped to create the pain body is probably why a lot of my work here is to help people get out of their pain, and work on creating a more balanced, and stress-free life. Once we have that, we react and create from a different place.

I also learned there have been many times when an enlightened couple has incarnated onto the planet to help bring humanity forward in their vibration and ascension. A few examples are Jesus and Mary Magdalene, Isis and Osiris, and Krishna and Radha. The feminine and masculine embodiment of each of these couples shares the same Soul. They supported one another to create great transformation and synergy for humanity. If you look into each of these stories, you will see a very similar storyline.

I learned that we are far more powerful than we could possibly know. I was shown that we hold every incarnation we have ever had within our cells and DNA. Because of that, the gifts and abilities that we hold from those incarnations could emerge in this lifetime when one has mastered higher frequencies of love.

For me, one of the most unexpected pieces of information happened when I returned from getting a glass of water while Iris tuned in. As I entered the room where we did our work, the hair on the back of my neck began to prickle. I looked over at Iris and could tell that she was having a really hard time holding an energy that was using her as a channel. As I felt into it, I knew it was the Devil. I was scared shitless, but wasn't going to leave Iris alone with it. I looked over and said, "What the hell are you doing here, and why are you in Iris?" He looked over at me and said, "Please don't ask me to leave, I just need to talk to you. I promise it will help you make sense of things." I sat there for a minute not knowing what I should do. I decided that I was protected and it would be ok. I told him he had five minutes and then he had to leave.

He thanked me and proceeded. He began by asking me what I thought a shadow body or shadow self was. I thought for a minute and said that I felt it was a body outside our self where we dumped everything that we couldn't handle while growing up and into adulthood. It was there to protect us until the time came where we could handle looking at it, heal it, and bring it back in as part of our self.

He told me that was correct. Then he said, **"Most people are being told to turn their backs on their shadow body and push it away, but it has protected you so that you could make it through life. If that is** so, then why would someone be told to do that? It is an intricate part of yourself, even if you can't visibly see it." He went on, "If that is its job, then what do you think hell is?" That I had to think a little longer into, as there was so much programming around it from church and people in general. After a minute or two, I answered that I felt it was the projection of everyone's anger, misdeeds, violence, hurt, all unresolved emotions and actions that had not yet been dealt with or taken responsibility for. He smiled and said, "Yes! That is correct! It is not a place where bad people go and burn eternally for their sins; it is a place where people reside within their own thoughts when they do something that they feel to be wrong. People create their own personal hell when they go to all these unresolved places and relive it over and over again. Many people consistently doing that creates a large amount of energy that creates the container you call hell. So, in a sense, there are individual hells that create a much bigger hell."

It brought me back to the time I was being taught about the energy field and the universal energy field while I was working in the bakery. I assumed it was the same principal as when the individual energy fields merge together to make the one huge universal field. He had me captivated even with the fear I was pushing down. I wanted to hear what he had to say until this talk was finished.

He went on, "Your shadow self holds your pain outside of yourself so that you as a person can move forward more easily without constant charges of hurt. It is an intricate part of you. At some point when you are more capable of dealing with it, it shows itself so you can heal it, love it, and bring it back as part of you; no longer separate. There are some places where one could go to the raw hurt and anger of the shadow self and use it for power to fight back and move forward. There is a lot of power in anger, hatred and injustice. If one could understand how to use that power in a positive way, it could move mountains. Hell is the same for humanity, as the shadow self is for the individual."

I could understand through what he was sharing that as each person begins to heal their lives, they begin to heal the collective consciousness. With love and healing comes the power to break down all the hatred, separation, and warring that everyone has used to create this place called hell. A collective could also use the power there to break down the old corrupt systems that have kept us enslaved by the few who own the majority of resources. Therefore, creating a better world for everyone.

He gave me a minute to process his words and started in again. "Earth is a planet of duality. In order to have love, there must be hate. To experience good, there must be a bad. In order to be a right, there must be a wrong. To have a yin energy, there must be yang energy. It is what creates movement here. Other planets aren't like this. In fact, there are few planets that are like this. Earth is called the school of hard knocks, and one can grow and experience more here in a very short time than most of the other planets. It is one of the reasons this planet is so revered. There are so many emotions that one can have and so many flavors of experience to choose from. There are those who look after the "good" energy and those who look after what you call the "bad" energy. Neither is right or wrong. It is just an experience one goes through to help propel one to their destiny."

Now I know most people wouldn't pick a talk with the Devil as one of their most enlightening talks, but I had to admit that I found it to be very enlightening. As he began to release out of Iris I asked if I could ask a quick question. He told me to go ahead, "Do you sit on the Council of Light?" He just smiled and was gone. Poor Iris, it was hard on her to hold that energy, but I was ever so grateful for that unexpected and amazing conversation!

I feel like since this was years ago, I need to say that what we are now going through is an integration of every aspect of ourselves. It is true that this is a planet of opposing energies. At this time, we are going through a process of integrating higher frequencies so that we can hold more and more light. At some point, we will be vibrating at a fifth dimensional frequency. In other words, we are going into a time when the dark energies are going to be illuminated and we will be able to go into a unity consciousness. I don't know what that is going to look like, but I know that the dark energies will need to be illuminated and integrated so that they have the chance to become light. I think the darkness has been here to help us take our power back. They called 2016 and beyond the start to the years of revolution. The individual and collective darkness that has enslaved us through fear is now coming into the light to show itself. When the truth is seen, it can unravel the slumber that we have all been in. If we see and walk through our fear, we gain freedom.

Several times during our work together, we were visited by a black helicopter. The black helicopters come from a branch of the military called the Black Ops. It would circle slowly around the property as if it was checking into things. Sometimes, we could see a man leaning out of the open doorway holding what looked like a hand- held microphone. Other times, it looked like he was taking pictures. Dana and I had experienced it another time before that, but our getting together to do this work certainly seemed to increase the visits.

When we asked the Star Beings about them, we were told that our government was constantly measuring frequencies on the planet. When they documented a spike of energy, a black helicopter was sent with machinery to check it out. There were several stories about people in Sedona who had black helicopters come around, but they seemed to be inventors of devices that could alter weather. I wasn't sure what we were doing that seemed so threatening, except perhaps learning the truth about things. When people can see through all the lies they have been programmed with, they begin to wake up to their true nature. They can no longer be controlled.

It wasn't long after that I had a sense that my phone had been bugged. When people called, they would say that they could hear a weird clicking sound, like our conversation was being recorded. It freaked me out at first, but after a while I figured if they were listening to my conversations, they must be pretty bored.

Iris was there for a couple of months and as hard as it was at times, I was acutely aware of the huge spiral of growth that I saw in each of us. None of us came out the same person we went in as. It also created a lot of tension, which put a palpable rift between Dana and I that we were never fully able to work through.

CHAPTER 88

The Follow Up & Anuk

SEVERAL MONTHS AFTER Iris left, my friend, Donna, from Minnesota came to stay for a few weeks. She was guided to come help set in the previous work, and get me more grounded into my own guidance. I have always been very thankful for Donna. I feel like many times we have been on escalators going in a similar direction. Sometimes we meet and do work together. Other times, we help one another get through things that would be harder to get through on our own. A lot of the time we are on different escalators and don't see one another for months, sometimes even years.

She always seems to get pulled into my life when something big was happening or about to happen. It feels like my guides talk to her when I need a little help, or need to be straightened out. Another thing about Donna is that she isn't all caught up in the glamor of being advanced or needing to be anything in particular. She just goes where she is directed and says what she needs to say, even if it is hard. I have had a few of those hard talks and it was needed to help me see something I wasn't being able to see or work through on my own.

This time she was being directed to make sure I was getting a good connection to my guidance. Being around other people's energies usually makes tuning in a lot harder. After her being there for a time, we decided that it would be helpful for me to go off on my own out in nature. I decided that I would go camping until the connection to my guidance was strong.

That first night I was in heaven as I set up my tent in a beautiful spot right next to a small lake up near Flagstaff, Arizona. I had a perfect view of the water and the mountains, and I was the only one there. Thank God, I had found it before the sun had set! I was just settling into my sleeping bag when I heard a bunch of loud, revved up trucks pull in. I unzipped my window to take a peek and was puzzled when they began to set up camp right around me. What the heck! The loud music started, and the beers began popping as they sat around a campfire celebrating the first day of duck hunting season. Are you kidding me? It was too late to take my tent down and leave. I was going to have to stick it out and leave at the crack of dawn to avoid the hunt.

There wasn't much sleep that night. They had no intention of turning in early. Evidently duck hunting for this group is a time for men to come together for comradery and drinking. It didn't make much sense to me to get drunk and then use guns, but then I guess it wasn't my hunting experience. That morning I woke up to shotguns being fired from every direction. It was definitely a holy shit moment! I threw everything in the car and left. This time I decided to drive down the canyon to see if I could find a spot in one of the camping areas. There was one spot still open in a part of the canyon that I loved. Camping there was a much different experience. This time there were people around, but the sound of the creek took away any distracting noise from other campers. I had the energy around me of silence and wanting to be alone, so people didn't come over to talk to me. The first day I decided to explore the river and get a walk in. I laughed because the trees here looked like they were eating rocks. I decided to spend some time sitting in a place where several little streams converged to empty into the creek.

As I sat on a rock, I could feel a very high energy nearby. I was directed by my guidance to a 20-foot-tall face naturally chiseled into the side of the cliff on the opposite side of the river. I could tell that it was a Being. It felt very masculine and spacial, as well as Lemurian. He began to talk to me telepathically. His name was Anuk.

He told me that he was going to download me with information. He also said that there would be a further opening of my third eye. I felt intense pressure in my third eye as a high pitch began ringing in my ears. I could feel the energy powering me up as words started coming through my mind in an affirmation to be who I came here to be. It felt like it was energy that supported me coming into my power. After about 15 minutes, it ended. I thanked Anuk, and asked if it was okay to take a picture of him. It took the whole night to integrate the energy so that I didn't feel like I was buzzing out of my skin.

Sedona is the first place that I was shown that **there are Beings who live in rocks. Ten years ago, I would have told someone they were crazy if they told me this. But once you see and experience these things, they begin to become more apparent. They begin to show themselves to you. Or maybe it is that the awareness of the possibility has been opened, so your eyes begin to see them more.**

The Natives knew of the Rock Beings or Guardians, and understood that they stood as a wise one and guardian where there was a place of power. They often went to commune with the Guardians and Kachinas in the rocks, and would gain knowledge about the area, or even themselves. There are many of them in Sedona that I have found and taken pictures of.

The next three days it rained. I covered my tent with a tarp and basically spent the time talking, and listening nonstop to my inner-guidance. I wrote a notebook full of our talks and I felt I had finally accomplished what I had set out to do. A lot of the writings were pretty hard to look at, but I knew that it was important to listen to what was being shared. **It's imperative to look at the things that aren't so pretty so you can clear them up. Again, you can't fix what you don't know about. The more unhealed energy** we carry in ourselves and our cells, the denser we are. In order to carry more light and higher frequencies, we have to release, or transcend the densities that have anchored into our body.

CHAPTER 89

The Breakup

IT WAS INTERESTING how many people showed up to visit me in Sedona. I thought maybe after I moved from Minnesota that it would be different, but perhaps it is my nature to draw that in. Everywhere I lived, my house seemed to have a revolving door.

I think all of the company and putting so much attention towards my spiritual growth took the time away that was needed to focus on my relationship with Dana. It all became too much for him. We were so much alike in that we wanted to grow spiritually, but there was also so much that we couldn't seem to match up. Not that anything needed to look the same, but sometimes those things are too important and insurmountable and the relationship doesn't last. About a year in, Dana and I decided to end the romantic part of the relationship and just be friends.

It was really hard for me to think that we could stay close friends. I had breakups modeled to me all my life. My belief system was that when two people decided to quit a relationship, they needed to move away from one another. That was just the way it was done. Dana wasn't going to let that be our reality. He was hurt to think that we would give up our friendship because the romantic part of it was over. We were best friends. I loved his gentle manner and beautiful heart. We could talk about anything and were such an awesome support for one another. I was in his life to shake him out of his comfort zone, and he was there to ground me so I was in the here and now. I decided to give it a try, and our roommate experience began.

CHAPTER 90

Mexico: Pyramids & The Mayan Goddess

THINGS WERE GOING pretty well, but I could feel that I was starting to stagnate so I decided to go on a trip to Mexico with my friend, Tiffany. My guidance told me before I went that it was fine, but that I really didn't need to. It was something Tiffany was actually called more to do. If I went, I was to make sure I just did what I felt I needed to do and not get too carried off on other people's agendas. That seemed to be something I did a lot.

We flew to Mexico City and were picked up by our mutual friend, Linda. We were to stay with her in her apartment for the time we would be visiting. Big cities are really hard on me because of my ability to feel others so easily. I couldn't seem to settle down there no matter how hard I tried, so we decided to stay with Linda's family in more of a rural setting, away from all the noise and traffic.

When we got there, they grabbed us by the arms and kissed our cheeks in such a welcoming manner I almost blushed! It didn't take long to figure out that I had known these people before. I felt so at home with them. It was like picking up where I had left off from a previous incarnation. They felt like Soul-family. I especially had a strong connection to Linda's mother. She and I both knew that there was something there, and I would often find her trying to look deeper into me. I was so happy that we were able to stay at a place that would connect me more to the people of the land.

I had so much respect for these down-to-earth people who had lived here from generation to generation and farmed the beautiful, fertile land. I found the people of Mexico to be very heart-centered and family-oriented. There was a lot of poverty, and things were very simple there, but they all seemed to be happy. There were several generations of the family that lived and worked together and I could see that they really cherished their Elders.

One of my favorite days there was when Linda's brother took us to the mountains in the neighborhood that they lived in. It was the morning after a rain, and he wanted to show us the waterfalls that develop on the mountains. As we followed the winding dirt roads, I could see the lush backdrops of the coffee groves ripe with their treasured berries. The pickers were skillfully collecting the beans into the bags strapped to their fronts. We also saw fields of vegetables that families were gathering for harvest. It was just like stepping back in time as the farmer pulled his weathered wooden cart through the grounds and headed up the road for home with his donkey pulling the load.

As we traveled the country roads, majestic water falls fell hundreds of feet into the pools where the water collected below. Everything there was alive and vibrant with incredible lush foliage of every color of green you could imagine springing from their fertile soil. It created a visual that blew my mind! If one didn't know any better, they would think they were in a tropical paradise. Unfortunately, tropical paradises create humidity. It took my comfort zone over the top.

While in Mexico, we decided to take a day trip to the pyramids. There were several that were clustered close enough together that we could experience them all in one day. I had never been to a pyramid so I was looking forward to seeing and climbing one. It was hot out, and even though I was excited to go, I dreaded the amount of walking we would be doing out in the sun with no cover.

At each stop, several men would present us with things they were trying to sell. I left most of my money back for that very reason. I would just keep saying, "no pesos," and avert my eyes. After the second pyramid, I started noticing that there was one man who seemed to keep back, but was watching me. When he saw that I had seen him, he came closer and showed me a beautiful carved black onyx piece. It looked to be a Mayan priestess. She wore a beautiful headdress with polished stones set into it. It was a stunning piece, but all I could think about was how heavy it had to be. He told me that it was for me. I told him I didn't want to carry it up the pyramids, and had no pesos, then walked away.

When I made my way down from the third pyramid, he was there. Again, he came up to me and said the piece was for me. Again, I told him it was too heavy, that had I had no pesos and walked ahead. I couldn't believe it when he was there to meet me again after the last pyramid. He said "Please lady, I need to go home! I have children waiting! It is for you!" Tiffany kindly told him that she would buy it and he said that it was only meant for me. What could I say? I told him I only had twenty US dollars, and that wasn't enough for his beautiful piece. He told me it was ok, then wrapped it in a soft yellow cloth. He thanked me for finally listening and departed.

The day before we left, a crippled man around the age of 20 showed up at the door without the family knowing he was coming. He said that he felt he was to meet us and had walked from town. I couldn't imagine how long that must have taken as he could barely walk. I was honored that he would do that just to meet us, but was confused as to why he had come. As I looked into his energy, I could tell that he was a Master in sheep's clothing. I could sense that he was very wise. As we all talked, I knew that he could see through every word being spoken by each person present. He knew each of our hearts well. There was no fooling this one. He shared some of the most holy and wise words I had ever heard from a person. I felt so much gratitude for all the wisdom he brought through for our benefit. **It is wise to remember that when one judges outside appearances, they often miss the golden nugget that is held within.**

It was coming to the end of this beautiful trip to Mexico with the family that I had taken us in like we were their own. Before going to the airport, the mom told me that she knew in her heart we had been in a lifetime together and insisted on doing an ionic foot bath for me. In return, I was able to hear her deceased husband who came through to give her a message of release and moving forward into a new life. I would truly miss this family I had grown to love.

CHAPTER 91

Nudging Around the Cities of Light

IT HAD BEEN several months since I had talked to Iris, so I was glad when I got a call from her. This time I could feel a bunch of energy swirling around her body. I could tell that there was someone that wanted to come through her channel and asked what it was about. As she relaxed into it, we found out it was the Galactic Federation, which we now called the Light Beings for short, and they wanted to talk to us. After a few formalities, they asked us if we had forgotten something. Neither of us knew what to say. After a bit they said "We have talked to you about opening Cities of Light on the planet. It is time to start that work." I told them that I thought it was too hard to do things like this when we were so far away from one another. I felt it would be best if Iris found someone there to do the work with. Again, they told us that it was our job, and we were supposed to do it together. Perhaps I could come to Europe, as there were three stones that needed to come together to do the work. These stones would be necessary for the cities to be opened, and I was to be their carrier. I told them that I would have to feel into it to see what I felt I should do and I'd get back to them. When they were done, I think Iris was as shocked as I was. She told me that I would be able to stay with her if I decided that I would come. Several weeks later, I got confirmation around all of it through my inner guidance. In four weeks, I would be on a plane to Amsterdam.

I was getting a strong push to go over to my friend Karen's house, and talk to her before going on this trip. Karen has always held a very special place in my heart. I was told she, and her daughter-in-law, Julie, would have things to share for my trip. The first thing they did was to bring out their Egyptian oils. They asked if I was drawn to any of them. Five stuck out to me with the number one being blue rose oil. They also brought out Lemurian Seed Crystals because they were told to gift me some for my work in Europe. Karen channeled and in it I was told that I would be going to an island in Scotland that was very important to Mary Magdalene and Jesus. Julie also channeled that I was to go to Ireland and that the leprechauns were excited. They said that Ireland held a lot of importance for me.

Dana and I decided to go to the creek the day before I left. I felt the need to clear and energize the crystals I was supposed to take with me to Europe. I liked to stick them in running water, so the creek was the perfect place. We were only there about 35 minutes when it started lightning and raining. As we headed back up to the top of the mountain to go home, a rainbow appeared. The end of it was on us and engulfed the car. It would go away and the next thing you knew, we were driving through it again! It happened over and over again. Soon a small rainbow began to arch off the right side of the front fender of the car. It did it all the way up the mountain and felt like it was a blessing from the leprechauns. A voice came through and said that while traveling rainbows were to signify that the leprechauns were with me, sometimes even testing me. I was told to pay attention when the rainbows showed up. As soon as the message was done, the rainbows disappeared. I have tried to find the end of the rainbow so many times. I didn't think it was possible. I guess you don't go looking for it. You wait for it to come to you. I said a silent thank you and went home to pack my bags for the trip to Europe.

CHAPTER 92

Europe: Meeting the Elementals & The Troll

IT TOOK ME 24 hours to work through the jet lag, but I was so glad I had come. I loved the farms in Holland that dotted the country with the turn of the century homes. Some still had thatched roofs and

I'd often see long-haired Scottish cows grazing in the pastures. The beautiful castles that dotted the country were surrounded by moats and their stately grounds were enchanting. The forests seemed to be pruned almost to the point of perfection. It was as if nothing grew by accident and everything was lovingly looked after.

The land was flat, but it was beautiful. Their dirt looked to be as black and fertile as the soil in Minnesota. One of their main crops was flowers. Extravagant, perfumed, bouquets of flowers were sold everywhere. They were so cheap that I couldn't imagine walking by without bringing some back to the house.

I was elated that instead of big conglomerate malls, they had mom and pop stores everywhere. Some were even out in the country. The stores in Holland were very specific. Some sold breads, some milk and cheeses, some chocolate, some vegetables. If they sold candy, it could be every kind of candy imaginable, but there was only candy. Because each specialized in specific things, there were a lot of entrepreneurships. When we went in to visit the stores, we were almost required to sit and have coffee or tea with the owners. There was always a table and chairs for people shopping to sit and visit. It was surreal, but very nice. I laughed thinking about having the same scenario in the U.S.

I loved that they were so energy conscious there. They truly cared about how much energy their houses were consuming. Not so much because it cost more, but because conserving energy was the right thing to do. They thought the western world to be huge energy wasters who used more than their fair share.

I also thought it was amazing that people rode bikes a lot. Everyone seemed to have several bikes parked in their yards. When we went shopping, we would leisurely ride our bikes through forest pathways and skirt streams and rivers to ride from store to store. The pathways were well thought out and intricate. It was a pleasure to connect to nature as we rode. Even the children rode their bikes to school from far out in the country. Their children didn't seem to be plagued by the obesity that is so rampant in the U.S.

The first thing we were guided to do together, was to go to Germany and meet with a couple near Heidelberg. I was scared because the one time we had gotten close to the German border, I went into a panic attack. I really had to work it through to be able to go. The fear welled from somewhere deep within. Perhaps it was about the Holocaust again, but as I felt into it, that didn't seem to be the case. The ride was a constant leveling of my fear while we made our way to Heidelberg.

As we got close to our destination, I felt a familiar energy filter into the car. When I looked at Iris, I could tell that she was in a trance. That concerned me a bit because she was the one driving. They must have felt my uneasiness because they began to speak. "It's okay, Barbara, there is no need to be concerned, it's the Galactic Federation." I asked them why they had come into Iris and asked if they knew how to drive a car. I think it was the closest I had come to feeling them laugh. I was told that if they could drive a spaceship, I'm pretty sure that they could drive a car. In retrospect, I guess it was a silly question to ask.

I asked them why they were here and they explained that they needed to show me something. They told me that they would have to put me in a fifth dimensional frequency in order for me to be able to see and asked if that would be okay. I told them that I didn't really understand, but gave them the permission to do so. Before long, I could feel the energy around me change while driving down a street in Heidelberg. They encouraged me to look around, and as I did, I began to focus in on the people walking down the sidewalk. I couldn't believe what I was seeing. Everyone was an Elemental! Some were Fairies and Elves, some were Leprechauns, and some were Gnomes. They were dressed like humans, but they were definitely Elementals. With that, I began to look at the houses. Each of them seemed to be a very unique Elemental home that looked far different than the ones that were there a minute prior. I just kept looking out the window in amazement as everything Elemental began to show itself. It was incredible!

They told me that each of us incarnated on the planet carry different parts of themselves from various incarnations. Some carry more Star qualities, whereas others carry more Elemental qualities. I asked them if it was like this everywhere and they told me that Heidelberg was unique because it was the capital of the Fairy kingdom. I asked why Heidelberg and they asked me if I remembered where the fairytale books came from. As I thought about "Grimm's Fairy Tales," I knew it was Germany. Just one more experience to blow my mind! I was only in that state for probably a few minutes and it all began to fade back to the way it was. I felt so lucky to be able to experience and see the things I got to see. Sometimes, I felt bad that Iris was the one holding the energy and wondered if she got to see what I did during some of those rare moments in time.

In a few days, Iris's friend, Liesbeth, was to start working with us. She was someone who had little spiritual training, but she was a good person with a big heart. She was to go with us to England to do some work there. Before we left, we were guided to go to a specific crystal store. The owner's name was Peter and it was one of the most amazing crystal stores that I had ever been to. We were literally drooling as we looked at all he had for sale. The specimens he had were off the charts and some of the biggest I had ever seen. All three of us went our separate ways as we dove into the proverbial candy shop.

I could hear some crystal skulls calling out to me, but couldn't see them anywhere. After I had gone through the whole store, I asked Peter if he had any. He winked and told me to follow him. I hadn't seen that there was a second floor. It wasn't a huge room, but it was where the finer stones and gems were kept behind glass. He pointed to a lit cove. As if he knew what was supposed to happen, he told me that he would give me time alone. He then closed the door behind him.

As I entered the cove, I could see four clear crystal skulls around ten inches tall sitting side by side on a lit glass shelf. I just stood there feeling the beautiful energy that they emitted. One of them telepathically asked if I would please activate them. I told it that I had never done that before, but it assured me I would know what to do.

When I checked in, I was given the go ahead. Standing in front of each of them, I toned the frequencies I was being guided to give. Each time I was done with one, they would gift me back energy. Finally, at the end of the fourth one I heard, "Here is your skull." I asked "Where?" and was guided to take a few steps to the right. There sat what looked to be three black wooden skulls that were only about three inches tall. I was asked if I would also honor and activate them. To be honest, they repulsed me, but I said that I would. After it was done, I heard again, "This is your skull." I didn't know how to respond because I had been told several times that my skull would be gifted to me. I left, and went back downstairs to see how Iris and Liesbeth were doing.

My focus was brought to the table where a guy who looked to be in his early 60's was visiting. He seemed an odd sort of fellow and was digging in his backpack. He kept saying he had something to show Peter and I knew I was supposed to see what he was going to pull out of the bag. I walked over and asked if I could join them.

Out came one of the strangest objects that I had ever seen! It was an obelisk about ten inches tall with a dirty bluish green color that looked to be made of a composite material. There were various things set inside which were held in place by some sort of hardened resin. He handed it to me to take a look. I could see flakes of gold and silver as well as crystals, emeralds, and a ruby. There were so many different things, I couldn't begin to name them all. I could feel the energy it held as soon as he took it out of the bag and knew we were supposed to have one to do our work. I was told that he was to gift us one of them.

By this time, Peter had been called off to help a customer. This strange man and I were left alone. As I sat there studying his work of art, I unconsciously blurted out "You're a Troll, aren't you?" His mouth dropped open in shock, as he looked deeper into my eyes and said "Yes, I came up from Middle Earth to help with the Human and Elemental kingdoms coming back together again. That is what these obelisks are for." He told me that Trolls were the protectors of the Elemental kingdoms and were born out of need. "It didn't used to be that way," he told me, "At some point, man had chosen separation from Elementals and nature. When that was chosen, it created a rift within the Elemental kingdom. The Humans and Star Beings began to use them for their own gain. The Trolls were created to protect the Elementals."

The voice told me that he was in need of healing and I was to ask him if he would like to experience it. He asked me what it was that I did because he could feel my energy from far away. I told him that I was an energy and sound practitioner and then asked him if he would like to experience it. He nodded yes and I told him all he had to do was to hold my hands. As we held hands, he closed his eyes, and energy began to surge through. He seemed to go into an altered state of consciousness and began to talk in a mottled whisper. It sounded like he was talking to someone who was guiding him. "Yes, yes, I know I am supposed to give her this, [long pause] but it took so much time, and cost me money to make. Yes, I know it would help. Yes, I understand, but I just don't know. [Long pause], Okay, I will. I promise I will! I'll give them one." Soon after, he opened his eyes and looked at me. He completely flipped energies as he explained that he just couldn't. His obelisks took so much time. They were too valuable. Poor guy, what a hard time he was having. I was still being guided that he was supposed to give of it freely, so didn't offer to buy it.

Just then, Liesbeth came around the corner and said, "Hey Barb, look what I found upstairs! There were three of them, and I wanted to gift you one." Of course, it was the three black wooden skulls. (Well, I guess it was my skull after all.) Then she looked at the obelisk that the man had, and asked if she could buy one of them from him. She felt we were supposed to have it for our work. Oh well, at least we had one. She also bought a big crystal that became the City of Light Crystal. This girl may not have had as much spiritual training, but she sure was tuned in.

CHAPTER 93

Germany: Seeding the Waters, The Stone, Hitler & a Fairy

WHEN WE WENT to meet Iris's friends in Germany, I was so glad that they spoke English. I had taken four years of German in high school, but hardly any of it remained in my memory. They were a nice older couple and I especially liked her. He was a handful, and I had a much harder time being around him. Probably because he felt to be so boastful and flirty, which I felt to be very disrespectful to his wife.

At one point, I was left in a room alone with him. I tried to make small talk, but he just sat there in silence staring ahead. As I looked at him, I could tell that he definitely wasn't there. He seemed to be in a trance. After several uncomfortable minutes, he began talking to me. I knew it wasn't him talking. Over and over, he said "Please forgive me, I didn't know. I didn't understand the true teachings, and because of it, Christianity was founded on un-truths. I am so sorry!" Then he broke down and began to sob. I had seen several of my past lives. The one person that I had hoped I would never meet again was the disciple, Peter. It looked like that was who I was speaking to now. All I could say was "I'm sure you did the best you could. We've all done the best we could." That two-minute talk seemed to erase any unease I had, and with it the rest of my Germany fears released.

This is not the first time that something like this has happened. I have had several experiences of people being in an altered state of awareness while talking to me. I have often wondered if they are talking from another aspect of themselves, or have agreed to being used as a vessel to let another Being talk through them. I can attest to the fact that I have been used as well. Sometimes people tell me that I said something to them and I have no recollection around it. There have also

been many times when I blurt out something and am in shock when I hear it being said out loud. It just flows out with no conscious thought.

We were guided to a well to do an activation. As we explored the area, I came across the first stone of the three that I was told I was to collect. It showed itself to me almost right away, but I didn't think it looked like anything special so I kept looking. All the while it was telling me it was the one, but I chose to bounce it off. Finally, Iris said she could hear a stone talking. It told her it was the first stone I had tuned into, but I wouldn't pick it up. I finally surrendered and went back to get it. It was a plain triangle shaped rock, and it had very high energy. I apologized for not picking it up from the beginning. After all, how many times have I told others not to judge a book by its cover?

Before we left, we were asked to use our voice to tone a download into a seed crystal and throw it into the middle of the water. When we were done, Iris told me that they said we should get back to the car as fast as we can. Later, when I asked what that was all about, they explained **"In order for people to carry more light, they must first release the things that have caused so much imbalance in their lives. Letting go of the darkness creates more room for the light.** You guys did the work that was needed to help people here clear that darkness."

While being in Germany, we learned that many of the people there were still recovering and programmed by Hitler's reign. I can't tell you how many times I heard someone talk about a family member who was the way they were because of Hitler's rule in Germany. **It showed me how hard it was for people of genocide and warring to completely heal. If one incurs enough trauma, their nervous system becomes fractured. Fear becomes the norm. That fear stops a person from moving through and creating forward movement as well as growth. They then become more easily controlled, which I'm sure is exactly what Hitler's plan was. To create a trauma so large that it would fracture generations to come.**

Before leaving Germany, we were guided to visit one of the forests. The Light Beings said that there was a Fairy, named Tianna, that wanted to channel through Iris and talk to us. The one thing I can say about Iris is that she surrenders into what is asked of her. Tianna was having a hard time channeling through her because it was so scary for her. She was very shy! Eventually, she worked through her fear and talked. It was a very beautiful talk about nature and how it used to be long ago before humans had become so unconscious.

When she left, I heard to go and take a picture of a specific tree and she would show up in the picture. When I looked at the picture, I saw a cute fairy with wings. Tianna had shorter hair with bangs and was wearing a short dress. She was right in front of the trunk by the ground. It was like she used the tree to create her form just like the trees in the Redwoods had shown me the Green Man. I hoped that at some point I would get to know and interact a lot more with the Elementals.

CHAPTER 94

The Tor, The Cow & The Calling Crystal

AFTER FINISHING UP in Germany, it was time for the three of us to go to England. Most of the time was to be spent in Glastonbury where we would be working around the Tor. The Tor is a very tall hill on the edge of town with a fourteenth century church tower on the top of it. It is said to be a place of pilgrimage where people come to visit from all over the world. You could tell that it was a powerful spot on the planet.

Glastonbury is a very strange town, although I got a huge kick out of it. Everywhere you go you run into people who look like they come straight out of a storybook. There's the pirate at the bakery slapping women on the bottom as he playfully spins out his pirate talk. A town crier yells out his concerns for the day on the street corner in century old clothing, as a man dressed in early London clothing, with a top hat, strums his guitar singing near the Abby. You go to have coffee in the hometown restaurant and get your order taken by the Hunchback of Notre Dame's daughter, while he's in the kitchen cooking the meal. You go down to check out the shops and see a Witch arm in arm with her Druid husband. It's almost like you're in another reality called Storybook-Ville. I've never experienced anything like it.

Unfortunately, we came during the rainy season. It seemed like every time we were supposed to do something on the land, it was raining. I don't mind rain, but it was also cold. Several times we wrang bowls of water out of our clothing as we waited to eat. At one point, we were supposed to go to the Tor and do an activation of the crystals that were buried underneath. It was sprinkling, so we sat at the bottom of the Tor in a protected spot until we understood what to do.

After a while, Tianna the Fairy came in. She was trying to teach us about how the knowledge of nature had been lost from the human race. We were given a meditation to do in which we were to close our eyes and meditate asking nature to support us. As we sat there with our eyes closed, we were to allow the energy nature was gifting us to siphon into our heart for support. When each of us were full to overflowing, it would automatically create a circle where we were also giving back to nature. It started a spiral of giving and receiving.

As we were doing the meditation, we could hear a cow walk up to us. There were several that were grazing and lying at the bottom of the Tor. Tianna just kept saying not to let it distract our attention. It had come over because it could feel the light. We were told to stay in our energetic space with our eyes shut. The cow was pretty big, and none of us was sure what was going to happen. Imagine our surprise when we felt a sandpaper tongue licking us all over! Over and over her tongue went up our arms, hair, wherever she could get access until we couldn't take it anymore. I guess we finally finished what we were supposed to do because she finally walked off. What was amazing to me was that when Tianna was channeling through Iris, the animals were attracted to her like a moth is to light. It was a beautiful thing to see. They would constantly come to her to be pet and acknowledged.

It seemed like we were always doing work with the waters and the churches. In one particular church, we were to call back in the feminine energy that had been pushed away. We were also to call forward the true teachings of Christ so that it's truth could start to work its way through the doctrine, as well as the people. In another, we were to set in healing for the darkness to come into the light. The seed crystals were getting shared all over Europe.

It was a really nice trip, but it wasn't without difficulties. Liesbeth was having a hard time being able to focus on things. In hindsight, she probably was just disoriented because of all the information and integration that was going on. She didn't really know if she wanted to put so much time into this kind of work or not. Liesbeth was in a relationship and had two boys to raise. It was all valid. I was having a hard time stepping into my power. It's hard when you have someone who is so good at channeling and pretty much takes charge. It makes it easy to follow.

We were staying at a bed and breakfast which was enjoyable at first, but by the end of our stay, the owners were getting into some pretty heated arguments. I wasn't sure if the energies that we were working with were causing a lot of their dark stuff to come to the surface, or they were a mirror to the dissension that we were beginning to experience in this group of three. More than likely, it was a little of both.

When we were nearing the end of our trip, I was being guided to stay behind. It was time to find the rest of the stones that were to be gathered. I felt it was a very private journey to listen and follow my own promptings. I would be staying on in Glastonbury for a bit, then head where my guidance led me.

On the last day there, we were at the top of the Tor and the Light Beings were telling me to look out on the horizon. I thought that weird, but of course, I did it. They asked me what I saw. It was something to do with an accident and there were police cars everywhere and a helicopter was flying in. It was very odd, and I couldn't figure out why they would show me something like that. What was it all about? Unfortunately, I was about to find out. The next day I took the girls back to the airport and started my journey to find the stones. The only thing I remember the Light Beings telling me was to not go to Stonehenge. They said that the energies there would not be conducive for me. Wow! Here I was in England and couldn't even go to visit Stonehenge. The place most people want to visit when they come to Europe.

I decided to stay in Glastonbury for a few days because it felt like I needed a bit of time to readjust after Iris and Liesbeth left. The next morning, I was shown to go to a book store not far from where I was staying. It would be a clue to where I would find the next stone of the trinity. The only thing I already knew was that it was in Scotland. I just needed to narrow it down a bit. As I was poking around in the bookstore looking for books on Scotland, a book energetically popped out. After setting it on the table, it fell open to a page showing the Cheese Well, and I knew that would be where I would find the second stone. Who knew it would be that easy?

During the night, I kept being called by a crystal. It kept telling me it needed to be with me and I kept saying no. I didn't want to carry a crystal around. As much as I resisted, it persisted. The next morning, I went to find it in the crystal shop I had been shown. It didn't take long to figure out which one it was because it never quit calling out to me. I can't say I had ever seen anything like it. It looked like a hot dog rolled in a crescent roll. Who would carve a crystal like that, and why?

The owner told me it was the last piece from a man in town who had been a crystal carver and that he had died several months ago. He'd never had any trouble selling his stuff, but this one had stuck around for a long time. Gee, I wonder why? The crystal was 86 Euros, but I got over it and walked out the door carrying the crystal in my hand. At least now I didn't have to hear it calling to me like a whiney child in a grocery store anymore.

I don't know why, but the crystal made me uneasy. It felt like it had been violated and I wasn't quite sure what I was supposed to do with it. Luckily, I ran into the old Druid and his wife. She could feel the crystal and asked "What have you done?" The words made the hair on the back of my neck prickle. They advised me to take the crystal to the Well of Avalon and bring it to the twin trees so it could be cleared. That was where the Lady of the Lake lived. I was told to call her forward with the Elementals and the elements to clear and bless it. As soon as I was given a sign that it was done, I was to pick it up and start my journey. When I found the two trees, I called the Lady of the Lake in. I could feel the work being done. When the wind picked up, I knew that was my sign. I was shown to wash the crystal first where the white water ran, then where the blood water ran, and that would be enough to clear it. I thanked them all for their assistance and left to start my journey into the unknown.

CHAPTER 95

The Accident

WHAT THE HELL! Not in my wildest dreams could I have imagined what was going to happen this day, nor would I have wanted to! It all started out so well. I was headed out to Scotland and would be skirting around Stonehenge. I remembered I wasn't supposed to stop there but I didn't think it would hurt to drive several miles away from it. After all, it was the most direct route to get where I was going.

I was about 20 minutes away from Stonehenge when I pulled over to get some gas. As I left, I pulled out right in front of a motorcycle. It was like a bad dream that was playing out in slow motion. I pulled out after looking left, then right, then left once again. I didn't even see the motorcycle. He came through a tunnel under a bridge with no lights on. It was a black motorcycle and he was wearing a black helmet, a black coat, black jeans, and boots to match. It was like it appeared out of nowhere. I saw the puzzled look on his face as he tried to swerve so he wouldn't hit the car. His handle bar just nicked my hood and it threw his cycle at least 15 feet in the air throwing him off. He landed in the middle of the highway. His cycle hit the road and slid across it sideways. By the time I could pull the car off the road to help him, he was screaming in pain, laying in a pool of blood! All I could do was keep saying how sorry I was and hold his hand as he screamed because of the pain that I had caused him.

The highway never shut down. People continued to drive by. There was only one other woman who stopped. She handed me a towel so I could try to help stop the bleeding. It was obvious that the bone above his left ankle was severed because his foot was hanging out in back of his leg. I took the towel, wrapped it and put pressure on his leg trying to get it to stop bleeding. All I could do was wait until the ambulance got there. I would have given anything for it to have been me instead of him lying on that road. As I sat in the middle of the highway trying to calm him, I remembered the accident the Light Beings had shown me earlier. I knew that this was the accident that they were trying to get me to see.

It felt like I was stuck in a time warp. Finally, several police cars, a couple of ambulances, and a helicopter came to help. I remember trying to stay as detached as I could so that I didn't add to the problem instead of helping him. The whole thing felt surreal. It honestly felt just like it was all being played out in a dream. I would have been incredibly thankful if it had been, but unfortunately, it wasn't.

Finally, the police put me in the back of their car while they took over. It was horrible listening as they reset his ankle before loading him onto the helicopter. It took four hours for the whole process to unfold. The police were very nice and after all the paperwork was finished, the car was hauled back to the rental company. Thankfully, one of the officers gave me a ride to the town where I would be getting a replacement car. He told me that I would need to go to a hotel until one came available the next morning.

Before I got out of the car, he had a talk with me. He said that it was important for me to get back in a car tomorrow and overcome my fear of driving right away. If I didn't, it would be a lot harder in the long run. He told me not to be too hard on myself. It was just one of those things that happen sometimes. I could let it take me down, or get back in the saddle and overcome it. I was very grateful for his kindness. It meant a lot being in a foreign country not knowing anyone. I thanked him and walked into the hotel.

When I finally got to the hotel room, I lost it. I screamed and cried and let all the emotion and fury I held at hurting someone so badly go. I was angry and hurt for not being protected from something like this happening. I had come to do work for the Universe. I was spending my own money to do so and this was how I was rewarded? I don't think I had ever been so angry! And as I released my furry into the room, pictures started flying off the walls.

When I could finally settle into a calmer state, all I could hear was, "Trust, Barbara, breathe! All things are for a reason, as well as this. You aren't alone, can you let us in? Could you open yourself up to feel us? It hurts us to see how you punish yourself. You don't have to do this alone. We are here to help if you would only allow us to." I cried until there were no more tears and collapsed into an exhausted fitful sleep. Tomorrow, I needed to get a different car and I was so paralyzed with fear I didn't know how I was going to be able to drive again.

CHAPTER 96

Getting to the Truth of It

AFTER BREAKFAST, I went to the car dealership to pick up my new car. I was beside myself because all they could get me was a manual. Now I would be driving on the wrong side of the road, sitting on the opposite side of the car, shifting gears with my left hand instead of my right.

It took everything I had to push past my fear and take the car. But then, what choice did I have? It wasn't like I knew someone I could call and ask for help. I knew no one.

I decided before going any further, I would drive back to Glastonbury until I could get on top of my fear. At least it felt more familiar there than anywhere else. I would go back to the place I had last stayed until I could settle my nerves down. I can't tell you how many times I had to pull over to the side of the road because I was in a major panic attack. It was one of the hardest things I have ever had to push through. All I could do is breathe until I could pull myself back into my body long enough to get going again.

As I drove down the main street in Glastonbury, a woman jumped right out in front of me. I almost peed my pants and had a heart attack! No more driving until I got on top of this fear, otherwise I was going to cause something else to happen. I was going to settle back into the place that I had stayed before and find someone to give me a massage. Maybe that would help work out some of this fear and trauma I was holding. It felt as if I had a gaping rip that needed to be fixed. What was this all about? Why did it happen? I wondered if I would ever know. Finally, information began to flow through from my inner guidance. I was encouraged to write my understanding of what was shared:

> **I wanted to share my experience of my car/ motorcycle accident in England. There is no need to go into the story, but after the accident was documented and things were cleared away, I was escorted back to a hotel to recuperate. There I went into a place of deep anger, and rage for not being taken care of or protected by the Universe, but even more so by God.**

> **I traveled a spiral of feeling the split that had been created between the masculine and myself. It felt to be far deeper than this one lifetime. I sensed it encompassed many lifetimes, like it was something that was carried forward in my cells from incarnation to incarnation. I was shown how it kept its hold as each lifetime replayed itself over and over in its singular theme.**

I also saw how it had gained strength in this lifetime, and how I had given my power away time after time to the men in my life. Then it went deeper, showing me how I was even mad at the masculine part of myself that had overrun my life and not allowed me to be the true expression of femininity that I so desired to be.

I always thought it was God that was holding me at bay, thinking myself unworthy of his love and attention, but then I understood. It was me who had turned away from him. I, was the one that chose to experience separation. I, had chosen to give away my power to the men in my life. It was me who had chosen to blindly accept and let things be, to just accept things I felt weren't right. Yet, I never spoke out to correct them. It seemed a lot easier to be the victim than having to fight for my truth to be expressed. It was easier than taking responsibility for my own choices. I just kept stuffing all my disappointments and feelings of being victimized within. I walled myself off and lost my voice. Even though I looked happy on the outside, I was full of deep hurt and resentment on the inside, which had colored my perception of the truth.

The men that I have had in my life have been an incredible reflection of what I have been doing to myself. They've been mirroring what I have felt about myself, and what women have, in mass consciousness, felt within. The energy went deeper showing me the disconnection that we all have from the Mother and the feminine Earth, which reflected the disconnection of the feminine as an equal in humanity.

The understandings went deeper still, and I saw how fragile and programmed men had become. They know that things haven't been right. The suppression of the feminine created a chasm for them as well. They were told not to show emotion. They were brought up with pressure to make a name for themselves and have money or they weren't worthy. They were to be the breadwinner for the family. From a young age, they were programmed to control things. They were molded to believe that they were superior to the feminine. They became detached from their hearts and now lived from their mental aspect.

If I could look past all the stories I had lived and created, I could see that the masculine energy was in my life now to get me to revolt and take my power back. I needed to find my voice and speak out, to say no. To respect myself so much that I don't allow disrespect from anyone.

Our individual lives are reflecting being out of balance within our masculine and feminine within our own self and that has created a world out of balance. There is now a call for balance between the sexes. It was time to bring the feminine back as an equal.

This is not one-sided by any means, there has been great injustices done from both sides. Women have been shrinking and not standing in their truth. They've shied away from being the feminine power of softness and love. They've had a fear of taking responsibility for themselves. At times, they have used their sexual energy to manipulate men into getting their way. To persuade men into doing things they shouldn't have been made responsible for.

And men have been shut off from being able to show and express their feelings and emotions. They've been preened to not show any weakness. Many have used their physical strength and motivation to get what they want no matter whose toes they step on, or how much it hurts the planet. There are many who have used their sexual urges without thought as to how it would affect the other person.

There has been a great chasm created between the feminine and masculine throughout our history. Maybe it is time for each of us to take a good look inside to understand our perceptions in this area. From what I've witnessed from those around me, it seems to be coming forward so that it can be healed for themselves and the collective consciousness. It doesn't need to be a hard process. Just look into your own life to see where you haven't stepped up to the plate, or worked through your hurts in this area. The walls of protection we have built around our hearts need to be healed and come down.

Of course, this doesn't fit every person on the planet. It fits those that have been programmed by society. It fits those who have not yet worked through and healed their own feminine and masculine parts of themselves. I see a huge shift within this next generation where the traditional roles we Elders have experienced are now merging and becoming more balanced.

CHAPTER 97

Scotland: The Stone & The Guardian

IT WAS EXTREMELY taxing on me to travel from then on. I don't exactly know why I always feel I need to push through what comes at me. The smart and nurturing thing to do would have been to fly back home and recuperate. The tenacious part of me always feels the need to push through something until it is finished. I would go to Scotland and continue to gather the three stones and be done with it.

Scotland's landscape is ever-changing. It could go from mountains to rolling hills within minutes, and most of them were dotted with sheep. One would think that it was the only livestock raised there. Come to think of it, one would think it was the only animal there. You really didn't see much of any wildlife except birds and sheep.

The people felt to be a rugged and hardy bunch. I quickly learned to find younger people to talk to. I was told before getting there that they spoke English, but it was no English I had ever heard! The older ones had such a heavy accent that I couldn't understand a word they said.

I was going to a place called Peebles where the Cheese Well was supposed to be located. I found out through a lady that it would be a four hour hike up a mountain. She told me I wouldn't be able to find it without a map, so I ended up getting one even though I was told that I would be guided to it. I just didn't want to take any chances of getting lost. After a good night's sleep, I started up the mountain.

How I was going to find a well on a huge mountain was beyond me, but I was willing to give it a try. The Universe made sure that I overheard a woman in the parking lot talk about the Cheese Well. At least now I knew it was near the top of the mountain. I didn't really understand the whole concept of a well at the top of a mountain. It would make more sense to be on some flatter land somewhere, but I guess wells have no discrimination. They are where the Earth feels it needs to be.

I'm pretty sure I must be the world's worst map reader. I had been climbing up the mountain for hours and had no idea where I was going. It was crazy the amount of people I ran into! Evidently mountain hiking was a huge thing in Scotland. After hours of climbing, I finally stopped a guy who looked like he had been there a time or two and asked him if I was going the right way to the Cheese Well. He told me that he was from there and had never heard of it. He wanted to know why I was going there, and how I had come to know of it. I just told him that I had seen it in a book of Scotland and wished him a nice hike. He laughed and said he was actually going to the next town over to have a beer at the local pub and then he'd be hiking back.

Wow! He was climbing a mountain to go have a beer at the local pub! Again, he asked me how it was that I knew about the Cheese Well as he had lived there his whole life and hadn't heard of it. Then he looked me in the eyes and asked if I was going there to meet up with the Fairies. I told him I didn't know. It would be nice, but I had no idea what was going to happen. He bade farewell and started down the mountain again.

An hour later, he came from behind calling out for me to stop. He asked me where I was from and I told him America. Then he asked me why I was really going to the Cheese Well. I told him that I was directed to by my guidance. He asked me if I believed in Fairies and I told him that I certainly did. I told him I had even been allowed to take a picture of one. Then he seemed to shift and began to share with me that he lived in a place with an amazing glen and forest behind his house that housed a whole Fairy community. He said he loved the Fairies and felt a very strong connection with them. He told me he could feel I was there to do good work and wished me a safe journey. He hoped that I would find what I was looking for. With that, he was off again.

What a strange encounter! **In my traveling, I have come to understand that there are guardians that watch over power places. Usually, at some point on your journey, you meet up with them. If they feel your heart is true, you are allowed to access what you need. If not, you will never find what you seek. It will be hidden from you.** I felt his coming back and saying what he did was telling me that I was now able to pass and do what I came here to do.

It was funny because not long after meeting up with him, I found the second stone. I had finally crumpled up the map and instead used my intuition to find the right pathway. I could actually feel the stone as I came closer to it. It was almost lying out in plain sight like someone had carefully placed it there. I found that very interesting. Hopefully, the well would be that easy to find.

I had climbed to the point of exhaustion so decided to sit and have a bite to eat. I also needed to rest my poor feet. If I didn't find the Cheese Well soon, I was going to have to give up. The last thing I wanted was to be stuck on a mountain I didn't know at night. After a leisurely rest, I grabbed my coat off the rock I was sitting up against. I could not believe my eyes! It was the marker for the Cheese Well. The well was literally 50 feet away, and I didn't even know it. I had to laugh at the irony of it all. Thank God, I had finally found it!

The marker said that when people pulled their wagons up and over the mountain, they were able to replenish their water at the

Cheese Well. It was a well that was protected by the Fairies and if the people drank of the water, they were well to remember to leave cheese or money for the Fair Folk. If you honored them, they would make sure your passage was unencumbered for the rest of the trip. I couldn't imagine a wagon being pulled up to the top of this mountain, but obviously it had been a regular route.

The well was a tiny stream not more than a foot wide. You could see where people had left little trinkets, cheese, and money on the drier rocks that protruded from where the water bubbled up. It was very sweet and I was open to the magic I felt stirring in the air.

When being instructed about the ceremony I was to do, I was told to take pictures before and after. It would help me to understand the importance of ceremony and activations. After doing so, I tuned in to the area and asked if there was anything, I could do for it. This is what I heard. "This well is not well known, but it holds the energy of the Elemental realms. We ask you to activate the well to a new level so that people become more aware of the Elemental kingdoms. The Fairy and human connection have been lost." They then thanked me. Sweet, short, and easy.

There were all kinds of Beings coming in while the ceremony was going on. With this activation, I was unable to see physical bodies, only colors. At one point, there was a feminine energy that came in with a huge fuchsia aura. She felt to be pure love and her aura showed up in some of the photos. Towards the end, a dog kept coming up to me with a huge stick wanting to play catch. I kept shoeing him away so I could finish. Finally, I figured out that he was trying to tell me that the well had been activated. It was complete. Animals are amazing!

I washed my rock in the well and let it sit there until I felt it had opened and was activated for its next purpose. It was time to get off the mountain. Thank God it took one-third the time getting back down. The hike had been eight hours mostly uphill. My feet were swollen, and my body was sore. I needed to soak in a hot tub and get a good night's sleep.

Note to self: When in Scotland never book a room over a bar. Holy shite! These Scottish men know how to party!

CHAPTER 98

Mull: The Graveyard & The Oracle

THE NEXT PLACE I was being pulled to was the Island of Mull. I missed the ferry I had booked earlier that day because of needing to pull over to calm my nerves every now and then. Because of the delays, I had a four-hour layover waiting for the next one. Mull was a whole new driving extravaganza. The island had single lane roads with little pull outs every once in a while. It brought in a whole new fear to overcome. Much to the other drivers' annoyance, I decided that it was easier to just pull over and breathe while I let them use the straight away.

I had a bed and breakfast booked for the first night. After that, I was being guided not to book ahead. I was encouraged to explore the island and go where I was being pulled. The voice came in and said that Mull was a very special place for me in a past lifetime. I was also told to spend as much time as I could with the water that surrounded the island.

Although the water was very calming and the land serene, I was getting more and more uncomfortable. It felt like the water was purging things up that I needed to see. Most of it was about having to do things the hard way and always thinking I needed to do things alone. The energy and thoughts that were coming up were often around separation and how I really didn't fully trust. I also wasn't asking for what I needed. **There was so much contradiction in every thought that I had. I could start to see the depths of sabotage that each of us plays out every day in life. We deal with so many insecurities and feelings of unworthiness that we literally become immobilized**. How was I ever going to find happiness and true purpose if I couldn't overcome this? The Light Beings keep talking about community being the way, but how can we be in community when we can't even get along with ourselves?

I was feeling lost and alone, when the voice came in and told me to call Karen. I thought maybe talking to her could help me figure out what was going on. It was so nice hearing a familiar voice and it helped to calm my nerves down a bit. She said that she felt there was something really important for me exactly 90 degrees from where I was standing. Once I found it, I would be free to go on to France where the last stone would be found. I had no idea what she was talking about, but I was going around the island anyway. If something was important, I figured it would show itself. I was almost all the way around the island when I was attracted to what seemed to be a graveyard. There were three huge Celtic crosses with moss covering them. I could tell they were very old. Each were around 20 feet tall and I thought they would make amazing backdrops for photographs. The minute I got out of the car, I knew that I needed to climb the wall to the graveyard and go in. It was as if the energy was pulling me there. I assumed that everyone could use the steps that went up and over the stone wall, but thought it peculiar that there even was a wall. Most graveyards I'd seen were open.

When I got to the wall, the voice came in and told me that I was buried there. I didn't understand and was instructed that I was to go to the building in the middle of the graveyard. Once I went through the doorway, I could feel a lot of energy stirring in my womb. The only thing there was a three-foot marker made of carved white stone which was in the very center. It had what looked to be a holy woman holding a baby on the front of the tombstone, with what looked like a grapevine that wove around them. On the back was a carved dragon by a boat, with the same vine running through it. The dragon was the same one I had seen inside a church in Germany. I was told to remember what it looked like as I would see it again later. In the church, Christ was standing on the dragons back with a sword held above his head pointing at the sky. Here, it was by itself.

The voice told me that this was where my remains were buried and that I was here to collect my energy from that lifetime. I was then told I needed to pee on the gravesite. To say that I was shocked was an understatement. I exclaimed that I just couldn't! What if someone caught me doing it? The voice assured me that would not happen. It was raining, and no one was there except me. Again, I was urged to do it. I was told that it was important to leave my DNA on the gravesite. I could only assume that it was my DNA that would unlock the codes that were to be gifted back to me.

It took a lot to overcome the feeling of being disrespectful and desecrating a sacred burial place, but I worked through it. I was told many times that part of my mission here was to collect pieces of myself from other lifetimes. It was like gathering parts of me that were spread around the world. As I did what I was being directed to do, a ball of energy came out of the grave and seeded into my womb. It felt like I had collected part of myself back to me. It was home.

As I started to leave, I was told to look out the key shaped window to the back of the building. It faced an inlet that looked like it would be a good place for a small ship to land. I journeyed through a vision to a time that I had watched a certain ship come and go from there on many occasions. This had been one of my favorite places to sit and wait for those I loved to dock so I could see their beautiful faces once again. Karen had been right. This graveyard was approximately a 90-degree mark from where I had talked to her previously. Amazing!

Towards the end of the stay on Mull, I was guided to take another ferry to the Isle of Iona. It was a beautiful small island where I could once again feel the influence of the holy family. It was there that I found an amazingly beautiful flat stone. It was to be the platform for the trinity of stones I was collecting to sit on. My back pack was becoming increasingly heavier and I was ready to be done with all of this.

The last night before going back to the mainland, the voice came in and asked me if I would be willing to do different activations with the water and people in France. It said that France was a very important place for me, and that I would be collecting a lot of memory from there for activating myself as well. I asked if I would have to travel a lot more to do it, and was assured that all of the activations would be pretty much in the center and a little farther north. I was told it would take me four to five days. Most of the activations were where I would be going anyway. I would be fully guided, but it was up to me whether or not I felt I wanted to, or felt like I should do it. I knew that it was part of what I was there to do, so I agreed.

The next morning as I left, I was greeted by the woman who owned the bed and breakfast. She asked if I could sit with her for just a bit before I took off. As she poured me a cup of tea, she told me that her mother had been somewhat of an oracle. She felt the gift had been passed on to her as well, and asked if it would be okay to give me a message. She said that she felt my energy to be very loving and kind and that I had completed what I had set out to do on the island. She told me that there was writing that I would be called to do. That at some point, I had a story to share with the world. She assured me that wherever I went, I needn't worry, as I was deeply loved and protected by the other side, and they were my constant companions. I told her that that was hard to believe since I had gotten in a pretty serious accident on the way there and that I was still trying to work through it. She replied, "Sometimes things don't make sense to us because we can only see the tip of what really went on. Even though we can't understand why something happened, doesn't mean it didn't do something big for us in our life. Know that you were protected as much as could be done. Trust that it was all for a reason."

As I was riding the ferry on the way back to the mainland, I was still working out my nerves. Was this fear ever going to recede? This accident had torn me in more ways than one. Even though it was hard for me to understand fully, I was beginning to see that one of the deepest things it was bringing up was a feeling of deep betrayal by the Light Beings. Why did they show me the accident that day on the Tor? Were they trying to warn me about taking off by myself? Were they trying to make sure I didn't go to Stonehenge by scaring me? Had the accident been inevitable, and they thought that by showing me it would lessen the backlash? If they knew the accident was going to happen, why didn't they just say I should rethink things, because if I didn't, the accident was what was going to happen? How could they show me something that was to happen in the future? If that is the case, then are we living a predestined life thinking we are making our own choices, but we're really not? I can't tell you why, but these questions going around in my thoughts had put a wedge through me that I didn't know if I could ever forgive or repair. I didn't know if I could ever trust another Being outside of myself again.

While I sat there breathing through another round of panic, I saw an etheric Bennie walk up and sit down next to me. He put his hand on my heart and kept saying "You're okay Barb, breathe deeply and calm down." As he sat with me, I could feel everything start to settle down and felt calmer than I had in a very long time. He sat with me for around five minutes, then he got up and disappeared. This man will never cease to amaze me.

I had a connection with Bennie that I had never felt with another Soul. No matter where either of us was on the planet, we knew what was going on with one another. He often called when he was in trouble doing his work. I could see exactly what was going on around him, and within his physical body. Then when he asked, I could help him correct it. He could do the same with me. It was as if we shared such a deep Soul connection that it created an energetic bridge to one another's physical and energetic essence. Time or space seemed to be no hindrance with our ability to feel and communicate with one another.

CHAPTER 99

France: The Dragon, The Ring of Fire & The Final Stone

THE NEXT MORNING, I felt softer. I think a lot of the energy I'd picked up from the gravesite had integrated, and a bunch of nervous energy had been released. I felt strong enough to make the last trek of the journey and was ready to take off for France where I would be meeting up with one of my Sedona friends. Nancy lived half of the time in Sedona and the other half in France where she led Magdalene journeys.

That morning before boarding the plane, I was told that France would be different than I thought. It would be stirring and triggering my emotions and feelings a lot. And I thought I had gotten to the end of it! I was supposed to make sure that I spent time alone at each of the places that I went so I could have the full experience I was there for. I was also told to journal as often as possible so I wouldn't forget anything.

Of all the places I had gone in Europe, France was by far my favorite. It seemed to be all about beauty and sensuality there. The women dressed to accentuate their beautiful form without shyness. The food was served to appeal to the eye and the wine was pleasing to the palate. The couples expressed their feelings openly and the land was incredibly fertile with all the vineyards that dotted the country. I could literally feel the passion this country held.

The first stop was to Lourdes to get some holy water. I wasn't being guided there, but it was so close. It's one of those places that people set out to experience. For me it was pleasing to the eyes, but I couldn't say I felt anything special there. It was surprisingly void of people, which I found interesting. I decided to cut it short and took off for Rennes-Les-Bains where I would meet up with Nancy. What I thought was going to be a four-hour trip turned into seven long hours. I forget that it takes way longer to go through windy mountain roads than a highway. At least I was back to driving on the right side of the road again.

Nancy booked me a beautiful flat on a river. It was situated on a small waterfall that flowed into different deep pools. They called the pools the Roman healing baths, and people came from all over to experience the healing they were famous for. It was exquisite hearing the water in constant motion from my room. That being said, staying near or on moving water tends to bring up a lot of emotion and I already had an overtaxed emotional system.

The first morning I felt I needed to connect to the land. I decided to hike a few miles up the river. It was so lush and abundant with beautiful greenery that was well-manicured, as if a gardener went to great pains to sculpt it. It didn't feel wild and free-formed. Instead, it felt as if it was designed to fit in to someone's vision of beauty. This stretch of land felt incredibly familiar. It was as if I had walked it many times before. I decided to follow the trails that ran parallel to the river until I couldn't go any further. The leaves were colored with the hint of fall while waiting for the last frost before giving themselves to protect the new seedlings through the winter. Several times as I walked, I came across a woman or a couple relaxing in the water with no clothes on. At first, I was shocked and averted my eyes, but it gave way to yet another example of the sensual nature of the people there.

As I lost myself in the beauty of nature, my inner sight became activated. I began to see alternate realities shifting into focus. As I followed the river path, I began to get a glimpse of the tunnels and chambers under the massive rocks and within the mountains. Interestingly, people began emerging single file from an open doorway. Women and men began walking down the pathway from where I had just come. Each, wore a long white sleeveless gown, with a golden clamp of a snake halfway between their elbow and shoulder on their left arms. They also had a golden band that came across the middle of their foreheads. Some were barefoot and some wore sandals. Each carried a single white candle that floated slightly above the palm in their cupped hand. The weird thing was that all of them had a white cloth tied across their eyes. I guessed it was an exercise to see as if they could walk the path with their inner vision. No one acknowledged or seemed to notice me, so when the last person had gone by, I walked back to meet up with Nancy.

The first place we went was to a pooling waterfall site not far from my flat. It was in the opposite direction I had just hiked from. Nancy told me that she was feeling very guided to bring me there. As we walked, I could tell my inner vision was still acutely activated. As is always the case while activated, the colors around me become heightened and otherworldly. When we got to our destination, I was shocked! There in the pool of water was a small reddish Chinese looking dragon who was playfully splashing around. In with the dragon were several naked women washing each other's hair under the waterfall. I was pretty sure that they were the ones that

I had seen earlier. There was also a couple making love in the water with others gathered around them. It felt to be a sacred ceremony or ritual, like Beltane rights were being performed. **Beltane is an ancient Celtic festival celebrated on May Day. It is celebrated when Earth energies are at their strongest and most active. Celtic beliefs are that all life is bursting with potential fertility, and/or conception. On the eve of May 1st, the sexuality of life and the Earth is at its peak. The Celts celebrate this day to bring fertility to their people.**

I was sitting at the side of one of the pools of water watching, when I felt a very tall feminine presence walk up to me. She said her name was Ixchell, who is a Mayan Goddess, and she started talking through Nancy. Ixchell was the name of the Mayan Goddess that I had brought back from Mexico while visiting all the pyramids. Ixchell relayed to her that she had come here to do an initiation on me. She then asked me to stand and face a certain direction. As I did, she unfolded a red piece of cloth and told Nancy that she was placing a moonstone that was in the shape of a crescent moon in through my chest, which I could feel. Then she placed several sapphires in a circle around it. Emeralds were placed to each side of the circle through my back. To the side of those, she placed two rubies, and at my third eye, she placed a single yellow diamond. She told me that she had waited a very long time for me to come there so she could do the initiation. She then bowed and said "Now you will be able to bring forward the information you carry, and do what you've come to do." She asked me to kneel and as I did, she activated the newly placed stones with energy from her hands. I could feel and see everything as it happened, but I couldn't hear a word. I was glad Nancy was there to be my ears and validate the experience. I feel it happens that way at times so that there is validation from one person to the other.

Nancy then took me to some places on the mountain near the property where two beautiful chairs carved out of stone were used to do initiations. They looked as if they had been carved eons ago, and were called the Isis chairs. Both were in the same approximate area, but one was way farther up the mountain. I would have never found them without a guide, and was continually grateful for Nancy being there with me.

That afternoon we went to where the salt water spring and fresh water spring met on the river. It was a magical place, and I began feeling the last of the trinity stones. It was pulling me to walk in the shallow part of the river. As soon as I did, I saw her. She was a beautiful, shimmering, white triangular stone that looked similar to a human heart. The energy it held was palpable. I was so happy to have the final stone to complete the trinity!

We spent the next three days following the Magdalene trail. She took me to several places where I knew I was picking up energies again. All the places felt very familiar. I knew without a doubt in my mind that I had been there before. Each place had such a different feel, and I enjoyed them immensely. But, as always seems to be the case, my favorite places were out in nature.

On the last day of our travel together, Nancy took me to what she called the Pool of Lovers. She said the story was that there was no bottom to the pool. It was said that sometimes lovers would meet here from other dimensions. It was starting to get dark, but we had our phone lights, and this place was really calling to me. I was told to gift the pool a pretty big crystal so I downloaded it with the codes that were given to me through my voice, then dropped it into the pool. Within seconds, the ground started shaking and I heard a big screech. In my peripheral view, I saw a huge dragon come out of the water with its wings spread wide open! As quickly as it surfaced, it went back under. Nancy asked what was going on. She could feel the shaking and heard its cry, but she didn't see the dragon. That was the one and only time it emerged. Part of me wanted to run, but the other was curious and needed to stay. Sometimes I wondered what they were having me program into those crystals, but in my heart, I knew it was all part of the great awakening for the planet.

That night was a sleepless night. The energy was running so high that all I could do was to lie in bed and shake. At one point, I heard a loud explosion and ran to the window to see what was going on. In my inner vision, I could see a mountain range exploding into fire. It would then run in an arched line to the next mountain range. That mountain exploded as it arched to the next. That went on over and over until it formed a complete circle of fire that looked like a wheel. From the looks of it, Rennes-Les-Bains was the cog of the wheel. The mountain ranges seemed to be the fire points or igniters. Once they fired up, the line of fire led to a center point. I didn't know what I was seeing as I had never experienced anything like it before. I finally drifted off to sleep just as the sun was starting to peek over the horizon.

A short time later, I was awakened by the most mournful cry I had ever heard. The kind that seared your Soul. As I looked out the window, I saw a woman sobbing in a heap by a nearby tree. I started to get dressed so I could go down, but when I opened the door, there were two women who had come to console her. Sadly, her son had been killed that night in a car accident. All I could do is to send her love and say prayers for the Angels to hold her through her grief.

Her mourning seemed to bring up a lot more around the accident, and the man who was hurt because of my mistake. I had tried several times to find out his condition, as well as where he was so that I could at least try to do something to help him. For some reason, I was never allowed access to any information. It felt to be purposely inaccessible. So many times, I would wonder how he was doing and how extensive his injuries were. But all I was able to do was to send love and prayers for his best healing possible or whatever was for his best and highest good.

Our lives can change in a second. One minute we're on top of the world, the next we're thrown into chaos and our lives change in ways we could have never perceived. Life is fragile. We never know what is around the corner, or how much time we have with someone. You learn to not take what you have for granted.

It was time to get on a train and go back to Drenthe. I asked for the train ride to be filled with ease and grace. I also said that I was open to all the help I could get with my suitcases. I didn't mind taking trains, but with the amount of luggage I had brought, it was a hassle. There was no one who came to grab suitcases like they do on a bus. I was responsible for bringing them on and off. At one point, I was at a station where I had five minutes to go up several flights of stairs, get the tickets, and then come down to catch the train. There was no way that it was going to work lugging suitcases, and I didn't know anyone that I could ask to watch them for me.

To my surprise, four young Asian men came up to me and asked if they could help me with my luggage. They kind of looked like gang members, but I had asked the Universe for help. I had to trust that this was an answer to that call. I told them I would really appreciate it. I asked if they would mind watching my bags while I went up and got a ticket. When I came back down to collect the suitcases, I was relieved to see that everything was in perfect order. I thanked them and we had a wonderful talk until the train showed up. These young men seemed to be in touch with their feelings and were wise beyond their years.

The train was 15 minutes late, and I was glad. I got to see the beautiful hearts of four young, respectful men. I also got to see how amazing people can be if you give them a chance. In the last leg of the journey no one spoke English. I really wasn't sure if I understood where I was supposed to get off. I couldn't read Dutch. Right as we were getting close to my exit, one of the men came to the back of the train to let me know that this was where I needed to go. I love people!

CHAPTER 100

Confirmation of my Initiation & Jasper Revolts

GETTING BACK TO Sedona felt good, but as always, after traveling I have a hard time integrating the accumulated energies and changes within myself. I also needed to release all the pent-up stress accumulated by the accident. I always felt a lot more grounded and safer when I was with Dana. Visiting him was like coming to a safe haven for me. As comfortable as it was living with him, I was also being guided to find my own space near the creek. I need moving water like I need air. Being someplace where it was so hot and dry didn't bode well for this northern girl.

A week after I was back, I went to visit my friend, Natalya. She was a very gifted animal reader and painted peoples' spirit animals for them. Natalya brought out the paintings she had finished up while I was gone. When she uncovered the last one, I almost dropped my glass! She told me that she had woken up with it in her mind and was told she was supposed to paint it even though she had no idea who it was for. I excitedly told her that it was a picture of my initiation that I had in France with the Goddess Ixchel. It had the pools with the little waterfalls, showered with the golden light that was all around us. In the middle of the picture was the tall woman with the long dark hair, red fabric in her hand, and me standing in front of her. I asked her when she had painted it, and found out it was the same day my experience had taken place. Amazing! Again, I was given confirmation through another person that couldn't possibly know what had happened to me in France.

During this time, my cat Jasper, started sending me messages (mind to mind) through the ethers. He basically told me that he didn't incarnate to be with my daughter, he came to be with me. I was then told that if I didn't come and get him soon, that he was going to leave the planet. I felt horrible, but I didn't know how I could have him in a place that already had two cats. I guess it was time to get serious about looking for a place of my own.

A week after the message came through, my daughter called and said that she had taken Jasper to the vet because he was sick. He tested positive for leukemia. It made me so sad. He was such an amazing cat! A voice came through and said that if I went to get him, he would kick the leukemia out within two weeks. I guess it was time for a trip back to Minnesota. I couldn't just let Jasper die. I was bringing him to Dana's until I could find a place of my own.

CHAPTER 101

Curing Feline Leukemia & Jasper Speaks

IT WAS TIME to bring Jasper on the plane to Arizona with me. The vet had given me pills to help him relax, but they weren't working as far as I could tell. He cried all the way to the airport. Thankfully, he was as good as gold on the plane. I couldn't believe it. He didn't make a peep. Luckily, no one sat next to me on the plane so I could put his carrier up on the seat next to me and keep him comforted.

I was so happy to have him back with me, but I could tell that his life force was weak. I had friends that had a machine to create vibrational water to help him heal his leukemia. Besides doing energy work, I put pure prayer and intent into his food and water. I waited three weeks for the leukemia to heal, then took him back to a vet to do a retest. It was gone. There was no trace of it. Jasper had kept true to his word and kicked it out.

I took him over to the house that had helped create the water to share the good news. While there, Karen told me that Jasper was trying to talk to her, then proceeded to give me his message. Jasper told her that we had been together in Lemuria and Egypt and that he loved me very much. He was very glad to be back with me again. Jasper said that humans were integral to the solar system. Then he explained how the seven planets around Earth corresponded with our organs and chakra centers. He shared that our etheric body, the first layer of our auric field closest to our body, is our true body. Not the dense physical manifestation we perceive as our body. He talked about how important it is to go inside and check in with ourselves. We need to receive and listen to our own unique and individualized information and guidance. He said that it was important to go to the heart when getting in-formation because that is where we are connected to the central sun of the Universe. The heart would always steer you in the right direction. He also told us how the moon would someday no longer be needed for our planet. This planet and humanity were going to look different in the future. For that, he gave no timeline. He also explained how at times some spiritual principles have become a blanket statement. Something that is helpful for one person, may be completely wrong for another.

Who would have known that animals carried such amazing information and intelligence? With all that he shared, it seemed to me that he was far more connected and advanced than most humans. Just think how much we could learn if only we would take the time to tune into these amazing Beings! How is it that we are no longer in tune with the animals around us? When, and how, had we lost that connection, or did we ever have it? I wanted to understand. It seemed to me the more technically advanced our civilization has become, the more disconnected we've become from nature and our higher understandings.

CHAPTER 102

Where is My Home? & The Lady & The Leprechauns

I WAS GETTING pushed more and more to find a place of my own. I knew that being with Dana was a safe thing, but it probably wasn't a good thing since we had split up. We both needed to start a new chapter in our lives. I decided to go down to the creek and see what I could find.

As I was driving down the road looking at different places, a lady with a rain bonnet came out of nowhere. She was waving her hands to stop me. I stopped, and rolled down the window to see what I could do to help. She asked if I knew how to keep an outdoor flyer holder shut that held her brochures. I said, "You stopped me for that?" And she told me that she had a feeling I would know. "Let's see, I guess I would use a wire or a paper clip and put it through so the wind didn't take it." She looked at me and said, "Oh that's a really good idea. I hadn't thought of that!" This was getting weirder by the minute. Then she asked me what I was doing here. I told her I was looking for a house to rent. She looked me directly in the eyes and said "Well, it's not over here sweetie. It's on the other side of the creek." Then she turned around and walked away. Well, weird, but I knew that it was a way of guiding me to my next place and I didn't take it lightly.

I decided since I was so close to the river I would go and sit by it for a while. Red Rock Crossing was my favorite place in Sedona. Whenever I sat next to the water, it instantly balanced, and calmed me. It was so helpful when I was trying to see things more clearly. I had so much emotion and thought running through me. So much had happened, and now I was letting go of the one steady and reliable thing I had here by moving away from Dana.

As I walked the path to get to my favorite sitting place on the creek, I noticed a bunch of young Native teens in different areas making prayer ties and bundles. I assumed that they must have been out on a field trip. The smell of sage was wafting through the air and it began to feel like I was going someplace very holy. I asked for a clearing of my emotions as I followed the guidance to where the Universe, and my heart was pulling me.

I was so grateful when I got to my favorite spot and no one was around. I just needed some time and space to myself. I snuggled into a tree and disappeared within my swirling thoughts and emotions. All the tears that had been held for so long finally flowed through and released. Sitting there in my emptiness, I began to hear a masculine voice singing from the other side of the creek. It was singing that went straight to the heart. I was grateful as it lovingly flooded through my body to fill the emptiness I felt.

As I peeked around the branch of the tree, I saw a young man around 15 years old in Native dress dancing and singing without abandon. I was mesmerized as he twirled and splashed in the shallow waters that flowed over the rocks dancing and singing from his Soul. It was one of the most beautiful things I had ever witnessed in my entire life. Part of me felt guilty, as if I shouldn't be watching something so personal, but I couldn't pull away. It was one of the most beautiful gifts I had ever been given by a stranger, and a masculine gift once again. I remembered how precious life was and how important that connection to Spirit was. I had so much gratitude in my heart for what I got to witness. I was now ready to move on and start over again.

A week later, I was back to Red Rock Crossing. This time I had promised my friend Julie, that I would take her there. She had never had the opportunity to go, and I wanted to make sure that she got to see it. As we sat there with our feet in the water, she said that the Leprechauns were talking to her. They told her to ask me if I was looking for a new place to live. I told her that I was, but wasn't sure where it was located yet. All I knew was that it was near the creek. They told her to tell me that it was just around the bend, and at the end of the rainbow. I looked at her and laughed as I said, "Well, it certainly would be a lot more helpful if they gave me an address!" I then blew it off. I changed the subject because I was a little uncomfortable. I mean, what are you going to say to the Leprechauns about a statement like that? Just quit the rhyme crap and give me some facts I can use?

The next week, I decided to take a drive on the opposite side of the river. I had often wondered what was on the other side of Red Rock Crossing. Besides, the realtor lady had told me it was on the opposite side of the creek. **That's how Spirit works at times, through other people, in odd encounters.** I drove to the end of the only road that goes back to the creek in that area. There, at the very end of the road, was a street sign that said Rainbow Lane. Under the street sign, there was a for sale sign by Magic Land Realty. Well, Leprechauns are definitely magical, I figured this had to be it. As soon as I got to the place, I knew it was where I was meant to be. I had driven right to my new home! Right around the bend from where my friend and I had sat the week before, and at the end of the Rainbow, just as the Leprechauns had told me. What a trip!

I called the number on the sign and asked if they would consider renting it out and they told me they would be over to show me that day. I was pretty sure it was a done deal until I got a call from the relator who basically told me that they had made her show the house to another party. She said she would pray for me to get it because she could feel that the house was supposed to go to me. I thanked her and told her that I would do the same.

Later that afternoon I got a call from Karen telling me that her friend, who was an Eastern Indian Master, felt guided to go into ceremony to make sure that if it was meant to be, the house was mine. He said he felt it was very important for the region and that there would be work done to benefit humanity by my living there.

The energy of this house was taking on a life force of its own. It seemed like everyone was helping out in some way. I was loaned $2,600.00 for the first and last month's rent without even asking. Someone else gave me a TV, rugs, lamps, pots and pans, everything you could imagine! A woman even called and told me her guidance came in and told her to clean up her beautiful couch for me. It was time to let it go. My living in this house was totally supported by the Universe, and I was excited to get in. I didn't know why it was important to be there, I just knew that it was.

When I finally got possession of the house, I knew that there were things that needed to be cleared. There were door locks on the outside of the bedroom doors. Not like normal privacy locks, but eye hook locks. It gave me the heebie-geebies. As I felt into it, I felt small children who were very sad. There was also a huge male energy here that felt to be Egyptian pharaoh energy. In the master bedroom, I could feel the energy of porn. It felt like someone used their computer to watch it constantly.

The property was originally the private home of the leader of a group that was booted out of Sedona. They were labeled a cult by the town, and I had heard a lot of unkind things about them. The leader lived on this particular property, but the group owned properties all around Sedona. From what I could see, they were on some of the most powerful pieces of land in the area. This guy definitely knew what he was doing.

The group had been relocated to another town where they felt they could start over without interference. The house I was in was one of the properties that they were trying to sell. The complex had six bedrooms with a separate extended building, a pool, several water features with a pond, a huge garden area, a covered sitting area, a gazebo, and a tree house. A lot of area to furnish, but in Sedona, the garage sales are amazing. The place was fully furnished within two weeks. Everything I needed showed up and Dana helped me haul and place it all.

I felt that this was to be a healing sanctuary. I cleared it as far as I could alone, then people started showing up without being asked to help with the rest of it. It took days, but we finally got it done. The land told me that it wanted to be brought back to the feminine ways. It had been pushed out by so many years of unbalanced male energy. I was also asked to open it up to the Elementals once again. They would help clear the sketchy parts of the land. It could never be total perfection because I didn't own the property, but I could help to change it in a good way. I'm not sure I really understood it all, but I could tell that it was getting a lot softer, and I could feel the Elementals all around the property. When people came, they didn't want to leave. It was like a place out of time.

My friend, Tiffany, was moving to Kauai around the same time I moved in. She told me that she had a huge 135-pound aqua lemurian skull that said it needed to be at the sanctuary with me because the land had been a Lemurian temple site at one time. It told her that it had energy to download into this area of Sedona and couldn't leave until it was done. We made a place for it by the pool where it would light up at night. The lemurian skull was absolutely stunning! With the light illuminating, it you could see Universes within it. I could sit and stare at it for hours!

It didn't take long to figure out that this property was way too big and expensive for just me. I decided to open it up to one or two roommates, and put a few rooms up on the Airbnb website. It felt like I was to share with people who would benefit by what the land had to offer. Within a few short weeks, the sanctuary was overflowing with guests. I was soon to see how this place was to connect me with a lot of amazing people. It was also here to teach me so many things that I couldn't have wrapped my head around it had I tried.

CHAPTER 103

The Sanctuary: Iris's Visit & The DNA Portal

IT WASN'T MORE than two weeks after moving in that Iris came to visit. On this trip, Iris, Dana and I were asked to open a DNA portal. We were told that the human DNA was to be opened from a two strand DNA, to a twelve strand DNA. In order for that to happen, a portal needed to be opened up on the planet. Then it could start opening up within each of us. We were told that we would open it, but someone else would write about it. It seemed to be the way with our work and it didn't matter. We would do it, and when it came out in someone's article, we would know it had been accomplished. I was glad to see it come through Lee Carol. He's a beautiful man who works with Kryon of Magnetic Service. I've always resonated with Lee. His messages were always uplifting and filled with love.

Once we had accomplished opening the DNA portal, the Light Beings started talking to us about opening Cities of Light again. They said it was part of our mission here, and now was the time to get started. As far as I could understand at that time, a City of Light was a place where a gigantic pillar of light was opened on the Earth. It held energy for the opening of our individual hearts to be more attuned to the oneness. It also helped to open and align us with our Cosmic and Inner Earth origins. The activation would help to hold the energy for the new Earth that was ready to be birthed.

There were nine places around the world that they needed to be opened. The first one being Sedona. I guess that was no surprise. They said they would be talking to us about it later, but it was time to make a commitment. They also laughed and told me that a lot of my children would be coming back to me at the sanctuary. I was told that all I needed to do was to help them understand some things, and encourage them to make little energetic adjustments. I could then give them a pat on the butt and send them off again. I guess they weren't kidding. I swear almost every person who stayed there felt like they were my child. It was crazy! I would always know, because at some point, they would say "I think you were my mom in another life." or "You feel like you're my mom." Most of them were women, but there were a few men. I bet I met at least 50 in the year and a half that I was living there.

CHAPTER 104

The Ball of Light & a Personal Encounter with a UFO

FOR THE MOST part, I really enjoyed the sanctuary. It attracted a lot of beautiful and amazing people that I was glad I had met. It also didn't hurt that Red Rock Crossing was my front yard. I could go to the creek when other people weren't even up yet. I could also spend my nights star gazing and watching for spaceships down on the creek. There were several times when a group of us were there when several ships flew by. One time there was even a jet chasing one. It was interesting because it seemed to be a game to the spaceship. It would let the fighter jet get half way close, and then it would shoot across the sky out of range. Spaceships were a big thing in Sedona, and I had many experiences with them, as well as other unexplainable things I saw in the skies.

One night I was making a trip to Dana's to have supper with him. As I was driving, a huge blue ball of light about the size of a large room slowly dropped to the side of the road. It was a bright blue transparent ball with spikes all around its perimeters. It was all the same color, and it looked very electric in nature. It slightly reminded me of the one I saw as a teenager. I couldn't stop the car because it was a one lane road, and I was on a curve. But I will never forget how it looked.

Another time, after driving home from a Thanksgiving meal, I saw a huge ball of light flying low across the sky. It was bright yellow and had a tail of bright orange and yellow fire that streamed behind it, hundreds of times longer than the ball was. It was extremely slow moving and in view for at least a minute before it was out of sight. Some people would say it was a comet, but I can tell you it was unlike any comet I had ever seen.

There were many ship sightings, but the best one had to be when a roommate and I were outside on New Year's Eve. We were doing a ceremony for letting go of things we wanted to be done with, and intending things that we wished to bring in. Both of us, at the same time, pointed into the same spot in the sky and said, "I feel a ship right there!" The minute we did, the ship lit up and started coming straight to us! We could feel the person who was controlling the ship was intrigued by how we could sense where he was sitting cloaked. There was a definite feeling of surprise and wonderment on his part. The ship hovered right above our heads around 100 feet off the ground. He began cloaking and uncloaking the ship. Each time he cloaked we could see through it like there was nothing there. But when we looked closely at it, we could see a faint outline of the ship just the way you would see a heat wave on the highway on a super-hot day. Again, it changed to a regular ship. This time when he cloaked, he showed how clouds could hide it. Then he uncloaked the ship once more. He ran the lights around the bottom of the ship one way, then turned and ran them the other way. We couldn't believe we were having this kind of an interaction!

Finally, we knew we could ask him questions telepathically, so we asked what he was here for. **He told us that there were many ships above the Earth. He was aware that we already knew that information. He explained that they were here as helpers and overseers of the planetary shift that was happening at this time. There were actually many different planets that had ships stationed here. They would be here until the ascension of the Earth and its people were secured. The driver went on to explain that some of them were here to make sure that nothing happened to stop the process. Others were here to help with the changeover of the human system, like an upgrade. And some were starting to make contact with their different family members. He said that all the things that haven't been working fairly were to break apart and a new way of being would come forward for humanity. There was energy from the center of the galaxy that was coming in to help awaken each of us to our true nature. They were also helping to make sure that our bodies were stable through all of it.** We thanked him, and with that, he ran his lights once more and shot straight up and out of sight. It was an incredible experience!

CHAPTER 105

The Bobcat & The Snake

One of the things that I loved about this property was the wild-life. One day, I was out on the gazebo just enjoying some peace and quiet. I was listening to the frogs, and watching the dragon-flies, when I saw something jump over the pond out of the corner of my eye. As I started to turn my head to get a better look, a full-grown bobcat walked within a foot of me. She was an amazingly beautiful wildcat and I couldn't take my eyes off her. The bobcat's markings were stunning, and I loved her little curly tufts of hair that bejeweled her ears. We just stared at one another while working through a bit of fear that was coming to the surface. I finally put my hand down and asked her if she wanted me to pet her. I think she could feel that I was a little bit nervous, because she started to slowly back away until she reached the pond. Then she turned around, jumped back over, and ran away.

After the bobcat came to see me, she came to visit on a regular basis. She felt to be a protector for the sanctuary. We would hear her on the roof above my bedroom at night. It was oddly soothing to be able to hear her settle in as she made her bed on the roof. I loved that she felt safe enough to make herself at home.

It was surprising to me how many animals actually lived on this desert property. I suppose because it bordered a national forest and had one of the few water sources. There was a rattle snake that lived down by the pool, along with a tarantula that made its home under a seashell. Frogs that sounded like goats hatched in the front pond each year. Pack rats ran around stealing our shiny stuff to stash under the gazebo and chipmunks were constantly taking off with produce in the garden. There were also colorful lizards and toads that scuttled around the property. The jack rabbits are huge in Sedona and seemed to be out more at night. They liked to dig their burrows into the sides of the red dirt walls that lined the road to my house. The deer, coyotes, bobcats, raccoons, and javelinas would often come to the property at night and wake me up as they padded down the sidewalk around the back of the house.

Animals are amazing teachers, and they're so patient with us. It seemed like every time someone had a problem with a bug or animal, it showed up and gave them opportunities to work through their fears and teach them something.

A beautiful young woman who had come to do some work with me was scared to death of snakes. One of the days it was rainy, so she decided to journal in the living room until it was time for us to start our work together. I was in the kitchen doing dishes and heard the loudest blood-curdling scream I had ever heard in my life. I ran to the living room to see what was going on. Paula was crouched on the couch with her legs folded up under her. She was staring and pointing at the front door. There, looking in, was the cutest little eight-inch garter snake I'd ever seen. It was just hanging out on the rim of the door, looking in through the bottom window. I told her it was trying to help her get over her fear of snakes.

It's pretty comical when you see a full-grown person go into hysterics because they see a tiny little snake. It wasn't like it was going to charge through the window and devour her. She told me it had been there staring at her for a long time and she felt it was trying to scare her. There was no talking sense into her so I said, "You know, it's best to work through that fear. Otherwise, you're going to draw in some experiences to help you do so in the future."

Interestingly, during her stay, she ran into two rattlesnakes on her hikes. It was rare to hear of a rattlesnake encounter. On the second to last day, she decided she would go swimming with me in the pool. The outside shower wasn't hooked up yet, so I had a sprinkler can with the sprinkler end taken off to use. When she was pouring it over her shoulders that little garter snake came out of the snout and landed right in her bathing suit top. I thought she was going to pass out! She was jumping and screaming, and throwing her arms around like a crazy woman! Still, she wouldn't touch the snake to get it out. I laughed at the incredibleness of it all. I mean, what are the chances of something like that happening? (Just so you know, I did eventually grab the poor little snake before she pummeled it on the ground.) I can say with certainty that once you get to a place of honoring and tuning into animals, you can receive their messages. Then you'll bring in magical experiences instead of scary ones.

CHAPTER 106

Jasper & Meeting Bigfoot

JASPER REALLY LOVED it at the sanctuary. From the start he became the resident healer. He would check out every person who came to spend the night. If they needed some form of healing, he would rock their bedroom door when they retired for the night until they would open the door. Once in, he would get up on their bed and do what needed to be done. He was relentless about it. Even if they didn't really like cats, he would keep it up until they finally gave in and let him do his work. Jasper had a job to do, and no one was going to stop him from doing it. It was odd to me that people who said they were allergic to cats never seemed to have a problem with him. Everyone told me that they could feel the energy he was running. They often said they felt different or better when they woke up the next morning. I found it interesting that they would often say they saw him as a white wolf. I felt like it was a part of his spirit that walked with him. He honestly did act more like a dog than a cat.

Every night Jasper would walk with me down to the creek where we would lay and watch the night sky. It was at this time that I started to feel Bigfoot. He was always on the opposite side of the creek. I felt it was so I could get used to his presence and not feel threatened. He was patiently waiting for me to get used to his energy. At this point, I could only sense him. There was a little bit of fear that I was working through, but I was never afraid that I would be hurt in any way. Bigfoots presence felt to be very peaceful and respectful. Often, I could hear him walking in the water. Sometimes when I would sit at the creek, he would give me a sign that he was there by throwing four very large rocks into the water downstream. After the fourth rock was thrown, I would tune into his presence. Usually, he only came when Jasper and I were there alone. However, once he came when Craig had come for a visit and was there with me. He got to hear the four splashes as the big rocks were being thrown in.

He must have felt I had finally worked through my fear because one day I finally heard him talking. It was not a verbal sound; it was more of a telepathic transmission. **He was a very kind and honoring presence and talked mostly about the human disconnection to nature. He explained how they wouldn't be able to communicate with us until we lived more from the heart. I asked him where they live and he said that you would most generally find them in very remote places in nature away from the intrusive energy of people and their machines. He explained that often times they try to come into contact with those who have cleared their energy and live from the heart. I asked if they lived in our dimension and he told me that they live in a different dimension, but could cross over into our dimension at will. He explained that sometimes the dimensions merge and cause difficulty. An example of that would be when a logging company comes onto a very secluded piece of land and starts cutting down trees. The energy from the destruction of the forest causes a ripple effect into their dimension.**

He called us their brothers and sisters and wished for us to wake up before we do destruction to the Earth that could not be undone. He seemed confused as to why humans do what they do. He hoped that one day soon we would remember our true nature so the Earth could be healed. I very much enjoyed my interactions with this male Bigfoot, but the visits were only there for a short period of time. After that, different Bigfoots showed up, and were always a surprise.

One of those times took place when I went with an Australian woman up to Flagstaff, Arizona, to get a session from a brilliant networking chiropractor called Dr. Milgram. Both Eva and I were having some skeletal issues and needed to get some adjustments. I had heard amazing things about this beautiful man and wanted to see what the hype was all about. Dr. Milgram was a cross between a chiropractor and an energy worker. He puts you in one of four rooms that has several tables and works on several people at once. He goes to each person over and over, listening to the bodies innate wisdom of what is needed to achieve balance. He makes small adjustments, then lets the client simmer until he checks in on the next round. I thought of him as a body whisperer.

Eva and I were put on tables in the same room as Dr. Milgram introduced himself and started his first energetic adjustment. He put me into a pose, went to my friend where he did a different adjustment, then left. I felt a presence come into the room and slide under my table. It had a very musky smell, and I knew it was another Bigfoot. It wasn't the one I had talked to before. This one was an off-white male. He asked me if I would give Dr. Milgram a message for him. He wanted him to know that his new medicine was going to be coming in soon, and that he wasn't to worry about it. It would come when the timing was right. Then he told me that Eva had been a Sasquatch in another lifetime. With the message delivered, he slid out from under the table and left. No sooner had he left, when the other lady asked me what that awful smell was. All I could say was, "It wasn't me!"

I was at odds. I didn't especially want to tell Dr. Milgram what had happened. It's hard for me to give someone I don't know well a message. You just don't know how they'll perceive it. Eventually, I figured with the energy work he did, he would probably be open. So, when he came in, I told him what had ensued in his absence, then gave him the message. Whether he believed me or not, it was now off my shoulders. As soon as I had given him the message from Bigfoot, a scream sounded from the secretary at the front desk. He ran out and I could hear him asking his secretary what was going on. She told him that something hairy and smelly had just come up behind her. It made some noise and startled her. I smiled because it was perfect validation of what I had just told him.

Before we left the room, Eva told us that when she was a little girl, she remembered being rocked to sleep by a very gentle female Bigfoot. She also said she felt she had been a Bigfoot before. Looking at her, it wasn't a stretch. She was a tall woman and carried a very different energy. The Bigfoot confirmations and sharing's were awesome!

When I went to settle the bill, Dr. Milgram explained to me that he had an infatuation with Bigfoot. Several times he had traveled to remote places to find them. They had shown themselves to him on several occasions, but he had never been able to get a close-up look, or been able to talk to them. He was very grateful for the message I shared. I guess you never know the way you'll be asked to be of service. I knew that he had received a lot of confirmation and healing because of what was said. **I could have chosen to be quiet because I didn't want to look crazy, but then I wouldn't have had the adventure I had, or given him the message he needed. Sometimes we just have to trust, deliver the message without questioning, and have faith that it serves a higher purpose.**

Bigfoot has visited me several times since. Mostly while sitting at the creek. We've shared some pretty in-depth conversations. Unfortunately, those transcripts disappeared. I'm hoping to have many more meetings with them in the future. I love the beautiful heart-felt innocent nature energy they carry and want to know them better.

CHAPTER 107

Doing Ceremony for the Ancestors & The Gift

I WAS SITTING at the gazebo having some much-needed quiet time, and could feel a group of Indigenous Elders start to gather around me. I had experienced this before, and refer to them as the Ancestors. I could see them through my third eye, but their words seem to be carried through the wind. I was being asked to do a clearing ceremony for them at a place called Smoke Signal Rock. It was a mountain not far from where I lived and was one of my favorite hikes in the area. They told me to bring my staff and drum, and that I would be guided to where and what was needed once I was there. I was also told that I would be receiving a new crow feather for my staff and would soon be losing the old one.

The guidance was to do the ceremony the next day. Unfortunately, the next day it was incredibly windy. This particular hike was off the beaten path and could get a little scary. I had taken a few people up there who had refused to complete it. I thought it might be a good idea to ask Dana to come along in case anything happened. He could go somewhere else to tune in and connect, while I went to where I was being guided to do ceremony. We started out after lunch, and the wind just kept picking up speed. Walking the mountain paths are always windier than on the ground. There were several times that I felt I was going to be hurled over the side. I asked for protection as we worked our way to the top of the mountain. When we finally made it to the last assent, Dana walked in the opposite direction. It would be where we'd meet when I was done. He was going to tune in and meditate, while I did what I was being guided to do. The minute he left the crow feather blew off my staff. I guess it didn't surprise me. I just thought I'd get a new one before the other one was gone.

The rest of the way up was scary and slow. I had never been on a mountain with the wind blowing that hard. The spot I was to do the ceremony at was what looked to be a large stone table. It was said that the Natives used to climb on top to send their smoke signals out. At the bottom of the formation was a twisted juniper. I unpacked my bag, then wrapped my legs around it so I could settle my nerves down. As soon as I opened all the directions, I was guided to start drumming and singing the song that the Ancestors were bringing through for the clearing. As I sang and played the drum, the force of the wind continued to build. It felt as if it was clearing hundreds of years of sorrow and pain. The wind finally hit its crescendo and I felt a wave of energy reverberate through the surrounding land. Then the wind, the drum, and my voice went still. I sat there in a moment of silence when I heard a crack. A rock had split off the mountain and dropped on my back. I remember being angry, and saying "What the hell! I risk my life coming up here to do ceremony for you and this is how I am repaid?" A voice came through and said "Reach behind you and grab the rock. It is our thanks to you and a blessing." I reached back and brought forward a slab of rock that looked just like an Indigenous grandmother with a shawl wrapped und her shoulders. All I could do is laugh and tell them thank you, but perhaps if there was a next time, I preferred to not be a cushion for the rock to land on.

I carefully put everything back into the backpack and headed down the mountain. There I was greeted by Dana holding up a crow feather with the biggest smile on his face. He had asked for one to be gifted to him. Spirit works in wonderous ways!

CHAPTER 108

What the Heck is Going On?

AT THE SANCTUARY, I decided to open up the building that was separate from the main house to an artist that was looking for a studio. It was the perfect place for her to spread out and do her art. Terri was a really sweet person, and yet could seem a bit standoffish to others. I found her to be free-spirited and refreshing. She knew what she did and didn't like, and wasn't afraid to voice it. Terri was a mixture of many nationalities. She was very intelligent and kind, but also very private, and at times, a bit neurotic. I wondered what had caused her to not trust people and was soon to find out.

At one point, we were talking in the kitchen and I could see that she had a large triangular shaped bump under her right shoulder several inches from the spinal cord. She confided in me that she was abducted when she was a little girl around the age of three. She knew something had been done to her on an operating table by three men in white coats. The weird bump showed up after that. She often questioned if it had something to do with her dad being a scientist.

I asked her if I could look at it since it seemed like she wanted to share it with me. To me, it looked like something had been inserted under her skin. There was no way that it could have been a normal growth in a human body. It was a raised triangle with black dots about the size of a tip of a dull pencil. The dots were equally spaced like a bowling pin set up. The first row had one dot, the second two, the third three, with the last having four. She said she hated it. It made her self-conscious so she dressed so that no one would be able to see it. I asked her what she thought it was, but she didn't seem to have an answer.

That night, I woke up to her screaming. I grabbed my flashlight and went to see what was going on. When I got to her bedroom, she was sitting up in bed with a scared look on her face. Terri told me that several men had come into her room. She then explained that ever since she had the thing on her back, there were men who came into her room at night on a regular basis. She felt they were trying to program her. Terri felt they were from the government and for some reason they had targeted her to do something. She was so tired of it all and wanted it to stop. After moving to Sedona, she had worked with a few people who were well-known for working with this type of situation. Unfortunately, it continued to plague her. She knew that there were people who had been trained as remote viewers that worked within the government. She felt that was who was messing with her, but didn't understand how or why.

It was a lot to take in, but I knew there was something not right about the whole situation. I was going to wait it out and see what happened next. I didn't know what I could do, or why it was showing up here, but I intended to help her if I could.

CHAPTER 109

A Well-known Visitor

I HAD HEARD about a young woman, named Kiesha, who was gaining a lot of recognition around the world. She was part Native, and part Caucasian, and I felt an instant connection to her. At one point, I got a call from a Lakota friend that was talking about her to me. The voice came in and told me to ask my friend if he would give her a message that was coming through. The message was that she was thinking in the old ways, where a Shaman had to take on energies and transmute them. She needed to look into the new ways so she didn't have to suffer or get sick. Her body was getting fragile and she didn't need to suffer anymore. She could birth a new way. I asked my friend if he could make sure that she got the message and he assured me that he could.

Weeks later, Kiesha called and told me that she was guided to come and stay with me so that we could work together. She felt we had something to teach one another and was open to us spending some time together. I, of course, said yes. It felt as if the Universe had lined it up.

When she got here, the first thing she did was pull out a medicine bag and asked where the big rock that held consciousness was. She told me that it had been talking to her ever since she had been guided to come to the sanctuary. It was telling her that it needed to be activated. I took her back to the pool, where we had placed the skull. She began pulling out all her tools to clear and activate it, then she led a ceremony for it. Kiesha was told that she needed to be buried. I kept that in the back of my mind but wondered how on earth that could even happen here. I would have to jackhammer a huge hole to do it.

We had a great time. Both of us could feel that we had shared a lifetime or two together before. It was just too easy and fun to spend time together. She told me that in the last lifetime we were together, she had helped me, and in this one, it was my turn to return the favor. I had no doubt it was true. It was through working with her that I understood at a deeper level how **everything and everyone is perfectly placed around us and used to help one see, understand, and heal what is most needed for the collective energies involved.**

I had a handsome young Australian man rent a room during Kiesha's stay. He had been there before and I loved him, but could also see that he carried a very strong sense of self. He knew how to use his good looks and personality to manipulate women into getting his way. He knew exactly how to play the game. I remember telling him that I had a guest coming to do work with me. I explained that she was here for healing and that he was to leave her alone so she could have her privacy. Over and over, he hounded her into going out onto the land with him. He was relentless and I was getting angrier by the minute.

But then I looked at it from a neutral place, and could see that he was being used as a tool for her to stand in her power and tell him no. She had to set strong boundaries and voice them. She also needed to point blank tell him to leave her alone. He actually played a huge part in her healing process. She felt empowered after being able to stand up to his attempts to pull her off focus. He, on the other hand, needed to know that there were times where he was out of line and inappropriate. She was able to get the point across on her own. I saw that I needed to quit trying to control how the healing was going to occur. The Universe is infinitely intelligent. It was using all the people who were here to orchestrate a collective healing.

At the end of her stay, all of the people with rooms at the sanctuary came together for a shared meal. As we sat there and talked, our beautiful guest let out a yelp and said she thought she had been bitten by a snake. She pulled her chair back and there was a bite mark on her leg with blood running down from it. We looked everywhere and couldn't find a thing. There was no way that a snake could have bit her without us seeing it slither away somewhere! After tearing the house apart, we had to come to the conclusion that it was a spirit snake. When I researched the spiritual meaning of the snake, this is what was written. You are in the process of transformation. Old emotional wounds are now healed, allowing you to move forward without guilt or fear. Wow!

CHAPTER 110

The Decoder & What Did This Crazy Skull Do?

AFTER KIESHA'S VISIT, I started hearing the skull. Over and over, it stated that it needed to be buried. The sooner the better. I asked how I was supposed to do that and it showed that I should carry it to a side garden. There I could dig a partial hole, set the skull on top, and cover it with as much dirt as possible. After that, I was to cover it with a wet blanket for two weeks. It was important that no one checked into its energy or uncovered it until the end of the two-week period. It took Craig, Dana, and I to do it, but we got it done.

During that time, I could feel the energy steadily climbing on the property. I was almost afraid to uncover the skull when the time was finally finished, so I waited an extra five days just for good measure. When I finally pulled the blanket off and uncovered the dirt, it was so high-vibrating that I had a hard time keeping the energy steady in my body. The skull told me to bring it up into the sanctuary where no one could touch it. Well, that meant my bedroom. Everywhere else was free space. After two nights, I knew I couldn't keep it up. I just lay there and buzzed all night. It could no longer stay in my bedroom. It was then placed in a spot by a window with a sign saying DO NOT TOUCH!

That next morning, I got a call. The person on the other end introduced herself as Brenda Julian Williams. She said she knew of me from a mutual friend that lived in Sedona. Brenda explained that she was a decoder for a group of scientists, and that a huge surge of energy had been traced from my house through the lay lines into North Carolina. Then, she asked if I owned a big crystal skull. I told her I wasn't comfortable talking to her on the phone so she asked if she could come to my house to finish the talk. She felt it was important that we meet. After tuning in, I finally agreed. In three days, she would be in Sedona for a visit.

How was it possible that the skull had done what she said? I knew it held a high vibration, but I sure didn't know things like this could happen because of it! I wondered if I was now being watched, and what the purpose of her coming here really was. I had to admit, this was way out of my league.

When she showed up, I was a bit shocked. For some reason, I didn't expect her to look like an innocent little granny. As she shared her story, I was able to understand things better. I have to admit, I had a hard time taking in what she had to say. She was highly intelligent, and because she came mostly from a mind perspective, I found myself checking out a lot. It had nothing to do with her, it was just that listening to someone talk from the mind tends to shut my receptors down.

There was another thing that was hard for me. When Brenda would start talking, I could see a window open up in the ceiling above our heads. It was as if the window was a table, and usually four to six people in white coats were sitting around it like they were observing us. At one point, my guidance came in and I was told she was a mechanical, which is a human/alien crossbreed who was part mechanical. I didn't really know what that fully meant, but I had met a male mechanical several months prior. Maybe that encounter was just so I could understand this encounter with Brenda better. I could tell he was a mechanical because he talked with a computer voice. Brenda was way more humanistic, personable, and definitely intelligent.

Being with a person who had a constant window opening, and scientists observing, was something I had never experienced before. I didn't know what to make of it. She seemed to know what I was thinking and told me not to be scared, they were her team. They helped her move from one step to another and were always with her. Brenda assured me that I didn't need to worry. They were the good guys. She then shared about her life and what she was here to do. It was a fascinating tale that she was going to write about. Some of the stories she shared were so far out there, that I really had to work at staying open. She spoke a lot about the government and what was really going on. She also talked about the Star Beings who were working on our planet to free humanity. She had been part of a team that created tools with healing frequencies, as well as tonal energy that could be a foundation for anything one wanted to create. It was called the Triad Wave. Both of her partners had been killed because of the information and technology that they were bringing forward for humanity. Those who are against humanity moving forward and becoming empowered had tried to kill her as well.

We met for several days, and at the end of our time together, Brenda shocked me to my core. She said that her team told her that I could make her more human. I have to say I didn't know what to say. I didn't understand what she was talking about. She asked if I would check in with my guides to see if they could talk to me about it. Then at some point, could I give her an answer? I was freaking out for days! I kept trying to get information around it, but nothing was coming through.

It wasn't until four days later that I finally got some guidance around it. That is when I finally calmed down. My guidance encouraged me to do it. I argued that I didn't even begin to know how, let alone what to do. That was when I was told that all I needed to do was surrender. Her team would come through to do the work. I was needed to hold the space with love and I would be shown what my part was. I was given the choice to decline, or accept. It was up to me. I was told that I would be safe, and it would mean a lot to her. A week later, I agreed to give it a shot.

As she lay on my massage table, I started getting the space set up by calling forward both of our teams and everyone who was needed to be there. I also put very strong protection around the room while we were doing the work, then surrendered to what the process needed to be.

Not in my wildest imagination could I have made any of this up, or foreseen what was going to happen. In came these big ant-like Beings! There were three, sometimes four of them, and they were about eight feet tall. They asked me to energetically open all her chakras and meridians to make sure she was in a good place. Then they began to make incisions in the trunk and upper body where they began cutting and pulling wires and different metal pieces out. As I looked into the incisions, there were all the normal organs just like anyone else. Those were never touched, just wires and metal pieces came out. I don't remember anything replacing what they took out, but I am sure that they did an upgrade. I really just felt like I was an observer to whatever was taking place. It took some time, but finally she was back together. When they were finished, there were no scars. There was absolutely no trace of the work that had been done.

She was told that she needed to be very calm and still for several days so she stayed at the sanctuary. When I came back from a short trip, I could definitely see a shift in her persona. She carried a lot softer energy and said that she was experiencing a lot of emotion that she wasn't accustomed to. I kept seeing her shifting into this softer, more effeminate person. I'm not sure on the whys of everything, but I could see that the shifts she had made laid the groundwork for an easier assimilation of information for those she talked to.

CHAPTER 111

The Human Dolphins

THINGS JUST KEPT on happening to help expand my consciousness. I had been told several times about a woman channeler with a suggestion that we should meet. I said that if that were the case, then she would show up at my door. I certainly didn't feel the need to go track her down. Amazingly, she called several days later, and asked if she could come by for a visit.

I could see why people were trying to bring us together. The conversations between us flowed easily and without any effort. After conversing for a few hours, she told me that she was working with the Sirians. They were prompting her to get into politics. There was definitely a need of people who are aligned with Spirit to run for seats in the political system. I couldn't have agreed more. The government is no longer working for the people it was put into place to serve. It has been bought out by a small group of people and conglomerates that try to manipulate and control the masses.

At some point, we decided to sit and talk in the gazebo. That's when one of my roommates showed up to join in. I started to feel an energetic wave open up between the two of them as they looked at one another. Then one said, "Oh my God! You were in my dolphin pod!" The other one came back with, "I knew it! I knew you were one of my dolphin family!" They then started talking dolphin to one another with high pitched squeaks and echoing clicks, just like they would sound in the ocean. It flowed just as normal as if they were speaking English. I just sat there with my mouth open. Finally, I excused myself saying I was going to get supper ready while they got reacquainted. This had to be another episode in the Alien reality show.

CHAPTER 112

Implants & The Human Microphone

A FEW WEEKS later, Bennie called to see if he could come for a visit. He had fallen in love and wanted me to meet her. I tuned in and she seemed to be an advanced and beautiful young woman, so I told him they were welcome to come stay for a few days. While there, Bennie got a phone call, and needed to travel a few hours away. I offered Kirsten the choice to stay so we could get to know one another better, or go with Bennie. She chose to stay and gifted me a nourishing deep massage. During my massage, Kirsten told me that I had an implant that was coming through the surface of my skin and worked it until it popped out. Unfortunately, she washed it down the sink before I knew what she was doing. That was the third implant removed since I had come to Sedona.

I once asked what these implants were all about, and was told that sometimes they are from non-benevolent extraterrestrials, but most of the times they are put in by us before we come here to keep us on task. They stay in until we reach a certain frequency or work through something we need to master in our life. Mine always seem to be around the base of my neck or high shoulder near my spinal Column. When they eventually work their way out, they look like a cobalt blue ball about the size of a stickpin head. As you pull them out, there is a sack like thing under it. If you pull the sack apart, it looks like two really fine wires that come down off the ball. Sometimes there is a crisscrossing wire that ladders off the two main ones. The first time I had one pulled out, I was going to take it to someone who could put it under a microscope, but it mysteriously disappeared.

It was during this visit with Bennie and his girlfriend, Kirsten, that I started noticing something with the artist roommate that I had never noticed before. She started showing up and spending a lot of time in the house when someone was visiting that was well-known in the spiritual circuit. Also, when we would be having a talk at the table, she would keep turning the shoulder that had the weird raised thing in it towards us. I watched as she did it over and over again, and finally the light bulb went off.

Bennie pulled me over that night and confirmed what I had thought. We had both come to the conclusion that the lump in her back was a microphone. She was being used as a spy. Now what to do? She was a good person and I didn't really want to kick her out. If we could help her, I thought it would be a better choice. After all, she was a small helpless child when it was put in. What kind of people would do something like that to a three-year-old?

I wondered what it was all about. Why was she here? Why would they, whoever they are, care about what I do, or what goes on around me? What was I supposed to do with all of this? Did this have anything to do with them tapping my phone? What was I doing that was so threatening to the powers that be? Or, is there something completely different that I wasn't seeing?

The next morning, I got up early to sit with it all. As I walked out of my bedroom, my roommate was waiting for me. I could tell that she was in a frazzled state and very nervous. She told me that she had barely slept that night and that she had finally figured it out. Teri felt the thing in her back was a microphone. She was crazed thinking that they were using her to spy on people, and asked if I could help get it out of her. I told her I didn't know, but I would look into it and get back to her. Until then, she needed to settle down and relax. It had been there for all these years. Another day or two wasn't going to hurt anything.

Bennie, Kirsten, and I looked into it and saw that it was wired into her spinal column. It was so intertwined after all these years that it would be impossible to take it out without doing serious damage to her body. But we could maybe do some things energetically to disconnect it. Whether they would hook it back up or not was anyone's guess, but at least we could try to do something that would help her. That night, we gathered together with Terri and energetically disconnected the microphone so that it was no longer able to transmit. We felt we did everything we could do. Hopefully, they would leave her alone, but I guess that wasn't up to me.

Weeks later, I was evicted from the house. Evidently, it was illegal to use your house as a short term stay for anyone. You can only rent if it is a month or more. I sure didn't see that one coming! I had heard it was like that in Sedona, but I was in the next town over. They told me that I needed to shut out any short term stays immediately or I would be fined $1,500.00 and the owner would get fined as well. Evidently, the timeshares here controlled the city council. I couldn't believe that what they were doing was legal. It's not like I was having drug or booze parties. I was having quiet, respectful, people come to stay who just wanted to help change the world for the better.

One has to concede when life alters itself. I had heard several times that I would soon sell everything once again and travel for a period of three to four years. I guess that time was at hand. I had been in this place for exactly 18 months, and done everything that was asked of me. I could leave with a clean plate and a clear conscious. The 136-pound skull was put in a shipping crate and shipped to Kauai. That was where she was needed next.

CHAPTER 113

Letting Go Again & The Trip to the Reservation

IT WAS ANOTHER incredibly hurried process of letting go of everything I owned. I would be staying with Dana for a week or two, then drive back to Minnesota to be with my family until I was shown what was next. My friend, Nancy, let me hold garage sales at her home and at one point, she decided to take a trip as well. Since we were basically going in the same direction, we decided to caravan across the states together. That way, I could help her with some of the things that wouldn't fit in her car.

It was an interesting trip back as Nancy is an eclectic natured person. She was part Lakota and had a very strong sense of her heritage and spiritual nature. Yet, within it all, there seemed to be a disconnect of sorts. I think it is like that for a lot of people who are living through a holocaust of their heritage.

During the trip, the voice came in and asked if we would be willing to do some clearing work on the land as we drove. Because Nancy's lineage was Chief Crazy Horse, her codes would unlock the land and call forward those who were ready. I could then use my field to clear the imprints and help them cross over. I had never attempted this type of work with a novice, but she was willing. That was only asked of us the first day. After that, it was just getting to where we needed to go.

The first stop was visiting my friend, Mel, who was living in Montana. She lived on a ranch with horses, and graciously put us up in her camper. That night after falling asleep, a ghost started slamming a door over and over. When he knew he had my attention he sat on the couch right next to my bed. I tried to pull the covers over my head so I didn't have to deal with it, but he was persistent. He told me that he was mad because all his possessions were missing off the land. He wanted to know where they were. I told him I would look into it in the morning for him and he finally left.

The next day I asked Mel about it. She said an old guy lived there for a long time. The people before her bulldozed everything off the land and buried it under the horse pasture. After he understood it wasn't her family that had trashed all of his belongings, he settled down. I asked him if he would like me to help him cross over and he told me he liked the children and watched after them a lot. He wanted to stay and keep the children safe. So, we did ceremony, giving him a choice of staying or going, and headed out for South Dakota.

We stayed one night with a family from the Sioux Reservation before making our way across the state. On the way, we stopped at one of the Indigenous Grandmothers who was Nancy's friend. I have always noticed that the Native people watch you for a while. If they see they can trust you, then, and only then, will they acknowledge you by looking into your eyes. That is when they will open up and talk to you. I must have gained her trust because she looked us both in the eyes as she told us a story about a young man who had come to her several times. The first time they met, he gave her a big hug and told her he was so happy to finally meet her. He then proceeded to tell her that she had come to him before he was born. She told us it scared her. She looked at me and asked "What does he want? I wish he'd stay away. He frightens me." I told her that I felt he was here to do very important work with her for their community. I suggested that maybe next time she could work through her fear and invite him to sit and talk. I told her that she didn't need to be afraid. He was a beautiful Soul and knew of the new ways to come. He was here to help their tribe heal. Hopefully she was able to.

From there we went to the Pine Ridge Reservation in South Dakota. My heart went out to all the people who lived in such an impoverished community. Looking at the living conditions, you could understand why there had been a rash of suicides with the young people who lived there. I am sure the young people felt hopeless. It was an emotional experience to see the undercurrent of their situation. My heart has probably always been closer to the Native Americans than any other culture. Being invited into Native people's homes and being able to observe their ways helped me to understand, and have more compassion around where they were at, both emotionally and psychologically.

One of the things that has always baffled me was why Native Americans were constantly honoring the dead by reenacting the slaughters and wars of the past. I understand the concept of keeping one's culture alive through memories and stories, but I feel that as long as one keeps reenacting and focusing on the negative aspects of the past, they will always stay in the old stuck negative energies of the past. I also have experienced that constant emotion with the reenactment, causes many of those that have died to be stuck here. Not being able to move on to the next phase of existence. I feel that is a huge part in where

they have gotten lost. I've always prayed that they begin to focus on the positive knowingness of who they are and what their connectedness to nature and the ancestors were, to create a better future.

It's like time has moved forward leaving them struggling and battered. One has to wonder if that is what the "powers that be" intended. Staying in the victim energy has caused incredible amounts of unrest within the people and their tribes. The death rate is incredibly high, diabetes, alcoholism, cancer and heart disease run rampant. I pray that one day soon there will be a massive healing for them. They carry such beautiful wisdom that we would all do well to learn and live by.

Perhaps they are a reflection of what we all hold onto. I know in my childhood the hurtful and scary things are what I remembered most. And because of those hurtful memories that I held and hadn't healed, I continually drew experiences to validate the very things that had kept me in my own prison. Those continued to show themselves to me until I was finally able to work through them and move on.

CHAPTER 114

Off to Peru

MY FRIEND JANE (another one) kept calling and asking me if I would be interested in going to Peru with her. I kept telling her I just wasn't feeling it, but it didn't seem to dissuade her. A week later, she tried again. She asked if I felt I was supposed to go to Peru and again I told her I didn't have any pull to Peru whatsoever. She then asked "What if it was paid for?" I told her that would be the only way I would even think of going. She resounded with "Good, because I paid for a ten-day all-inclusive trip for you to Peru. That is how much I know you are supposed to go." Well, crap!

I decided I would go back to Minnesota to visit the kids and my family until I left. There was a bit of fear coming up around this trip to Peru. One by one, my sons called and told me that they weren't feeling it was a good idea for me to go. They said they didn't want to get a call about me getting kidnapped, and being found dead in a bath tub full of ice with my organs missing. I was also told by a psychic that it would be a very strenuous trip on my body. Maybe that is why so many people said that they felt they would be going with me energetically. Either this was going to be a phenomenal trip, or a really hard one. I guess I was about to find out.

I stayed in my little home away from home above the garage in Jane and Mike's house while I waited for the trip. To prepare for the high altitude, I hiked up hills while carrying a backpack full of weights. I'd hoped it would get my physical body ready and help with the high altitude breathing in Peru. Since this was such a long flight, I decided after the tour was over, I would fly into Puno on Lake Titicaca, which is at 12,556 feet elevation to stay for a month or two. Then I could spend more time getting to know the people.

I flew into Cusco, Peru, for the first week so that I could get used to the altitude before meeting up with the group. I decided to stay with a family whose home I found on Airbnb before the group gathered. The elderly woman who owned the house was charming, but she didn't speak a lick of English. I had to draw pictures a lot, or wait until someone who could speak Quechua and English showed up. It's traumatizing not being able to get what you need across.

Even after a week at a lower altitude, I was waking up in a panic trying to catch a deep breath. I wondered how I was going to make it through this trip. I honestly wished I had stayed home. That being said, I was there, and I was going to try my hardest to find things that would help with the altitude sickness. I also walked as much as I could to keep building the capacity of my lungs up.

While exploring the town, it was easy to see the influence of the conquistadors who invaded Peru, especially through the government and churches. In the churches, the pillars were lined with gold, as well as all of the beautiful gold inlay on the ceiling and walls. The churches held incredible wealth, while the people were experiencing so much poverty. As usual, churches were built over the top of the Peruvian's sacred sites. They then used their sacred objects as a door stop for the church as if to say "You are welcome to come here and worship, but you need to leave your ways behind to be saved." I guess I shouldn't have been surprised; it's a typical repeat of all the things that I have seen with the invaders taking over a culture and its people.

I walked the town often, so I could be among the locals. They were so beautiful in their simple ways. It saddened me to see the influences created by the tourism that filtered through. You couldn't walk twenty feet without being approached by people trying to make some money by peddling their wares. Often, there was a child with a baby lama asking to be paid for photo opts. Sometimes, they would even try to bring you to their house where they had floors of things to sell. It took one time and I knew to never do that again. The guy was a Shaman and had everything upstairs. At one place in his house, you had to tightrope across a thin board to get to the next space where he stored his wares. That was when I bowed out and decided that it wasn't a good idea to go places alone anymore.

At one point, I met the son of the woman who owned the home I was staying at. He'd often bring over people who worked with him at a privately funded school for the younger children in town. It was surprising how many people came from abroad to teach and help out in whatever way they could. The school was a simple building with very poor resources. If it hadn't been there to serve the community, there would be children who didn't get to go to school or have a regular meal.

Peru is a third world country. They still washed their clothes by hand, and it was rare to have an oven. Some still had to carry water, or take their dishes to a stream to wash them. The electricity was very primitive. A lot of women still wove their own fabric and wore traditional dresses. The men wore more of a loose cotton shirt and pants. I did notice that some of the teenagers wore jeans, but traditional clothing was the norm.

The school was where I met the people who I would have synchronistic events later on in the trip. **It is truly amazing when you get to see how the choices you make creates a ripple of events to happen. Things that couldn't have happened had you not had that one experience, met that one person, or gone to that one place. That is when you see how the Universe's divine intelligence works, and how guided you truly are.**

One of the women who worked at the school and I became friends. The first time she walked with me through town, a man from the other side of the road kept pointing at me while yelling. I had no idea what he was saying so I tried not to pay attention. When he saw no reaction, he started coming across the street still pointing and talking very loudly. Finally, Anna interceded. She told him I didn't know Quechua. He would need to tell her what was wrong, so she could explain for him. He told her that there were some very bad people here and I needed to be careful walking the streets. He explained that he was from the Sacred Valley and he felt he needed to warn me because he could see my light. He told me I needed to guard it, or hide it, so it didn't attract attention. I didn't know what to say besides thank you and that I acknowledged what he had to say. It was beginning to carry the theme of my son's words. I made up my mind that on this trip I would put up protection until I felt comfortable, and then, and only then, would I put it down and relax. I would be mindful, and aware of my surroundings.

Putting up protection can be done in many ways. I will share some of the ways I do it for myself through the thought process of imagining.

- In one, I put a bubble of rainbow light around me, and fill the bubble with cosmic love. The bubble creates a barrier

that holds the energy of the cosmic love, creating one of the strongest protections you can use.

-Another could be to bring a pillar of light down around you, connecting you to both the Father, which is Cosmic, and the Mother, which is Earth. Its power is in the knowing that you are in a tube filled with their love for you that keeps you connected, and protected by those energies.

-A third way is to just emanate pure love from every cell of your being. Love is the ultimate superpower.

-You can also call in your Angels and Archangels for protection.

There are many more ways, but these are the main ways that I use.

CHAPTER 115

Macha Pichu & Sacred Valley by Horseback

I WAS SO surprised to hear that my friend, Angela, from Canada, was going to be in Peru with a group. Angela and I have a very strong connection and we seem to randomly meet up all over the planet. I guess you could say that we often times seem to be on parallel paths. We were able to get ahold of one another and meet for breakfast in a really sweet restaurant that catered to foreigners. She was traveling with a group of young adults that were feeling the call there, and we promised to meet up again before we left. There were several people in her group that I felt pulled to meet. Before the end of the trip, I felt we would all converge. I just didn't know at the time that it would be sooner, rather than later.

Our group finally came together and I was soon to see that we had a guide that was here to make sure that we were going to pack in as much as we possibly could. She was very connected to Peru and had Peruvian Shamans, as well as a couple of locals who worked with her to set everything up. I loved that she got local people involved. I also loved that what we were doing was prospering different towns and farmers.

Our first stop would be Macha Pichu. It was incredibly majestic and I could have stayed there all day just to be in the beauty. Everyone was running around babbling about how high the energy was there, and how powerful it was. I was surprised because I couldn't feel a thing. I was starting to see that on this trip that I was going to do it in a more normal fashion. There was very little seeing, feeling or hearing. It was like I was completely cut off from my inner guidance. Only, very rarely, did I get anything communicated to me.

Our group seemed more interested in watching the Shamans make their despachos (A Peruvian Shaman's way of building an offering with a prayer to Pachamama) then tuning within to see what they felt. But then perhaps that is what the guide was trying to give us all a taste of. She was bringing us a Peruvian experience. I really didn't like to watch the making of the despachos. It was a long and boring process and I'm not one to sit still for very long, especially within repetitious rituals. Usually, I chose to take off and explore the land while they did it.

The main part of this tour was a horseback ride through Sacred Valley. It had been more than a few years since I had ridden a horse, but it was definitely not new to me. However, riding a horse adapted to Peruvian sizes was a whole new ball of wax. They were very small people so you couldn't get your feet into their stirrups and the saddle was meant for a little person. It was extremely uncomfortable, and we were skirting mountain trails with a pretty good drop to one side. I'm afraid of heights, so I felt as if I were holding my breath constantly.

During the trek up to the campsite, it started to hail. Luckily, we had stopped to have lunch in a big tent, so we weren't out riding during the worst of it. It was pretty neat how they had a full stove set up and tents to go into while we waited it out. I'm pretty sure the horses were glad for the rest as well. The meal they had prepared was amazing, but I didn't have much of an appetite. My stomach started acting up almost right from the beginning of this trip.

The hail wasn't letting up much, and at some point, they had to make an executive decision to get started again. We couldn't afford to get stuck halfway up the mountain in the dark, so off we went. The poor horses were slipping and sliding all over the place. All I could do was to try and work through the immense fear that was beginning to well up in me. At one point, one of the women slid off her horse and said she couldn't do it anymore. She wanted to walk the rest of the way.

I looked ahead where it was getting backlogged with horses. It was at a place where we needed to go down a very narrow trail and make a corner at the same time. It was right at the edge of the cliff. The person in front of me started sliding, and that was it for me. I was starting to jump off my horse, when one of the guides grabbed the halter and yanked the horse down and around to the level part of the cliff again. I thought I was going to pass out and pee my pants! I don't think I have ever been so tested in one of my fears! I made a solemn vow that I would never do a horseback ride through mountains again!

Farther ahead, there was another stop when they came across a cow that had just given birth. The poor little calf laid directly across our path, so one of the men had to pick it up and carry it back to the scared mother. All the delays created us not being able to get to the campsite before nightfall. As the sun started setting, we had to dismount and walk the rest of the way. It was actually dangerous for us to ride any longer. Thank God there were a few flashlights in the group! Around an hour later, we finally reached camp. We were wet, cold and hungry, but at least we didn't have to crawl like the two ladies that had abandoned their horses. They couldn't see the tracks to follow anymore, so they had to crawl and feel them until they made it to the camp.

When we got to the campsite, they had the tents up. The guides ushered us in two to a tent and brought us a big bowl of steaming hot soup to keep us from getting even colder. There was still hail on the ground, and it was a miserable night of fitful, shivering, sleep. In the middle of the night, I unconsciously sat straight up and screamed "I hate this Godforsaken place!" My poor tentmate. Between the screaming and her waking up with me almost on top of her to glean a bit more warmth, I'm sure she wondered what she was in for.

The next morning, I slipped out of the tent to find the make shift bathroom. Not surprisingly, there was still hail on the ground. As I scanned the surroundings, I feasted on one of the most beautiful vistas I could have ever imagined. It literally took my breath away! No wonder they named it Sacred Valley. It almost made up for the extremely cold sleep that night. Unfortunately, I was so exhausted from trying to get warm, that I decided to stay back alone at camp that day. I needed to rest. The others would be gone for the day doing ceremony with the Shaman.

That was one of the few times that I had some guidance during the whole trip. That morning, as I got ready for the day, the voice came in and told me that under no circumstances was I to let the head Shaman tap into me, or work on me. Well, I guess that wouldn't be too hard to follow, I just wouldn't go near him. That morning, after everyone left, my stomach began churning. It was the start of a forty-five-pound weight loss program that I hadn't signed up for. The toilet became my best friend for the rest of my time in Peru. I made sure I knew how to say bathroom in every language that came at me! I'm not sure exactly how or what I had picked up, but I had a feeling that the campfire cooking may have had something to do with it.

After everyone came back from the ceremony, the head Shaman came over to me. It was easy to see that his ego had been bruised because I hadn't been part of the ceremony. I guess the others had laid on a giant rock one by one, while he did a healing on them. In sign language, he told me that he was going to come to my tent that night to do a healing for me. I kept shaking my head no and he kept nodding yes. Finally, I had to go to the leader and tell her what my guidance had said. I asked if she could have a talk with him since he wasn't listening to me. After that, he kept his distance.

At the end of the horse tour, we stopped at the guide's hometown. As we rode in, most of the people who lived in the village were gathered in what seemed to be the town square. As soon as they saw us coming near, they welcomed us with a band playing their traditional music. We sat and listened as they asked us to spread the word of their beautiful country so that more people would come to visit. They were looking at ways for their town to prosper. I gained a lot of respect for our guide as I saw his true intent was to help his community out of poverty. You could feel the love he carried for his people. I was also amazed at the complicated networking of farmers who rented their horses out for the trip. It wasn't like there was one person with all the horses, there was one or two horses per farmer. What a feat to coordinate all of this, and gather all the help needed to pull it off.

One of my favorite things was when our guide took us to meet his grandmother. He told us that he often stayed there. It wasn't hard to tell that she meant the world to him. The house they shared was incredibly sweet and primitive. In this part of the country, they still lived on dirt floors with old woodstoves to heat and cook on. The stove was heating the cold and damp air, as animals chased one another through the house and into the courtyard. The walls looked as if it had been decades since they had seen the end of a paintbrush. There was the peeking of cement under the peeling paint making a contrast of color everywhere you looked. My favorite place in the house was the alter honoring Mother Mary that they used for their prayers. It was in a room all its own. The people here may have been very poor, but you could tell they were happy, proud, and had a beautiful spirit.

One of the most unusual things that happened in this group was when we were taken to a ninety-year-old woman's home. We were there to experience a group session with her channeling the spirit of a particular mountain. They led us into the basement of the house where she and her sons lived. The sons invited us to sit on boards supported by concrete blocks. As we all got settled in, they turned the lights off. We were told to be quiet while she contacted the mountain spirit. It was so dark in the basement you couldn't see your hand in front of your face. After about ten minutes, you could hear pop bottles popping their tops off. It was like the bottles had been shaken and now they were exploding. Everyone was jumping because of all the noise and getting hit by bottle caps. They also had warned us that she would throw down rocks when a spirit would come in to contact her. After throwing several rocks down, it felt like she was fizzling out. After a bit if silence, she said she was just too tired. She was angry at her sons for being lazy and not helping her out enough. It made me laugh. I guess even mountain spirit channelers have to deal with everyday life.

The next day, we took off on a boat tour across Lake Titicaca where the Uros islands are located. The islands are entirely made of reeds, and were born out of necessity. When the area was being invaded by the conquistadors, there were Peruvians who went far out on the lake to escape. They began to create floating islands that were made by weaving the lakes abundant supply of reeds together. Each island was anchored into the lake floor by ropes twisted from reed fibers which were tethered to posts made from native trees. The ropes had to be replaced every year, so at various times during the year, the women gathered to replenish the tethers that held their islands in place.

There were many small islands hooked together that supported around twenty people. Each cluster created different communities of islands. Every family had a private hut, but they shared a common bathroom and kitchen. Their diets consisted of whatever they could harvest from the lake. I did, however, notice more than a few chickens running around, so felt they also bartered on the mainland at times. I was bothered that tourism was beginning to change their pristine island communities. It felt disturbing and invasive like introducing someone to candy when they had lived off the land and had a pure diet. I was amazed at how well they existed outside of the modern world, even though you could see that tourism was starting to have an influence.

I was surprised and saddened at how much pollution there was there. Because of outside influence, this once pristine land now had trash that wasn't decomposing. I saw a lot of plastic starting to amass as well as disposable diapers. You could find them laying everywhere. They were even dumped into their beautiful lake. The air quality was even harder on my physical body than the parasites. It was over-the-top at times, and I really found it taxing on my already strained lungs that were trying to fight off a bad cold and infection.

My favorite part of the tour with this group was visiting the Island of Amenti. The Native people there were really friendly and the air was clean because they had no cars. Getting to our quarters was a very strenuous uphill walk, but I just went at my own pace. It was here, that I had one of my few spiritual experiences. As I was walking the pathways around the island, a voice came in and called me Appu and told me this was once my home. Appu is what they called someone that carried spiritual knowledge for a village. The voice said that in that lifetime when I died, I was buried into the face of the cliff overlooking the water. Placed below in the water where I was buried, lay a huge golden solar sun disc. A vision began to unfold showing how I and a group of people had levitated the disc into the water for safe keeping many hundreds of years ago to keep it away from the invaders. After the vision faded, I saw a spaceship hover in and bring the disc out of the water. It was then activated with audible tones and placed back down into the water. I could hear low, harmonious tones sound from the disc for several hours after, then it went still. I figured that because it had been shown to me, that this had to be another collecting of my past life energies, and/or an activation of some kind.

The bulk of the rest of my stay was to be in Puno. When we got there, I made a decision that I couldn't go with this group anymore. My health wasn't going to allow it. Angela could feel that I was in distress and offered to have me come stay with her for a while. I decided to jump ship and stay with Angela where things were more laid back and serene. She was traveling with a beautiful group of light workers who were very even-keeled and going with the flow. It was there that I met Mara, a beautiful young woman from Ireland, who I would, like Angela, keep meeting up with all around the globe. I also met a talented musician and his girlfriend, Dana, an amazing free spirit who I would be traveling with for the next stage of my journey.

Their group was going to Bolivia and they invited me to go with them. Unfortunately, I was so sick that I knew if I didn't lay low for a while and just sleep, I would end up in the hospital. I slept for five days straight. By the time they got back, I was finally strong enough to start out again. I went with their group to explore a few places like Urubamba & Pisac, where we stayed at a beautiful sanctuary. There I experienced the second panic attack of my life. I felt so incredibly out of place, vulnerable and alone, traveling with this group of young people that had a far different lifestyle. I decided to take off on my own to an island called Amantine. It felt like a good way to tune into the water, and give me a quiet stay for a few days. Hopefully, it would help me get my head on straight again.

Once we docked at Amantine, I was put with a beautiful young host family that had two small daughters. They lived in a very quaint and primitive house with an outside bathroom. The mother had a bad lung and heart condition and I was really surprised when the husband told me in extremely broken English that he knew I was a healer. How, I never understood. He asked me if I could do some healing work on his wife to help her. It was awkward, but of course I honored his request. That night they made me a very special plate of food. It was piled high, even though I had stressed my digestive system was taxed and I couldn't eat much. In Peru, it is very disrespectful to not clean your plate and I knew that there was no way that I could even eat half of what I had been given. While they were in the kitchen getting the rest of the plates, I panicked and scooped half of my plate onto their three-year-old girl's plate. The poor thing just sat there with her eyes wide and her mouth dropped open. I don't know what I was thinking! I'm sure she could tell them, but maybe this way they would think I was trying to share. It never ceases to amaze me the crazy things you do when in a panic.

My most memorable experience was while I was out exploring the island. I was taking a break and sitting on a pebbled beach eating lunch when a woman, who looked to be in her late twenties, came by herding sheep. She motioned for me to come over and sit by her so we could have lunch together. Both of us sat there using sign language to try and get across what we wanted to say. She had a beautiful smile that shone from her eyes, and you could tell she had a good heart. I shared what I had brought to eat and laughed because every time I handed her something, she would take a small nibble and then make a face. I'm sure it tasted way different than any food she was used to. After tasting what I gave her, she would carefully stick the rest in her pocket. I felt she wanted to share it with someone else so they could taste it, too. It was priceless!

Being in a third world country really helps you to see things from a whole different perspective. You begin to see just how privileged we are in America, and yet how disconnected we are from one another. I always tell people that traveling around the globe will open your mind more than school or ordinary life can. I feel it's the best education you can acquire, and worth every penny spent.

CHAPTER 116

Puno: The Pan Flutes

I FINALLY FELT it was time to settle down in one spot. It was time to head back to Puno where I would be spending the eight-week remainder of my stay. I don't know why I felt so pulled to Puno. I'm pretty sure it had more to do with Lake Titicaca. I'm always pulled to the water.

Puno is the pan flute capital of the world, and it doesn't let you forget it. On any given day there is a festival marching down the streets twirling, dancing and making music in their beautiful Native dress. I loved watching it all, but developed a huge dislike for pan flutes. By the end of my time there, after hearing them day in and out, I was at the point of hating them. Whenever another wave of music and celebrations would start, I'd be on the verge of tears.

I mistakenly thought this would be a quiet nurturing, nature place, and instead it was a very loud and obtrusive place. Everywhere you went, there was a huge speaker blasting out a political speech, or loud music blasting as a group of teenagers played ball. There was the constant honking of the cars as they made their way down the streets, and the festivals went late into the night with walking demonstrations that were blocks long. At night, the dogs barked nonstop, with the occasional yelling of a person that was trying to shut them up. In the houses there were televisions on in every room, each on different channels. It was rare that I heard silence.

I made friends with a local tour guide named, Marita, who was a beautiful Soul, and my saving grace. I would go to spend time with her and her family, and it was the only place that I could actually eat without getting sick. I think it was because of all the love she put into the food as she cooked it. She also shared the history of Puno from the books she had written.

We took several day trips to places only locals knew about. Sometimes we would have to catch many different forms of transportation to get where we were going. On one of our trips, we were in a very sparsely populated area by the lake. We had walked miles before the van stopped to pick us up. It was late and we were beginning to wonder if something had happened. As the sun started to hit the horizon, the last van for the day finally showed. Unfortunately, as they opened the door you could see that there was nowhere to sit. A guy quickly hopped out of the van and helped us in. Marita pretty much had to sit on my lap, but at least we didn't have to walk all the way back. I looked around to see where the man had gone who had been so kind as to make sure that we weren't left behind. I soon realized that he had given up his seat and was now riding on top of the van. Talk about bringing chivalry to new heights! I felt terrible that we had unknowingly put him out, and was perplexed that the driver would even let him ride there. I kept sending out protection so he wouldn't fall off.

CHAPTER 117

The 11-11-11 Gateway & Getting Smuggled into Bolivia

ONE OF THE reasons I felt I was in Peru was for the 11-11-11 gateway. After that, I would be going home. Wherever that was meant to be. On 11-10-11, I decided that it was time to go to Bolivia and take a boat out to visit both the Island of the Sun and Moon on Lake Titicaca. I had heard that there were many groups coming from all over the world to meet and do ceremony on the Island of the Sun. That was where I felt I was being called to go for this particular alignment. Making that journey was probably the most in tune and supported part of my whole trip. It was also the scariest.

I knew in order to travel across the border into Bolivia I was supposed to have had certain shots and a Bolivian visa, but I'm not much for planned trips. If I was supposed to go, it would somehow just work out. During the long bus ride from Puno to the Bolivian border, a man came around to check on visas and shot records. After finding out I had neither, he told me that a visa would cost 175 USD, plus I would need to get my shots once I got there. I told him that I didn't have any shots, nor would I allow anyone to give me one. I had just made up my mind to come to Bolivia, so I didn't have a passport and I wouldn't be spending 175 USD. I would just go back when the bus turned around.

He then asked me to come to a private seat. As he sat me down, he said that he would help me get through for 80 USD, but I would need to make sure to be back exactly by 1p.m. two days later. That way he could help me re-enter the bus he would be chaperoning so I wouldn't get caught. He warned me that if I missed the boat and didn't get back in time, we could both end up in prison. It was imperative not to be late. He gave me his name written down on a piece of paper, a return ticket, and the date I'd need to be there for reentry back into Peru, then left.

I exited the bus and quickly located the area the boat would be docking at. Within minutes, two young men walked over and introduced themselves as Leom and Maxi, from Argentina. They asked if I could hold on to their guitar and backpacks while they went to find some food. One felt and looked a bit like my oldest son, Randy, and they both felt to be beautiful heart-centered people, so I told them I would be glad to. People started filtering in behind me as they waited in line for the boat to show up. Evidently, there were a lot of other people being called to come to the Island of the Sun as well. I turned around to see how many people were gathering for the boat ride. Standing not more than two people behind me was one of the women from the school in Cusco named Maia. I could hardly believe it!

It was an awesome ride out to the island on Lake Titicaca. I couldn't get over how huge this lake was! During the ride, I decided that I was not going to carry the stones that I had collected during the trip through Europe anymore. I felt that I had downloaded them and carried their energy within me now. It was time to set them, and the weight of me having to carry them free. I threw the biggest stone out near the Island of the Moon and the second biggest one near the Island of the Sun. I was about to throw the last one in and heard a loud "No, my work is not done yet!" So that one I repacked, agreeing to carry its weight and energy until it had finished what it needed to do.

I'm not sure why, but the boat dropped us off on the south side of the island and we were supposed to be dropped off on the north side. We all came together as a group and hired a lone boater to take us the rest of the way. Thank God we found someone! To make it to the ceremonies by 11:11 the next day, we would have had to walk all night in the dark, up and over mountains.

The north side of the island was extremely beautiful and there was a white sand beach with a very old and poor hotel. Like a lot of hotels on these islands, it had a shared outside toilet. Leom, Maxi, Mia and I decided we were going to travel the island together. We girls decided to share a room and met up with the guys after we got settled in. I was soon to find out that Leom was an amazing singer and musician. I could have listened to him for hours on end. There was no doubt in my mind that he could be famous if that was what he intended to pursue. Music ran in his bloodline. He had a twin brother who was a concert violinist. Leom could play violin, but his talent was in his beautiful voice, which he accompanied with the guitar.

I wished that I had studied Spanish a lot more before I came. I would have loved to have had deep one-on-one conversations with these two amazing men. I was grateful that Maia was able to translate for all of us. It just would have been nice to have a flowing, spontaneous conversation.

Everyone was starving that first night so we decided to check out one of the local restaurants. Little did we know that it would be a whole night affair. After finding a place to sit, two children who looked to be seven and nine came up with notepads to help take our order. Only one order could be made at a time. They'd get their food, then another kid would come up to take the next order, and so on. When it got dark, there were no inside lights except for pop bottles that held a single homemade candle at each table. I am sure that they used a propane stove to cook the orders. That's how most people cooked there. It gave you a huge appreciation for the food that you received.

The next morning, I got up early and tuned in while sitting by the lake. It was odd to me how there were large continuous waves rolling in just like in an ocean. I guess I would liken it to Lake Superior mixed in with a good dose of ocean. I watched as the locals took turns raking the kelp that had washed ashore into piles, and wondered if they ate it or used it to feed their livestock.

The children were running around in shorts and underwear, turning a prized piece of wood that had washed ashore over and over, then flexing their biceps to show how strong they were. Isn't it funny how children's play is so universal? You can plop a kid into any country and they can make friends and play whatever is being presented. Wouldn't it be nice if we could keep that innocence and acceptability as adults?

After breakfast, we all packed up and took off for Puma Rock. That was supposedly where a bunch of the ceremonies were to take place. It was so cute, Leom took my backpack, and Maxi wanted to hold my hand all the way to the top of the mountain. I felt like a little old grandma, but it was very sweet, especially since my altitude sickness was still plaguing me.

There were people from every walk of life on the mountain by Puma Rock, doing every kind of ceremony you could imagine. I even ran into a fellow I knew from Sedona who was with a group of Indigenous Elders. I didn't feel energetically pulled to anyone's ceremony. I felt all I needed to do was to come there with the codes that I carry, tune into the Earth, and send her love. I stayed in my own little world until I felt what I needed to add to the day was done. Then I went back to find our group of four that I had ascended the mountain with. I was in bliss as Leom played and sang his heart out. He shared his gift openly and with joy. What could be better to share with the Earth and humanity? I was grateful that instead of being with a large group for this 11-11-11, I was with three beautiful young Souls who just wanted to share their love and passion with the world.

That night, I said my goodbyes, because I didn't want to wake anyone up as I left the next morning. These guys had really captured my heart, and I was going to miss them a lot! It was such a short time together and I doubted I would ever see them again. The next morning, I got up early to make sure that I didn't miss my boat. Sitting in a Bolivian prison wasn't something I planned on experiencing. I went down by a restaurant with an outside coffee area to wait for the ticket office to open where I ran into a man named Mitch, and his girlfriend, Liane. We had a lot in common and I knew we were supposed to stay connected. I had meant to get their cards so that we could stay in touch. Unfortunately, at some point I figured out that what I thought was the ticketing office actually wasn't, and I had just missed my boat! I went into full panic mode as I ran back to wake everyone up and tell them what had happened. They were dressed and out in a matter of minutes. The three of them ran from place to place trying to help me figure out how to get back in time. As we walked down to the beach, there were two boats filled to the brim with people. I was told that there were no more boats until 1:00 p.m. That meant there was no way I was going to make it back in time. I was in a panic for a bit, and then a calming washed over me.

I began to sense that all this was the way it was supposed to be. I felt that the right solution would present itself. Finally, Maia, Leom and Maxi came over and told me that I was to get in a line with a group from Argentina who were at the beach loading. They had a private boat and were going to see if they could smuggle me on. If the captain asked if I was part of the group and had paid, I was to lie and tell him I had. They took me to the line, gave me a hug goodbye, and were gone. The lady in front of me leaned close and whispered to pretend I was one of them.

I felt terrible lying, but it was better than sitting in a Bolivian prison. Several in the group quickly took me up to the top of the boat and crowded around to hide me. I was very grateful because the captain had kicked several other people off the boat as we were finding our places to sit. It was definitely over legal capacity and sitting low in the water. I prayed a lot during the trip that the boat wasn't going to capsize as the waves rocked us a little more than was comfortable.

The woman who was in front of me in the line was the only person who spoke English, albeit broken. The rest spoke their Native tongue. She came to sit next to me and asked me where I was from. I shared with her that I was from Sedona. She gasped, got up, and took off. I heard her telling people excitedly about what I had said. Pretty soon, a lady came back with her to sit next to me. She was a beautiful lady with long brown hair around thirty-five years old. I assumed that she was the leader of the group. She asked me if I had any connections to Mt. Shasta. I told her that I had stayed there and done many ceremonies on the mountain. Again, she started saying things to people and they were getting very excited and started to gather around.

I was confused and asked her why people were getting so excited and asked her why she was asking me these specific questions? She told me that the group had been led to the Island of the Sun to do ceremony and open Lemurian portals in Peru. They were told that at some point on their journey, they would meet a woman from Sedona who had ties to Mt. Shasta and that would be the signal that they had actualized their work. It also meant that the Eagle and the Condor had come together. They were all elated that it had finally happened.

They asked me why I was there. I explained it all, and told them that my only regret was that I didn't get to visit the Island of the Moon. Two ladies each dug in their pockets and handed me a stone that they had brought back from there and handed them to me. I was so touched. They were such kind and giving people.

We talked and shared for a long time. A message came through to give my amethyst skull to the lead lady. As I handed it to her, she looked shocked, then began crying. After a while, she explained that her grand-mother had a dream before she left. In the dream, she was gifted a skull. When that happened, she was to use it to open and activate the rest of the skulls hidden in Lake Titicaca. She was amazed and grateful. They slowed the boat as they took time to do the ceremony and activate the skulls that were hidden under the surface of the water. After that, everyone broke apart and sat in silence. In that silence, I was tapping into the stress and tiredness of the travel on my body and emotions. The tiredness of traveling on my own.

As I sat there, I noticed three young men who didn't look Argentinian so I went over to see if they knew English. They were from Sweden, Germany and Poland and seemed to be seventeen or younger. I asked them where their parents were. They told me that they had been called to come to the Island of the Sun on their own. At one point in the trip, they had met up with one another. Each of their stories touched me deeply, and I rejoiced in the knowing that our next generation of light workers was falling into place.

When we docked, the group asked if they could honor me with a going away ceremony since I had chosen not to go with them. Forty beautiful people gathered around and sang me a song. Then they gifted me with the stones that they had brought together to represent the Eagle and the Condor. I was very honored, and gave them all a hug as I left to find the bus that was going to save my butt from a Bolivian cell.

CHAPTER 118

Getting Smuggled Back into Peru

WHEN I GOT to the bus, it was pretty stressful. I kept showing men who were there helping with the bus the piece of paper with the name on it. They just kept saying "No, here." The man who had told me that he would give me safe passage through was a no-show. I had to talk to one of the new guys to try to explain what happened. Thankfully, he agreed to help me. Of course, once again for a fee. These guys really had it going on! I told him I would gift him with 20 USD and he agreed to smuggle me back out of the country.

I was put on the bus and told not to move or make a peep. If the guards came in, I was to slide under the seats and be as still as I could. He also told me under no circumstances was I to sign in if asked to. He shut all the curtains and said if anyone heard anything, or saw any movement, that I would be found out. Okay, I got it, be extremely still and quiet. This time around things were a lot scarier. There were numerous guards with guns circling the bus, checking the luggage, and looking for anything that would alert them to something amiss.

The bus was stalled an hour while luggage was looked through and the underside of the bus was checked out. Finally, people started boarding. One girl looked at me puzzled as she walked by and asked out loud "Did you get smuggled on?" I just put my finger up to my lips and asked her to please be quiet. The driver came to me several times asking me who I was, and telling me that I needed to sign a sheet. I kept telling him to talk to the helper. The guards kept going through the luggage as if they were looking for something. Perhaps this was a place that deals with drug smuggling. For some reason, they never came inside the bus to check it out and for that I was extremely grateful!

It was interesting that being in Bolivia was the only time I wasn't sick while on this trip. As soon as I got back to Puno, my digestive woes started wreaking havoc again. By this time, my clothes were loose on me and my hair was starting to get brittle. I knew that there were things I would need to address when I finally made it back to the U.S.

I was excited to come back this last time to Puno because I found out a dear friend, Leslie, whom I knew from Sedona, was going to be there with a group. I was anxious to see someone I knew and loved. Perhaps it felt some semblance to going home. It's funny how so many people would die for a chance to come here, and I was dying to go home and wished that I hadn't decided to come. I guess different strokes for different folks. I would be leaving in a few days on a bus to see the condors. Then it was time to head back to the airport in Lima. It would be a grueling ten-hour trip, and I was beginning to wonder if it was more than I could physically handle at this time.

Before I left, I wanted to find a violin for my daughter. She had said so many times that she wished she had learned, and I really wanted to find her one. The cost of it was far more affordable here in Peru, and it would be something special that I could bring back. Marita was going to show me all the shops that sold instruments, but once I went into them, I didn't really know what to look for. I didn't want to buy a piece of junk. I didn't know a single thing about them. I decided to wait and think it through.

On the way back to the hotel, I was grabbed from behind. As I turned around, I was in utter shock! It was Maxi! He grabbed my hand and led me back to Leom and Mia. They explained that they felt our time together wasn't done yet, so they decided to come to Puno and find me. They wanted to spend the last few days with me before I had to leave. It was a wonderful surprise!

I actually got Leom some gigs with a couple groups of people who would pay him. He lovingly offered to help me pick out a violin for Paige. Leom played the violin so beautifully that he drew crowds wherever we went to look. I was so grateful for his help. It meant a lot that he had a hand in picking out Paige's new instrument. I would never forget all the beautiful synchronistic events that took place with these three.

I am constantly astounded at how everything is connected energetically. As I went through to edit this part of my writing, I received a message on my phone with a link sent to me from Leom. He put one of his songs on YouTube that he wanted to share. We haven't talked for five years, and on this day, as I'm writing this, he sends it. :)

CHAPTER 119

Time to go Home!

IT LOOKS LIKE I wasn't the only one sick. There were three people in Leslie's group that ended up in the hospital with their leader in really bad shape as well. Leslie took one look at me and said that she was leaving early and thought I needed to go with her. I couldn't argue. She brought me to a ticketing office and bought me a one-way plane ticket to Lima with her. There was no way I would have made it on a ten-hour bus ride through the mountains. Thank God she intervened! I also never would have made it through the airport without her because I was in the bathroom, more than I was out of it. She was truly an Angel.

When I finally landed in Minneapolis, I could have kissed the ground! Paige picked me up from the airport and after taking one look at me, she exclaimed "Oh my God, Mom! What the hell happened to you?" It took a long time to be able to eat normal again. For the first time in my life, I got fungus in some of my toenails. My skin blistered and peeled over every square inch of my body, including the top of my head. I had to take steps to get rid of the parasites, and six years out I was still cutting the repercussion of this trip out of my hair.

To this day, I still don't think I understand what all went on within that trip, but it did forever change me. I had a lot more appreciation for my ease of life. I also appreciated not living in a third world country. Although it was a very hard trip, it didn't take long to understand that the gifts I gleaned from it were plentiful:

-I gained an even greater appreciation for my children and family.

-My detachment found its balance and that was an amazing gift in itself.

- I lost my need or want for material things.

-I don't have as many pulls to do things that aren't aligned with my heart.

-I felt and understood the common thread we all carry no matter who we are and where we live. We all just want to be loved and feel like we have purpose. We all want to be healthy, happy and experience freedom.

-I learned that what someone projects themselves to be, doesn't necessarily mean that's what or who they are.

-I now honor that my intuition is keen, and I should listen to it.

-I learned that thoughts of lack consciousness, creates more lack consciousness, putting you in a prison of your own making.

-I am always better off going where I am pulled to in my heart. Otherwise, there is an opportunity for a lesson to come around and show you how that choice negates your true happiness.

-That following my heart is where I feel the raising of energy and nourishment for my Soul.

-If you allow yourself to become vulnerable and speak from your heart, it touches people deeply and changes who they are.

- I saw how people changed just by being with me, and in turn their beautiful energy changed me. It didn't matter how famous, wealthy, or beautiful I was. It only mattered that I was willing to go and share who I was from my heart.

CHAPTER 120

Kauai: Government Interference, Storms & Sickness

I SPENT SEVERAL months in Minnesota with my family and friends and then I flew back to Sedona to spend time with Dana and all the people I knew there. I was beginning to feel that Sedona would always be a base where I spent time, but pretty soon it would no longer be where I lived.

Even though Dana and I were no longer together as a couple, I still felt he held a huge grounding for my physicality on the Earth. We would probably always be connected. Dana was one of those people who you could be gone from forever and still be just as close when you came together again. He's always felt to be a very intricate part of my life, whatever the part he played in it. I honestly think he knows me better than anyone ever has and sometimes I wonder if he knows me better than I know myself.

Iris and I were getting the message that it was time to start opening the Cities of Light. The first one would be in Sedona, the second Kauai, and the third Glastonbury, England. Both Iris and I knew a lot about Sedona, but we didn't know anything about Kauai. I decided that it was time to go and visit a friend so that I could scope things out for the upcoming trip.

Kauai feels to be a mixture of beauty and raw nature. It was apparent why they called her "The Grandmother." Her land feels ancient. It is amazing how much natural food grows there, and how different it tastes when you pick it fresh verses letting it ripen on the way to the grocery store. You could actually live off the land here with no problem at all. And with all those crazy ass chickens running around that had swam ashore from a boat when it sank, it would be a very balanced diet at that.

It confused me that there were a lot of free medical and dental clinics popping up all over the island put on by the military. It had been going on for about a month, and I couldn't help but wonder what the ulterior motive was. Kauai seemed to have a lot of things going on, which became apparent as I got out on the roads and met the locals. They were fighting against a huge Monsanto company that had its headquarters on the southern tip of the island. Sadly, everything was dead for miles around it including the ocean. They had a government that was trying to get rid of the people living off the land by tearing out and destroying any food sources that didn't belong to a private party. The Native people were trying to get back their land that had been sold off and reclaim their sovereignty. And the Marines were playing war games offshore using sonar that was literally exploding the insides of dolphins, whales and other marine life. It really sickens you when you see the pristine beauty of Kauai being destroyed by the government that was supposed to serve and protect them. The greed of the seed and chemical companies and how they affected Kauai, was just as sickening.

It made me think of Atlantis. Atlantis was a group of people, who used technology that wasn't created through the vibration of love, causing a shut down on the planet and her people. What they experimented with created a spiral of destructive energy that had cataclysmic repercussions. That is one of the times that great floods occurred, wiping out most of humanity.

While staying at Tiffany's Goddess temple in Kauai, I was invited to help out with a group of women who were there to do a long retreat. It is where I met Laurie Reyon and Master Cat Puddah, Grandma Chandra and her mom Cat, and Judith Moore. They had put a large retreat together and were smack dab in the middle of the temple while I was there. It was intriguing to meet this group of women and through them I met two of the people who would always mean a lot to me. Jennifer McLean, who has an internet show called Healing with the Masters, and Mary Hall, who is an incredible abundance coach. We instantly became friends and I was invited out onto a Napoli coastline boat tour. Unfortunately, that ended abruptly after we came across a dead woman floating in the water. She had been swept away trying to cross a river while on a hike that I had earlier declined.

I also ended up running smack dab into Liane who was the woman I had met on the Island of the Sun. I hadn't been able to get their contact information because I'd missed my boat. What a coincidence! I guess if you are supposed to be connected, the Universe makes sure that it happens.

A string of very powerful storms raged through the island and caused a lot of destruction while I was there. Wouldn't you know it would happen while I was camping! I thought I'd be scared to death, but it was actually amazing being so connected to the Earth during the storms. It poured for ten days straight and felt like a huge clearing was taking place. One of the last nights of the storms, Grandma Chandra woke us all up and urged us to pray or the storms would continue in severity and loss of life would occur. It didn't take long for everyone to gather and try and help weaken the storms that were racking the island. The next day, things finally calmed.

During this trip, Mara and Angela were both there. It is so odd how we keep ending up at the same places without even planning it. We were able to get together and kayak down one of the fresh water rivers. At one point we found a wonderful swimming hole and decided to do some cliff jumping. Even though I was really afraid of heights, I climbed to the top of the cliff. Then I froze. All I could hear was a lot of yelling to jump so I could conquer my fear. I finally jumped in at the same time holding hands with Mara. Unfortunately, she landed on top of my shoulders. As I struggled to come to the surface, I swallowed a bunch of river water into my lungs. I was in bed for ten days with a high fever and thought I was going to die.

It was here where I finally saw how I didn't honor my fears and limitations. **There are two types of fears. One is there to keep you safe and it is wise to listen to. The other is unfounded and good to work through so you could move forward in life. I was learning a lot of hard lessons around which was which.**

As soon as I gathered the resources that I needed for the Kauai City of Light opening, it was time to go back to Sedona and get ready for the group from Holland. The first City of Light was ready to be opened.

CHAPTER 121

Sedona City of Light: Survival Programming & Two of Me

IT IS HARD to describe what a City of Light actually is, but this is how I understand it. Each place that a City of Light is to be activated is near water so that the water is encoded with its frequencies. Within each of these places, a huge pillar of light is placed that raises and activates the frequency of the land and all who come into its field. Because of the frequency that it holds, it can be a connecting place for humans, Star Beings, Middle Earth Beings, Mythical realms, and Elementals. When people come to visit the area, they can feel that there is a notable difference in the vibration. You can tell, because things feel clearer there, and you can connect to your guidance more easily. Physical things also look more colorful and vivid. One becomes activated with energy that will awaken them to the truth of their birthright. It awakens the divinity that they have always carried within them. The hope is that we, as a whole, can wake up from the slumber that we have been programmed with. Then we can create and live

from the heart. Hopefully bringing peace, harmony, abundance, and love together as we create with our multi-dimensional, multi-faceted self.

Once we come into understanding the truth of who we really are, and heal what has become out of balance, we begin to open that healing up to others around us. Soon, we understand ourselves to be Universal citizens instead of just Earth citizens. At that point, we begin to use our gifts and abilities to work together. And when we are ready, and the timing is right, we will be reunited with our Star and Inner Earth Lineages. City of Lights are in place to help create an upward spiral of frequency for the Earth and Humanity. Anchoring in these City of Lights would eventually alleviate war and hunger, bring in oneness instead of separation, and create living from the heart, new ways to teach, free technology, a much-needed cleaning up of the Earth, and much, much more.

I feel each City of Light will become an actualized place that we can see with our eyes but it will be further into the future before that aspect of it will be able to physically manifest. I could see the beautiful crystalline structures as if they were already there, and it was hard on me to finally understand that it couldn't happen until humanity was ready for it to happen. Each time a City of Light is opened, it triangulates with the others. It then creates amplification for the Earth's field of energy to occur. It also anchors a grid in place. That anchor holds the energy for rebuilding humanity around the world.

Each of the first three places that we opened had a keeper for its blueprint. Once I would ask the Universe for help that I wanted to find the blueprint keeper, the identities would start coming to me through different people who lived in the area. For Sedona, it was a couple who were in their late eighties. The husband had died, but his wife showed me the physical blueprints and was keeping vigil until it could be anchored in.

I found from the start that doing this work can be a huge challenge. Wherever someone is out of alignment, or hasn't fully realized their power and potential, it is brought fully into the light for everyone to see. It is also an amazing privilege and can help each participant to evolve at a far quicker pace. If you can use it as a tool to help you see things about yourself, it can be wonderful. But more often than not, people don't care to see what they don't want and aren't ready to acknowledge. That usually meant an intense time of processing with the group and within ourselves. There always seemed to be this period of adjustment that we needed to work through and clear, so that each of us could hold the energy needed to do the opening. Both Iris and I were getting tired of feeling like we had to do so much processing. It was exhausting! Now as I look back, I can see it was also a clearing for what was residing in the collective consciousness within humanity. Back then I didn't feel I was able to understand this clearly.

It seemed to be my piece to find whoever held the blueprints for each City of Light, as well as put the lodging and logistics into place. I also needed to feel into where it was to be anchored. Iris was the computer expert who did the flyers, channeled the Star Beings, and brought in the outside information that was pertinent to the opening. We definitely didn't have a set agenda. It seemed like it was to unfold day-by-day, and hour-by-hour so that we wouldn't get our heads into it and screw it up by projecting what needed to happen.

There was a defining theme for each opening. The Sedona City of Light themed around mind control and expansion within each individual as well as the collective. It also addressed the fear of money and death. To me, it made sense, because how could we create a New Earth within the old ways of separation, survival, and lack? Each time a City of Light was in the process of being opened, it seemed to have someone challenge where it was to be placed, and someone who was there to sabotage it from being opened by causing dissent within the group. It was very interesting to watch it play out.

In Sedona, I felt a lot more Galactic interaction guiding us. Perhaps that was because it was our first one and we were unsure of ourselves. At one point, we were guided to go to Montezuma's Well. On the way in, we were greeted with a circular rainbow around the sun. It was surreal with all the colors, and yet in the middle, it was crystal clear. When we stopped to check in, we were told that it held codes that would be downloaded into us. You could feel the codes filtering into your body as you stood there.

Montezuma's Well is a very special place. It is said to be the where the Root Race emerged out of the water and traveled to the four corners of the Southwest. It is also where Native people come to collect water for their ceremonies. There are deep caves that were used by the Native people to live in, but were now blocked off. One of the participants was being contacted by an Inner Earth person who asked for her to meet up with him in one of the caves. We watched out for forest service workers while she jumped into the cave and went searching for the voice that was guiding her. This Inner Earth Being would have influence with our group through all of the openings.

There were eight women and one man participating for this opening. It took about five days to help everyone work through their programming, baggage, and belief systems. Doing this work is incredibly freeing, but never fun. We finally came to a place where we knew we had raised our vibrations high enough. It was time to open our first City of Light. We were all out on a large expanse of red rock, in the middle of the creek, where we created a small altar and cleared one another and the area. Then we were guided through channeling from the Galactic, Earth and Middle Earth Beings. We sang and drummed while we called forward all our guiding energies to unify as one, and anchor the energies needed for the City of Light opening. It was incredibly beautiful to be part of. At the end, I felt an ancient Star Being come into one of the women participants. I could see her starting to hunch her back and her fingers were becoming all gnarled and crooked. I knew that it was her Galactic self, and that it was here to thank and honor us for the work we did. As I studied her, she began talking in a language I had never heard before. It almost sounded like a form of Chinese with clicking overtones as it was being said. Even though none of us could understand, the energy behind the words were captured by us all.

After it was all done, we placed two Gatekeepers (In this case, they were Beings from another dimension.) to make sure that the City of Light was protected, then went back to our home away from home to celebrate.

The next morning, I woke up and went out on the balcony to have a quiet moment and connect to the river. I was confused when I heard a woman at the edge of the property calling out my name to a woman across the creek. I couldn't figure out who she was yelling at. When I looked, I realized the person across the creek was me. How could that be? When my double saw me on the balcony looking at her, she hid behind a tree. I rushed downstairs to try and get a closer look. The participant was still calling out to her to see how she had made it over there. When she saw me walking over to her, she looked very confused, and asked me how I was able to get back over here so quickly. We both turned back to get one more look at the other side of the creek, but there was no longer anyone there.

I couldn't for the life of me figure out what was going on! All I knew is that I definitely felt different energetically after the opening. I could feel I was experiencing everything around me a lot more intensely. I also felt like my heart had doubled in size. I was incredibly sensitive to energy that was of a lower frequency and found myself to be easily overwhelmed. Even walking on the sidewalk with cars driving by, felt like an assault on my physical body that threw me into a panic. It literally felt like they were driving right through me!

Later that day, I had to drive Iris and Mara up to the grocery store. We needed a few things to finish up meals for the rest of the stay, and I was the only one legal to drive a car. I pushed the cart while they went off in different directions to gather what we needed. Before long, they both came hurrying back to tell me that they saw me in different aisles and I needed to bring the other "Me's" back in, before people figured out what was going on. I went to the edge of my auric field and began to bring it in. It must have worked, because there were no more extra Me's running around the grocery store. It took months to smooth out and integrate the new energy that was creating havoc with my body. It didn't feel to be good or bad, it was just harder to navigate any kind of normalcy. Why, or how it happened, I wasn't 100% sure. It had to have been because of the frequencies that had bathed me for the whole week. When you raise your frequencies significantly, unexplainable things can, and often do happen.

CHAPTER 122

Kauai City of Light: Connecting Back to Nature

THE SECOND OPENING was in Kauai. Once again, I found the blueprint keepers and they were a beautiful elderly couple who were ninety and had lived on Kauai for many years. This City of Light opening was about a reconnection back to the Earth Mother/Nature, and knowing that each of us is fully supported by the Earth with food, shelter, oxygen, water, and medicine. We were shown that everything is provided by her for our survival and is given freely. She was asking us to understand the symbiotic relationship nature had to offer. Each of us was asked to connect back to the land that we live on and remember to commune with her. She also asked that we work on seeing a "thrive, instead of survive, synergy" with nature fully supporting us.

Again, we were asked to clear our energy so that our frequencies could be raised to a sufficient frequency. After everyone had worked through their belief systems, programming and baggage, we were to tune into the aquatic life that lived in the ocean. We were told that the dolphins and whales were our brothers and sisters from Sirius. It was important for us to understand that they fed and cleared the lay lines under the oceans with their energy. They were also very intelligent and high vibrating Beings. They were asking for our help raising the frequency of the water because of the pollution and sonar, as well as the war games that were played out off the shore of Kauai.

This was an opening that was to be simple and organic. We had six women and again, one man. At the opening nine more joined us; four men, three women, plus two female harpists. It was a beautiful ceremony on a beach, where we were guided to lay in a circle with our crowns facing one another. All that we were asked to do was to allow the energy that was being sent from the Universe to run through us like a sieve. When it finally slowed and quit, it was our signal that it was done. The animals are always a good gauge for knowing that. As soon as the energy quit, the dolphins started jumping, a bird flew across us calling out, and a turtle strolled out of the ocean and sauntered near us. The energy shifted when it started sprinkling, and the waves started crashing over us creating a spiral of laughter that was easily reignited. We could all hear the beautiful harps and voices from the sidelines. It was like we were being serenaded by the Angels. It couldn't have been more organic or beautiful.

After everything was finished up, we all decided to take a ride on a sailboat. We wanted to connect with the dolphins in a more natural setting. Being on and in the water is a great way to set everything in that we had gained by doing the activation of the City of Light. While we were out on the boat, we began to hear a loud siren going off on the captain's radio. It was sounding a warning to a boat that was anchored offshore. It was right in an area that the government was targeting to send a missile. Obviously, docking the boat there was an attempt to stop it.

Almost as soon as the siren went off, there were several submarines that began to emerge from the depths of the ocean. We saw six of them in a very short span of time. They seemed to be from all over the world. One I knew was from Russia because of the markings on its side. The captain shared with us that sometimes they used the waters off the shores of Kauai for testing their missiles as well as sonar testing. Unfortunately, many felt it was causing great harm to the aquatic life. He said that there were people who knew about it and used their boats to stop it when they could.

Dolphins began to swim beside the boat and flying fish flew behind us in massive schools. It was incredible, but hard to be joyful when you knew what was happening to them. We all sent love and peace for the beautiful Beings that inhabited the oceans. We also sent prayers of healing for the people who lived on these beautiful islands. We prayed for an end to the bombardment of man-made disruption and ignorance. It made me even more grateful that we were doing the work we were doing. Just imagine how incredible it would be to have a balanced society, where people lived from the heart.

Unfortunately, during this opening, there was a rift created between Iris and myself that we just couldn't seem to be able to work through. It was to be a clearing within each of us that would take years to come to terms with. The next City of Light was done on my own, and I can say it sure would have been easier with her help. I could definitely see the unique gifts that both Iris and I brought to the table. I could also see why we were brought together to do the openings. Unfortunately, sometimes there needs to be disruption in order to see clearly and to be able to change and grow.

CHAPTER 123

Glastonbury City of Light: Crop Circles, Giants & The Dark Attempt

THE THIRD OPENING was in Glastonbury, England. Like I said previously, Glastonbury is like Fairytale land. You see everything you can imagine there, just like you were reading a book of lore. Besides the

Fairytale feel, there is the overtone of Druidism, King Arthur, Lancelot and the Grail Knights, and the Holy Family. It was far from a normal town. I've heard that Glastonbury, Sedona and Kauai were sister cities and it isn't hard to see that they have a similar energetic feel to them. I also thought it interesting that they were the first three to be opened.

This opening was to center around magic and folklore. It was about calling in the multi-dimensional self and bringing it into wholeness through the physical body and experience. It was also about merging back together with all of the Beings who have walked the Earth before us; forward and backward in time. Within that, one can jump timelines and gain information from their other aspects to help them within any point in this lifetime. It is becoming the diamond embodiment of the Hu Man, or God man. The Hu Man creates through the one heart and mind and weaves joy and magic back into their life. It was also about bringing all worlds together with openness and tolerance for each individuals way of existing without judgement, as are all a spark of the Divine.

I was told that for this City of Light, we would be working more closely with the Middle Earth people and that there would be a crop circle that would be created specifically for the opening. Glastonbury's opening was far different as there was a lot of travel before and after in order for it to be actualized. I first needed to travel to Ireland where I would meet up with Mara and stayed in her family home that lay on the bay in Calamara. I loved Ireland with its rolling hills, mysterious moors, and earthen bogs. It had such a magical feel to it. You could literally still feel the "Fair Folk" here in the ancient trees and lands that still held the ways of old.

While walking across one of the beaches, I started having terrible crushing pain in my chest. It was so bad that I had to stop walking. It felt like what I would have imagined a heart attack to feel like. I dropped down onto the ground and closed my eyes to ease my breathing, and started to see a picture unfold within my inner vision. I was being shown a Vikings boat coming on shore during the night and attacking the village that once stood there. People were being slaughtered. The village was plundered and burned, and the women raped and kidnapped. I asked for the physical pain to lessen from my heart and knew that I was being called to clear the imprint from the land and help those to cross over that had been trapped here. As Mara and I worked on releasing the imprinting of the violence, and helped the ones trapped to leave, the pain began to fade away.

I then began feeling the heart ache of the mother whales and was shown the babies that had been washing up on shore. Their delicate little systems were being affected by all the pollution and sonar that the government used in their submarines. We were asked if we would program some water with a high frequency and deposit it at different places around the bay. Perhaps with a rising of the frequency, there would be a reprieve for these amazing little Beings and all the rest of the aquatic life that was being so stressed.

It saddened me to think that we were doing such awful things to these innocent Beings. It always hurts my heart as to how unconscious, we as a people, have become. Sometimes it is hard for me to be shown things, especially things like this. **How did humanity get so desensitized and disconnected? How were we ever to clean up all the harm to the planet and our children that we have done? We have not been good stewards of the planet. We seem to have lost our way. Was it possible for humanity to wake up and come out of its slumber before the seriousness of what was being done becomes irreversible?**

There were certain places we were to visit and Mara was the perfect guide to where those places were. The one that was calling the most was called the Cat Stone. We were being called to do ceremony there. It was way out in the middle of a field. Once we got there, we saw that there was a herd of about 30 cows lying down scattered around the pasture. They were all female except for one lone, muscular, and very lucky bull. I was amazed as Mara took out her brass singing bowl and started to tone a beautiful Celtic song. The magic began to weave through the air as each of the cows got up one-by-one to make a semi-circle around us. I looked over at Mara and saw that her eyes were closed. She wasn't seeing all the action that her voice was invoking.

When the song ended, she opened her eyes, screamed bloody murder, dropped all she carried behind onto the ground, and ran up onto a big stone. I followed her because I felt the poor cows were scared. I didn't know how they were going to react, especially the bull. I had experienced a run in with a bull before and wasn't taking any chances.

The cows were friendly and I had to move back because they were crowding in and rubbing their heads on my legs. Farther out in the field, the cows began head butting everything Mara had dropped, her purse included. When the keys to the car started to get pushed around, I knew I had to do something. I took my drum and beat it loudly as they backed away from the spilled pile. I quickly picked it all up and ran back up onto the stone.

As we sat there, everything started to settle down, and I began to tune in. I was shown that we needed to bring twelve stones from the site there to help open up the energy at Stonehenge. It would also link Stonehenge back to here. I was told that this was a powerful place for the Druids to do ceremony and was the original Stonehenge. They said it was moved at some point because they were afraid it would be used by dark forces during an unsteady time. We gathered the twelve stones and did a ceremony we were instructed to do. When everything felt done and the cows finally lost interest in us, they filed away to lie down. We quietly asked for protection from the bull, then quickly made our way back to the car.

We spent two days visiting a few more of the ancient rock ceremonial places, then took off for England. I needed to meet up with another lady before the start of the opening. She had been in every one of the openings thus far and held codes for Middle Earth. She would be helping to hold space for the group during the opening.

I met Elayna near Avebury and she showed me around Wiltshire Hill and Long Barrow. They were very interesting places, both vastly different in their energetic feel. At Wiltshire Hill, I could feel the energy tied into cosmic energy. Elayna had been shown a ball of light that went through the fields when she visited there. She said most people think that spaceships are the architects of the crop circles. She had been shown that the balls of light were what had really been creating them.

Long Barrow is where I felt and saw the Giants. They showed me how they came in and out of the ground through an interdimensional doorway there. I saw that Giants were masters of sacred geometry, and created the blueprints for all the sacred places in the area, as well as built them. They also showed that they worked in conjunction with the Star Beings. At that time, I was told that there would be six Giants with us at all times until the opening was completed. They would be our guardians until our work was done. I could hear and feel their footsteps with us as we took off.

That night as I slept, I could literally feel the crop circle that I was told would be for the opening of the City of Light being made. I knew it in every cell of my being upon waking. We drove all over asking if a new crop circle had been found. Everyone assured us that there had never been a crop circle found in October, especially not in late October. They always ended in early September because by then, the crops were harvested. They looked at us like we were crazy, but I wasn't going to let them dampen my knowing that it was somewhere nearby.

Finally, after half a day of searching, we conceded and drove back to Glastonbury. Not more than ten minutes later, Mara got guidance to look on the computer and there it was. The crop circle was an incredibly beautiful and exquisite work of art! By the description of where it was located, it was only about a mile as the crow flies from where we had slept that very night. It wasn't in a field where crops had been planted, it was a field of wildflowers. We hopped back in the car and went to find it.

I had not yet been in a crop circle and can tell you it is probably the highest frequency that I had ever experienced. The crop circle was about the size of a football field. I was fascinated how every flower, grass and plant that was in this field had been bent in one direction or another. Some were laid over closer to the ground, and some had less of a bend. That was how its intricate patterns came to life.

We were very careful to visit the circle causing as little damage as possible. We understood how touchy the farmers were who had this happen on their land with people traipsing through their fields. It was not desirable to have one show up for them. They were bound to lose money on their crops with all the people coming and going. There were crop circles that people never got to see, because as soon as the farmer was aware that he had one in his field, he went out to plow it under. Evidently, that was preferable to having to experience all the people who were avid crop circle followers. They disliked all the people coming and going, especially when they had to walk through other fields to get there. Some of them finally began putting a can out to collect donations instead of trying to fight or control it. People just wanted to experience the energy of the sacred geometry and encoding that the crop circle had to share.

I received the message that this crop circle was the pinnacle of the meeting of the worlds. It was connecting Middle Earth, to Earth, and the Cosmos to Earth. As above, so below. The worlds are coming together and within that, the veils of separation are becoming thinner. The paradigm shift is upon you and polar opposites are integrating and balancing. As the sacred feminine and masculine are becoming balanced and also integrating within each of you.

The seven planets are aligned, as the seven sacred centers come into alignment. Earth is the nucleus for all that is going on. It is she who is leading the way into a vast unknown and unchartered shift in consciousness. For as the world shifts, so does the Universe. This is more than a global shift; it is a universal shift.

What is being experienced now has never been done before. It is unprecedented and not even your Galactic Families can predict the exact outcome. It is why we bow to humanity. The tenacity and velocity in which you move through the energies that flood the Earth is something to marvel at. You have moved through many shifts of energy which has brought much forward to look at and to be healed. This is being done through your lineages and ancestry, as well as your human physical body and state of being.

We support you fully and are always there for anything that you need. We ask you to open your hearts to all energies that are here to support you. The Universe is a kind and loving place, but not many people trust that they are fully supported or feel they deserve it.

After around thirty minutes in the crop circle, I was told to gather small stones from the middle circle to distribute to the City of Light participants. While doing so, I got the message to tell Mara she needed to leave because she was getting overloaded with the energy. I tried, but she said she wasn't ready to go. About fifteen minutes later, the voice came in very strong and told me that if she didn't leave, she would fry her energetic system, so I became a lot more adamant and finally we all left.

Unfortunately, it had already affected her. By the time we got back to our rooms she was incredibly nervous and going into a meltdown. The only thing she could do was to go out and connect to the Earth and run her energy until it felt evened out and clearer. I didn't think she was going to be able to help in the week ahead, but within 24 hours, she had finally gotten on top of it and was able to be of service to the group.

There were eleven women who were to participate in this opening, and how it was possible for each one to carry such different and opposing energies was mind blowing! I have the gift of being able to tell what a person carries as a dominant energy, and we certainly had a variety of energies at work within this group. I saw a Shaman, a Star Being, an Elf Princess with a quiver on her back, a Fairy, a Giant, an Old Sailor, a Rock Being, a Crone, a Priestess, a Dark Sorceress, and a Rainbow Unicorn Rider. How this group was to come together and be unified was beyond me!

The challenge was that for this opening, there were to be no boundaries put into place as to what a City of Light was. I was to help guide the women, but not tell them exactly what their piece was. It was up to them to figure it out. It was like herding cats, and I would never do it again. It was excruciating and exhausting! You see the true depths of how we sabotage ourselves and one another, as well as all the games people play through the stories they are living out. This opening was not for the faint of heart.

At several points during the opening there was a dark energy that I had to contend with. When I'd check in, I kept getting the same message. I was to love whatever was there. To try to control, or fight it, would only cause it to grow. It wasn't about pushing away the dark now, it was about bringing the darkness in to illuminate it and give it a chance to choose love and heal. It was time to welcome both polarities, as both dark and light have played key roles on this planet. That being said, it was extremely hard on me to be with that dark energy and not try to throw it out or dismiss it.

And so, I was constantly trying to hold both energies to see if we could unify them with love and nonjudgement. It took every ounce of energy I could muster to keep the group from splitting off in different directions. Finally, on the day before the opening, things shifted. And although that last dark piece wasn't fully able to heal, we were able to come together despite it and do the ceremony that needed to be done. I am sure I had the Angels to thank for that.

The day of the opening, I was intrigued that a group had just left the top of the Tor. They had come to do a major clearing on it, and the surrounding land. It is amazing how different groups go to do their work not even knowing that they are part of a major contribution to what comes before and/or after what they do. Perhaps it is this way so that one doesn't go into ego, or put too much of one's own thinking into what they are being asked to do.

As I began to climb the Tor, I was saying a silent prayer for everything to fall into place the way it needed to. I began to notice a woman a level above me that acted as if she was waiting for me. As I got closer, she yelled "Where have you been? We've all been waiting for you, hurry!" I was confused. I turned to see who she was talking to, but there was no one there. She was definitely talking to me. When she knew I heard, she turned and started climbing the stairs again. As I reached the top, I planned on talking to her to see who she thought I was, but no one was there. Not one single person! Who she was, I hadn't a clue.

I set the space and started to pray. Then I asked for assistance from all realms to help the group do what we had come to do. While in prayer, I was shown the exact spot to create the altar. When the rest of the women got there, we laid out flowers and collected gifts from nature to support the opening.

There were around 40 people from the town who felt to come and join in. I had no idea where they all came from. Complete strangers came together and shared their love, hope, and dreams for the Earth and humanity. People gathered that I had never laid eyes on. I did know that there were Middle Earth Beings there to help hold the energies. They were some of the participants that had joined in. You could feel their energy was far different. I also knew the dark force was still trying to throw a kink in the opening. I continued to pray for divine intervention that the opening was successful. As we began to start the ceremony, I saw men walking around the outside of the circle counter clockwise, and women walking clockwise. They looked like every day normal people but as I looked deeper, I knew that they were Priestesses and Wizards that had been sent to make a circle of energy for support. The sabotage was not going to be allowed. I could feel magic in the air.

We drummed and sang and toned until the beats were fevered and fast. Finally, I felt the pillar take form. The whole ceremony took about 30 minutes, and I knew that we had gone as far as we could go. As quickly as we gathered, we disassembled leaving only the flower petals behind as an honoring to the land. I was at a place of unrest because I didn't feel like it was fully finished. I didn't feel the pillar fully anchor in. There wasn't much I could do until I was given information around it. So, I waited.

Later that day I was talking to Daisy who was the proprietor of the Airbnb that we were staying at. She let me know that she was called to go to the Tor because she had been told that there was going to be an attempt to stop the opening. I guess she knew far more than I had given her credit for. She said that she had called on the Magicians and Angels to come and hold the energy so that it couldn't be sabotaged. Daisy had also been instrumental in a few other things that I knew about. Guess we definitely had come to the right place to stay!

Our group had one more important thing to do, and that was to visit what was called the White Springs. I was able to get a private time there for our group. Even though I had tried to set it up for the day before the opening, the only day that it was able to be actualized was the day after. Again, I was to see that all is in divine order. It was the most beautiful experience of the whole trip.

As soon as the door was opened, I knew that we were in a very holy and sacred place. The White Springs was near the Tor and the Chalice Well. You could feel the divine feminine energy was strong there. It was a huge, wet and dark room illuminated with candles. There were several above ground pools made with stone and mortar that held water from the spring. The energy there was primal and called out for us to sing a song from our Soul. That primal energy came forward from each of the women as it blended into the most heartfelt, raw, and powerful song I had ever heard! It was as if we were singing ourselves whole again. As we sang tears ran down each of our faces. There was no dark energy trying to sabotage here. Just us fully naked within the embodiment of our highest and most beautiful feminine power. The song reflected by that was hauntingly beautiful.

The ceremony on the Tor, left a nagging feeling that the pillar for the City of Light wasn't fully activated to protect the dark energy from filtering in. But here near the Tor, under the ground, it felt completed. We were able, with the rawness of letting everything go and letting our true selves come through, to fully activate it. Our work now felt complete. The group began to split apart, each knowing that we had gained a better truth of who we were. We also parted with an understanding of our strengths and weaknesses.

The three of us who had held the group together decided to check in on the Tor one last time to make sure that it was doing well. After I left, Elayna told me that a black helicopter had come and started flying very close to the building sitting on the very top. It would charge it, then back away. This it did over and over like it was energetically ramming it. Then it zoomed in close to where Mara was in the pasture below it and came down very low. She thought for sure it was going to land and was more than a little shaken.

Elayna and I had noticed several times that we were being followed by the typical black car with two men in black suits and sunglasses. They never did anything. They just tailed us throughout different parts of our journey there. When Elayna flew home, she was picked up by another mutual friend and said that six police cars surrounded them as they went to leave and searched the whole car. They were not taken into custody and let go after finding nothing that could incriminate them. What all of this was about was never fully understood. Evidently, what we were doing was a threat to the powers that be.

After a small rest, Mara and I decided to go to Tintagal and visit the Merlin Cave. We were just going to stay one day exploring the area and then were going to move on. Merlin's Cave was interesting in that you could only visit it during low tide. That is the only time that the opening was visible. I have to admit, there wasn't really that much to the cave, but it definitely had a feel of magic there. There was a crude chair that seemed to be carved out of stone that I was guided to sit on and meditate. I was also guided to pick up a few of the stones that lay on the sand for later tuning into the energy held there.

That night we both felt like we needed to have our own room and be in our own energy. I left the car keys with Mara thinking she may get up sooner and need something from the car. I was utterly exhausted! I pulled off my clothes, put on my pajamas, and fell fast asleep.

The next morning when I woke up, I didn't have a stich of clothing on. I looked around for my pajamas thinking I had just ripped them off during my sleep, but they were nowhere to be found. There was also none of the clothes I had worn that previous day laying around. I got up and looked in the bathroom hoping they had somehow been taken there. There was nothing. Not in the closet, or under the bed, or in the bathtub. There was not a piece of clothing to be found anywhere. I even looked under the mattress. What the hell?

The only thing I could do was to get ahold of Mara and have her go out to the car to get some new ones. My phone wasn't working in my room, so that meant I needed to wrap a blanket around me and walk to her room.

I just had to go for it. Hopefully everyone else was still asleep. After waking Mara, she came with me to my room to help look. We tore the room apart. At one point, we wondered if I had thrown them out the window. We both went over and looked out the window, but there were no clothes laying on the ground. As we were looking, a large orb of light shot up from the ground, hovered at eye level, then shot up and out of sight. We both stood their dumbfounded. I made a crack about maybe having sex with an Alien, then we started in tearing the bed apart. The clothes couldn't just disappear. Each blanket and sheet came off one by one and finally we pulled off the mattress pad. There we found a folded towel. When we opened it up, we found my clothes. They were meticulously folded, as if we had just picked them up from a laundry service. What the hell they were doing under the mattress pad, folded in a towel, at the foot of my bed, was beyond me! To this day, I still wonder what went on. I'm pretty sure that it was connected to that ball of light. I just don't know in what way. What happened that night has obviously been erased from my memory.

CHAPTER 124

Fuck Spirituality, I Just Want to Be Normal!

MY FIRST STOP back to the U.S. was to California to spend a little time with my friends, Jennifer and Mary. Since I met them on Kauai, we had spent a lot of time together. Jennifer was one of the most giving and beautiful people I had ever met. The first time I met up with her, there was an instant connection that I knew transcended this lifetime. I admired how she had worked so hard to heal her own life and be of service to others. I could see where her work with Healing with the Masters had brought a lot of healing on the planet, and I will always be grateful for the time we spent getting to know one another.

From there, I flew back to Sedona. While at the airport waiting for the shuttle, I got a really awesome surprise. My daughter phoned me, and she was in the same airport on a layover. What were the chances? We got to meet up and have lunch together! I was constantly watching the time, concerned that she was going to miss her plane. She finally confessed that she feigned getting sick. They had given her a new ticket for a later flight. I was so grateful that it all came together, because I hadn't seen her in such a long time. She shared some incredibly beautiful and honoring things that touched my heart deeply. That one hour I got to spend with her was priceless.

She took off for New York and I shuttled off to Sedona. It was the perfect place for me to be still and integrate all that had happened in my travels. I was exhausted! The City of Light openings and all the travel was harder on me than I thought. Looking back, I had flown 44 times in 13 months. No wonder I needed to rest. I rented a room from Dana to stay through the winter, and then was going back to Minnesota for the summer. I decided I had had enough of traveling and doing this work. I needed stillness. It was time to focus on myself.

That summer I began to see that I had had it with everything. My motto was fuck spirituality; I just want to be normal again. During that period, I didn't do prayer or healing work. I didn't process all my mistakes and pull apart my thoughts. I just enjoyed people and decided to have a laid-back life. I drank and swore and I even had a smoke once in a while. I enjoyed myself with no judgement. I had fun, and laughed my ass off. It felt heavenly! I was tired of being so responsible all the time. I had done so much traveling and work for the Universe, that I was done with it all! Everyone and everything could fend for itself. I didn't much care anymore.

By the end of the summer, I was laughing at myself. No matter how hard I tried to let it go, a Spiritual Being was my essence. Even when I didn't meditate or pray or run all over the world, I could feel the deep spiritual nature that I held. It coursed through every cell of my being and every thought that I held. Spirituality wasn't an action; it was a way of being. There was no way once I understood as much as I did, that I could turn my back on it. It just wasn't possible. I was, and have always been spiritual. It's who I am.

The reason I had been so tired, and fed up was because I wasn't creating a balance for myself. Too much of one thing creates an imbalance in other areas of your life. I was putting all my energy into doing for others, and wasn't taking the time I needed to recharge and pursue my own wants and needs.

I was sitting in an outside gazebo journaling before I was to leave for Sedona and an eagle landed in the tree right next to me. He made sure that I was paying attention to him by his constant chattering. Acknowledging him, I went into silence to see if I could hear what he had to say. Animals have always been a great messenger for me if I take the time to listen.

The eagle wanted me to know that he was glad that I had figured it out. I was a Spiritual Being and no matter what I chose in life, that spirituality would always be the nature of who I am, and what I chose to do. He also told me that he knew that I had asked to have my will aligned with God's/the Universal will. My asking for that would open an amazing and beautiful part of my life as I aligned to my destiny.

A humming bird landed right next to the eagle in a branch near his beak bringing in the aspect of joy. **It was explained that it was okay to have fun, in fact it is necessary. The trick is doing everything with balance.** It was amazing having the smallest to largest bird sitting right next to one another in front of me. I likened it to my life coexisting with God's/the Universe's existence. It had such a huge and vast presence and mine was but a drip in the ocean. And yet, becoming one with it allowed me to sit within that presence and become part of the vast field of consciousness on this planet.

That morning I woke up in a dream where I was in a car driving somewhere, and my eyes dropped shut. No matter how hard I tried, I couldn't get my eyes to open. I seemed to be going really fast and was veering around curves on two wheels. Of course, I was getting pretty scared and was wondering why it was happening. At one point, I pried my left eye open but I still couldn't see anything and it snapped shut again. I kept thinking "Oh my God, I'm going to die!" And finally, I started to wonder… Hmmm, why was the car staying on the road even without me being able to see where I'm going? I knew it had something to do with trusting God/the Universal flow of energy for my direction. And even if I couldn't see what was ahead, I could surrender to what was. In that state of surrender, I allowed the energy to lead me to where I needed to go. Then I heard "Time to regain your trust, Barb." and woke up.

Here is some wisdom I gained while rebalancing my hectic life.

If we choose to see ourselves as a victim, we bring more victim consciousness to ourselves in our experiences. The Universe has no choice within its agreement of freewill but to comply with what we continually think. It brings back an experience through a replication of our beliefs and thoughts. The Universe has no judgement of good and bad, or right and wrong, everything is just energy. If you wish to change your outer experience, you must first excavate the negative one and replace it with what you wish to see. That is how you change your world.

As I look back on different places within my life that were less than pleasant, I can see that I learned a lot from them. If I got what the lesson had been about, it would fade away never to return, but if I didn't figure it out, another harder one would come in to teach me in its place. Each of those places created propulsion forward into an easier and more balanced path, and has shaped the very fabric of my existence and who I am. This is a principle of life for us all.

Would I have rather not had to experience them? Of course! No one likes to have what they consider bad things to happen to them.

But if having them helped me to grow and heal, then I am grateful for the gifts that they brought. It seems to be a part of the polarity here on this "school of hard knocks" planet. There isn't one person that I know that hasn't had a hard time at some point in their life. Or, for that matter, hasn't made bad choices for their life. It is only when we can work our way through it, and see it for the gift that it brought, that it fades away never to return.

I think the most profound thing that I have walked away with in all my 66 years of living is the knowing that there is a divine intelligence that threads through each of our lives. I know that everything that I have experienced, and every person that I have met, has been there for a reason. Even though I don't always understand what that reason is. Each experience has created a shift and a realization that I needed to see and acknowledge. It didn't matter how much I had studied or experienced, there were deeper and deeper layers of programming and beliefs that needed to be excavated.

Trauma, like an onion, holds many layers. Don't get discouraged when you hit another layer.

CHAPTER 125

Going Full Circle & Healing the Child Within

I STAYED IN Sedona for several years while I got my spiritual practice more financially stable. During that time, my heart was constantly pulling me back to Minnesota. It longed to be back with my family, and my roots. When I felt I was more financially stable, I would once again be selling everything I had, pack up my car, and head for home.

It took me eight months to manifest my new place after I got there. I kept looking, but nothing seemed right. I finally said out loud that I didn't understand why my next place wasn't showing up. The voice came in and said that I wasn't finding a place, because I wouldn't commit to staying here. I was vacillating on exactly where I really wanted to live. I said that I would commit to at least a year or more and laid out the area I was feeling pulled to. That night, I dreamt about an old boyfriend and his mom. They were from a family that I loved and grew up with. His sister and I were good friends and she often invited me to stay at their farm when we were in school together. That night, in my dream they told me that my house was ready. They showed me the house that the mom was living in currently. I was confused, and asked if they meant I was supposed to live with the mom. They just smiled and the dream ended.

The next morning, I was called by my friend and was told that her mom had passed. Of course, I freaked out. Their mom had been a very special person in my life. It was through her that I got a true picture into the nurturing of a mother and the normal role they played in a family. This whole family meant a lot to me. I knew in my heart that it was destined to be. However, my mind could not conceptualize how it would all come together. I was uncomfortable telling the family about the dream. I said out loud that if it was meant to be, that it would be brought to me by a member of the family. Then I let it go.

At the funeral, I was giving my condolences to the family and then sat for a bit on a bench. There was a beautiful young lady there with a couple of children and we started a conversation. Long story short, she asked if I lived in the area. I told her I was trying to manifest a place to live. She asked what I was looking for and I told her I needed to be in a place out in nature, on a river, with lots of privacy and land that I could plant a big garden. She looked at me thoughtfully, and said "I think I know why we met, I know a place just like that." I later found out that it was the wife of the man who had inherited the farm when his dad died. I moved in a month later.

What a gift this place has been. It is one of the purest energy places I have ever lived. What I love the most is that it feels like home because it housed a family that I had been close to growing up. This place is steeped in nature and it's been my salvation. It has also brought me full circle back to where I was born. There were so many gifts waiting for me here. One of the biggest was being able to heal some of my most fragile and broken pieces. It has also been the perfect place to write this book. As I sat writing one day, I felt a little tug on my pants. When I looked down, I saw me as a cute and timid six-year-old. She began to talk to me about things that had happened to her. Everything that she had been so scared of and how much she hurt. It was a hard story to hear, but I let her speak. Then I set her on my lap and just held her until she felt safe again and melded back into me. Two more came to me, one-by-one. Each voiced the pain and hurt they had experienced and held for so long. Each sat on my lap and wept until all the hurt and fear was gone. Finally, they also, melded back into me. It has been the most grounded and whole I have ever felt.

It is so different being here after living at one of the most beautiful places on the planet. A place where meeting those who are spiritual is more common than not. This place may not be full of healers and psychics, but I have always been much more in tune with down-to-earth people. And even though I haven't had crazy interdimensional experiences here (at least as of yet), that's okay. I live in one of the most profound places of peace I have ever lived. It is here in my aloneness that I am learning how to love myself, and see what an amazing person I am. I no longer need to look outside myself for happiness or validation. I know that I carry everything within me that I need.

We are all going through a metamorphosis of our lives. The world is changing and we are all being encouraged to let go of the things that have caused so much pain and misalignment in our past. We can hit it head-on when it comes to us as an experience for growth and heal it. Or, we can put it off and wait for harder and harder experiences to come forward. Then we're forced to look it in the eye. There is no right or wrong, only a choice of if one feels ready to do the work or not.

This was a very sensitive and vulnerable story to share. I have sat on it for quite a while because I was afraid of the judgement it could bring forward from those who may not understand. I was also afraid that it would hurt several people. But nothing heals by silencing it, and no looking outside the box can happen if you never look beyond what's right in front of you.

My hope is that it has helped each of you in some way. Even if just to heal those deepest places of hurt that keep showing up for you. If you keep pushing your hurt away or down into your body to bury it, it has control over you. Its mission is to cause constant miscreations to learn from.

May you open your perimeters to far greater understandings of what life is really about. We've all been programmed and more often than not hold on tight to our belief systems. Try to have an open mind and explore things that help you stretch yourself. Remember, just because you can't see air, doesn't mean it's not there.

Turn off the television. There is all kinds of negativity, violence, and sex to dull our senses. There is also fake news to keep us all angry, upset, divided and fearful. Television has all kinds of subliminal programming that is hardwiring our minds, not to mention the mind numbing it does. It has an even more profound effect on your children. Their brains are a sponge.

These cell phones are amazing, but have you ever looked into what its energy does to the physical body? Try not to carry it in your pockets. If you sleep with a cell phone near your bed, it affects your physical body and mind negatively the entire time you're near it. Don't believe me? Try sleeping with it at least twenty feet away and see how much better you feel. There is so much research out there on the effect they have on your physical body. Did you know that they continually monitor and gather your information when you are on your phone? Talk about a particular subject and see how it pops up the next day as an add on Facebook or elsewhere.

Wean yourself off, or limit social media. Quit experiencing life through a phone or computer. Get out in the real world and create real interactions. People are losing the ability to communicate face-to-face.

Get out in nature. You will soon see how intelligent and supportive it is. It's been waiting for you to remember your connection. Nature is by far your fastest connection to your spiritual nature.

Explore love to its depths. Be the love you've always wanted to be. Show the love you always wanted to express. It is our true inherent nature, and life is nothing without it.

Talk to the Universe about your hopes and dreams, and ask it to teach you things. The sky's the limit. It will take you places you could never have imagined.

The world is your oyster. You can choose to experience life with the shell closed and close yourself off from the rest of the ocean. You can stick part of yourself out into the ocean of life and drift along on the bottom, letting the current take you where it may. Or you can fully open the shell and feast on everything that is available, exploring new ways of being and places to go. The ocean doesn't care. It only supports you in what you want to experience.

I hope my story helps you to understand your story at a deeper level. I believe there are far more people on this planet that are waking up to their true divinity and nature. I am sure that many of you are experiencing things that you have been nervous about sharing, or perhaps even have been experiencing things that you have no context for. Perhaps the sharing of my story will help you to be able to make sense of what is going on in your life.

We all came into this life with our own unique qualities and gifts. Don't strive to be normal. Strive to be all that you came here to be. Allow the Universe to guide you to your own unique path. Remember, no two paths look alike. Everyone came here for their own unique reasons. Try not to compare.

You can never find yourself and what the truth really is, until you find the courage to work through the programming and beliefs that have created your life. You have to unlearn everything you have been programmed with. All it takes to start opening the truth, is a desire to know. When you ask for it to be opened up, there is no choice but for the Universe to respond. In that one conscious act, you will find more treasures than you ever dreamed of!

Life is what you make of it. Your thoughts, and emotions, create aspects of your reality. Watch them closely, and master recreating them when you catch negativity creeping in.

May your journey help you to understand yourself to your depths, so that you may have the courage to be who you truly came here to be. Then you can share your gifts, and your beautiful self with this amazing world.

You can never find your truth without practicing silence, stillness, and going within. It is the only way you can find your inner guru. Everything you need to know, you carry within.

Love is your superpower.

I'm wishing you a journey that expands you to your fullest potential. May you flow with the universal energy that is here to steer your life onto its own unique path. Hopefully, one day, you get to meet the mystic you were always meant to be.

BIO

BARBARA IS A sound and energy practitioner, life coach, psychic, spiritual councilor, activator, teacher and interfaith minister. She has helped people around the globe to unravel their childhood programming, belief systems and imprinting to help create a life more in alignment with their Soul. Barbara resides in Minnesota. If you would like to know more about Barbara, you can email her at mysticmisfit555@gmail.com or check out her website at www.aligningthesoul.com

CPSIA information can be obtained
at www.ICGtesting.com
Printed in the USA
BVHW040241300323
661426BV00002B/3